1964
In Memory of
Kingsley W.
Congrove

BLINDNESS

WHAT IT IS, WHAT IT DOES, AND HOW TO LIVE WITH IT

Reverend Thomas J. Carroll

BLINDNESS

WHAT IT IS, WHAT IT DOES, AND HOW TO LIVE WITH IT

LITTLE, BROWN AND COMPANY
BOSTON • TORONTO

LIBRARY OF CONGRESS CATALOG CARD NO. 61-12808

Second Printing

Nihil Obstat: John G. Hogan
Diocesan Censor

Imprimatur: ✠ Richard Cardinal Cushing
Archbishop of Boston

Date: May 10, 1961

Published simultaneously in Canada
by Little, Brown & Company (Canada) Limited

PRINTED IN THE UNITED STATES OF AMERICA

Acknowledgments

So MANY people have contributed to the making of this book that it would be impossible to acknowledge their individual help. In various manuscript editions since 1953, the volume has been read by numerous blind persons and authorities in the field of rehabilitation who have suggested changes and improvements; it has been used as a teaching manual for over two hundred newly blinded adults; it has been a staff training book for many professional persons. From all these have come reactions which have led to the inclusion of new material or the changing of old material. Typists, proofreaders, and others have volunteered many hours of direct work on its transcriptions.

Although it would be unfair to single out individuals, I gratefully acknowledge the assistance of all those listed above as well as that of all the other people who taught me the things reflected in these pages.

T. J. C.

Preface

THE MANY blind and sighted who know and love Father Carroll are aware of the psychological profundity of his work, of his dedication to his faith and to the blind, and of his inspired influence upon so many individuals. But many of us, perhaps, do not fully appreciate the extent to which his creative ideas will influence work with the blind for years hence because they are so fundamental and at times so revolutionary.

Father Carroll wrote this book as a practical guide for the blinded — and for those who mean to help them. But this book is not designed to make the blinded reader feel happy about his blindness or take comfort in the good will of the sighted. It takes courage to live as a blind person, and strenuous efforts to make a successful adaptation. Despite his handicap, the blinded individual can do no less *than* the sighted, trying to live successfully as an independent and socially responsible person. The present book provides any person who possesses such ambitions with the methods and tools necessary to achieve this goal. As one who has done some work and thinking about these problems from the psychological point of view, I can vouch for the validity of these ideas.

To be sure, blindness is not only a more severe handicap than most, it is also a different one. But this does not mean that the readjustment problems which confront the newly blinded person are fundamentally different from those of any other individual, handicapped or not. On this basis, Father Carroll dispels many superstitions and false notions about blindness and the blind. It is because these have proven to be pitfalls in the path of the blind that at times his words seem angry. His faith in the basic inner goodness and strength of man, handicapped or not, is communicated to us in this book. It cannot but prove an inspiration to us all.

JACOB LEVINE, PH.D.

Contents

PART THREE

Special Problems of Various Groups

Charts

BLINDNESS

WHAT IT IS, WHAT IT DOES,
AND HOW TO LIVE WITH IT

Introduction

For whom this book is written

FOR WORKERS with the blind — professional and nonprofessional, paid and unpaid.

For those blind persons who have been seeking a fuller answer to the problems of their blindness.

For the families of blind persons.

For workers in the general field of rehabilitation.

For social workers.

For teachers in public and private schools, who to an increasing extent are meeting blind children in their classes.

For doctors — especially general practitioners, ophthalmologists, psychiatrists.

For hospital personnel, proprietors of nursing homes, and the increasing group working with geriatric patients.

Its purposes

This is a book about blindness: not about its medical aspects, not about preventing it, but about what it does to people when it has happened.

And mainly about a special kind of blindness. The blindness that visits the adult who once had sight.

Here we attempt to analyze blindness, what it does to the ordinary person struck by it in his adult years, and what could and should be done about it.

Other authors have made distinctions between the "blind" and the "blinded," between those who never had sight and those who had it for a period of time before they lost it. They have used terms like "congenitally blind" and "adventitiously blind"; or "born blind" and "newly blind." But whatever the terms used, they have not defined clearly the essential difference in kind between "having seen and lost sight" and "never having seen." And they often speak as if they believe that it makes little difference whether someone is born blind or becomes blind at an early age, as a young person, or as an adult. It has been too easy, therefore, for the casual reader to conclude that the only difference between blind people consists in the age of onset or the length of time since blindness occurred. "After all, they're all blind."

But this book holds that the realization of a qualitative difference between congenital and adventitious blindness is an essential prerequisite to intelligent efforts toward rehabilitation of the blind. This difference is vastly more important than any differences among blinded people in the length of time that the blindness has existed or the age at which it occurred. It is a difference in the very nature of blindness as it affects the person.

Those of us who retain our sight can only come to some understanding of the congenitally blind by gaining understanding of the person who once had sight and has lost it. For we can at least begin to imagine what this would be like. No closing of our eyes will teach us what it is like never to have known what color is; but by closing our eyes we can get some notion of what it is like not to see color. To imagine what our lives would be without any visual imagery is impossible — visual imagery is too interwoven with our whole way of thinking; but it is not impossible to imagine what it would be like to be left with visual memories only.

In this book, then, we are dealing not so much with the poignancy of "lack," but rather with the pain of "loss." We are concerned primarily with the problems involved in the rehabilitation of those who have become blind. But by gaining a greater insight into these problems, we can also come closer to a recognition of the problems of those who have never seen — and this is the only way in which we can do so.

As of the date of writing, statistics tell us that some 350,000* Americans are blind, and that the great majority of them were blinded as adults. And an increase in adventitious blindness is predicted.

Even if blindness were not on the increase, it would be important for those already blind, and for all the rest of us as their fellow men and fellow citizens, to understand the meaning of blindness and know about the possibilities of rehabilitation for those who have been blinded. If this is to come about, the fear and emotion which surround the subject must be dispersed; we must analyze blindness objectively and analytically before we can attempt to make the blinded person feel the subjective warmth of our love.

It is tempting to try to deal with blindness in the aura of an emotional glow. But too often this glow means that the blind person is being given something that masquerades as love — even to the person offering it — but that contains the seeds of hatred and rejection. Too often neurotic sympathy, shuddering rejection, possessive overidentification and a form of pity not unrelated to antivivisectionist fanaticism are forced upon the blind.

There is no easy way to find how to give true sympathy, help, love. But the approach that tries to see the real meaning of blindness and the meaning of some of our feelings about it is a beginning. If it does not necessarily and of itself lead to love, it can at least remove some of the difficulties that stand in the way of loving.

This book is not intended to go into disabilities other than blindness, save as these affect blind persons. But all major handicaps have much in common. An exploration of the meaning of blindness and of what can be done about it, then, may help its readers also to a better understanding of the nature of disability itself. And if the

* The United States National Health Survey (July 1957-June 1958) included a question on whether the respondent could read ordinary newsprint with glasses. The survey results estimate the number of blind persons in the United States at 960,000.

method of "analysis-resynthesis" worked out in this book is useful in the approach to blindness, it may also prove useful in the approach to other major difficulties.

Primarily, however, this book is intended as an introductory survey for the thousands of people who come into the field of work with the blind every year, whether as paid or as volunteer workers. I hope that the book will help them through the first days when they are filled with confusion, entangled in their own emotions as they face the trauma of blindness, baffled both by the complexities of this new field and by the contradictory platitudes they hear all around them concerning the "normalcy" of the blind, their great need for help, and their amazing ability to function without any.

Plan of this book

As a glance at the table of contents will show, the method used in this book is that of analysis followed by resynthesis. Part One analyzes the losses which go to make up the multiple handicap of blindness; Part Two takes up the problems of restoring or substituting for what has been lost, building up to the total rehabilitation of the blinded person. The rest of the book deals with various special questions concerned with the blind themselves and with those who attempt to help them.

In studying the analysis of the various blows dealt by blindness, the reader needs first to keep in mind the fact that no analysis can completely separate and distinguish the various effects of blindness. They are blows to a human life, to the life of one organism, one person; and so they necessarily interweave. The analysis given here is the result of more than twenty years' experience in the field, and of as many years' consultation and discussion with blinded persons themselves and with authorities in work for the blind. There might easily be other methods of analyzing and classifying the various losses of blindness — this one has, at any rate, proved its usefulness over a period of time.

The second fact to remember is that these losses, which are unequally severe in themselves, are also felt in different ways and to different degrees by different people.

Here we shall discuss primarily the blinded *man;* but as feminine psychology differs from masculine, so the various losses affect a woman rather differently than a man. Again, the loss which to one person may seem the most shattering of all may seem to another only one of the minor inconveniences brought by blindness. It is the whole and unique person who receives the multiple blow, and he receives it according to his own personality structure, his own way of life, his own interests and circumstances. Any analysis of the losses of blindness must be applied to each blinded person as an individual — as must the resulting program of rehabilitation.

How to Read This Book

THE BLOWS which blindness deals to a person, the losses he suffers, do not come on him one by one to be dealt with one by one, but all together — whether blindness itself overtakes him slowly or suddenly. To get any valid picture of blindness it is necessary to get a complete picture of these losses as they add up to the total handicap. This is the reason why the first part of this book lists and analyzes these losses as exhaustively as possible before going on to the means of rehabilitation.

But the reader may well be unable to face this complete picture all at once without some alleviation. Whether he be a worker with the blind or closely related to a newly blinded person, he may find that studying in succession the twenty losses which make up the total handicap of blindness is too much to bear. Such a reader is urged to turn, at the end of the analysis of at most two or three losses, to the corresponding study of the possibilities of restoration, before he resumes his study of the losses themselves. The sighted reader is studying this book to learn how to help the blind; he will help them better if, as he makes his way through the long list of losses that make up the total picture, he sees concretely what he can do to help.

PART ONE

Analysis of What Is Lost

1

The Sighted Man Dies

LOSS OF sight is a dying.

When, in the full current of his sighted life, blindness comes on a man, it is the end, the death, of that sighted life. This death may be the rapid one that results from accident or from some fulminating disease. Or it may be the slow, lingering death to a sighted life that often comes with glaucoma, with uveitis, or, as so often in our day, with diabetes. The death may come without warning; its onset may be hidden by false hopes or false promises; it may come with a terrifying slowness, inevitably.

However it comes, it is death to a way of life that had become part of the man. It is the end of acquired methods of doing things, the loss of built-up relationships with people, of ingrained relationships with an environment.

It is superficial, if not naïve, to think of blindness as a blow to the eyes only, to sight only. It is a destructive blow to the self-image which a man has carefully, though unconsciously, constructed throughout his lifetime, a blow almost to his being itself.

Is it so strange, then, that many people who cannot face this type of dying voice the feeling "I would rather be dead than blind"?

I hope in the course of this book to show how unjustified in fact this feeling is. Although the onslaught of blindness is a tragedy, with its multiple effects on the person blinded, on his family and on his whole circle of friends and neighbors, life holds worse tragedies than

And the first thing to be done is to admit its reality and to meet ace to face.

The late Dr. Louis Cholden* of the staff of the Menninger Clinic analyzed the condition of the newly blinded person as consisting of a first stage of shock followed by a second stage of grief or bereavement. The first is a stage of numbed inability to function, even to comprehend; the second is a period of mourning for the life that is gone, the lost self.

Dr. Cholden strongly warns medical men of the harm they can do to the patient by holding out false hopes. From his own experience with blinded people, he shows how the tragedy of new blindness is only deepened and prolonged by encouraging the patient to escape from facing the reality that is upon him. He shows that it is false kindness to try to spare the person the shock and grief. These must be undergone before there can be rehabilitation. Practically every patient must touch bottom before he begins the long road up.

Thus, in dealing with the newly blinded person, our first job is not to tell him that it is not bad, certainly not to tell him that it is not blindness. Rather it is to communicate to him the recognition that he is lovable and loved, and that in his grief he is not grieving alone. Then gradually we can let him see that it is possible that "life is changed, not taken away."

But the terms in which we say this must be without the Pollyanna note which still seeks to escape reality. They must not spring from a mode of thinking which tries to throw the sop of braille or guide dog, cane or Talking Book, or even the possibility of employment. The "death" of blindness destroys a whole complex pattern of existence. We must be prepared to offer something whole in its place.

For there *is* a new life ahead. But this is the paradox: the sighted person is "dead"; the blind person who is born can once more become

* See his articles: "Some Psychiatric Problems in the Rehabilitation of the Blind," *Bulletin of the Menninger Clinic*, Vol. 18, No. 3, May 1954; "Psychiatric Aspects of Informing the Patient of Blindness," *American Academy of Ophthalmology and Otolaryngology*, 1953, Instruction Section, Course No. 221; and his collected papers, *A Psychiatrist Works with Blindness*, published by the American Foundation for the Blind, June 1958.

the same person, but only if he is willing to go through
death to sight.

In a sense, we die many deaths in our lifetime; life is
dyings. Emotional sickness is so often the result of the
undergo, to "accept," these deaths. Often enough, the di[illegible]
of various stages of life are the disturbances caused by the conflict between the biological urge to grow and the psychological urge to cling to the safer life that was.* A reflection of this is found in "new school sickness," whether in the first grade, in high school, in summer camp or in college. It is found in the homesickness of the rookie or boot. It is the pause outside the door before entering a new situation.

The losses forced on the blinded person are many. They interlock; they overlap one another. Any one of them is severe enough in itself. Together they make up the multiple handicap which is blindness. Each loss involves a painful farewell, (a "death"). But with the death of the sighted man, the blind man will be born. And the life that is his can be good.

* See *Holiness Is Wholeness* by Josef Goldbrunner, Pantheon Books, New York, 1955.

2

Basic Losses to Psychological Security

1. LOSS OF PHYSICAL INTEGRITY

THE FIRST bitter blow in the multiple handicap of blindness is loss of physical integrity, of wholeness. The person who grew up, who built his life as a whole person, is now only a part. He is shattered.

To him now apply all the cruel words which mark the person who is not whole: — "maimed" — "crippled" — "afflicted." And the word freighted with horror — "*blind.*"

His fright has a nightmarish quality. With the loss of sight has come something long and deeply feared. He is different from what he was. And worse, he is different from those around him. He is a blind man in a sighted world. This physical difference from "normal" people is something over and above all the problems of living that he will have to face.

He has been striving all his life (in one way or another) to be a member of the "in-group," or at least to gain its respect; now he finds himself pushed into an "out-group" from which there is no escape.

His feelings are by no means as clear-cut as this. Often they appear only as formless terrors, as anxiety that cannot be described, as depression which has no logical base.

So far as his conscious thinking goes, the blinded person may be sure that blindness has not made him essentially different, that physical disabilities are not the worst things that could happen, and so on. But his feelings come up from the hidden wells of his unconscious, and they refuse to retreat before conscious logic.

And, interwoven in the feelings of the newly blinded man, are all the feelings that he turned on blind persons in the days when he had his sight.

If, during his sighted life, he thought of the blind as a group of mysterious people, if he thought of them as having certain mysterious supersensory powers, if he felt vaguely ill at ease in their presence — how does he feel now?

If he thought of blind persons in terms of the various stereotypes: the blind beggar, the blind genius, the blind musician — what are his feelings now?

And if a part of his feeling was due to the very physical presence of blind people, how does he now feel about his own?

If the physical blindness of a man moved him to rejection, to pity, or to a shudder of revulsion, what becomes of all these feelings, now that he himself is blind?

He may well be filled with special feelings of bitterness and hate because of his treatment of blind persons in the past, even for his donations to the blind beggar — now that he realizes the sentiment behind them.

If among his former feelings about blindness there was a deep and hidden fear, now he has even greater reason for disturbance. Fear of blindness is an important aspect of the normal instinct for self-preservation — witness the reflexes that protect the eyes, and the age-old phrase "to protect as the pupil of the eye." But with most people, this fear is to a great extent unacknowledged, something to be ashamed of, and therefore deeply buried in the unconscious, whence it gives rise to revulsion and to much of what is called "pity." (see page 69.)

The blinded person, then, may well be experiencing feelings of guilt for his past attitude toward blind people — his rejection of them; his maudlin pity for them, which gave no real help; and for the revulsion with which he passed their problems by.

These feelings of "difference," of fear, and of guilt may be tied to many other aspects of blindness besides this loss of physical integrity, but here especially they come in to confuse and add to the impact of the "reality" loss.

It must be remembered, however, that feelings of depression, of confusion, of difference are not clearly connected with one loss alone. Nor do these feelings occur in exactly the same way in all the people who lose their sight. Every human being is unique, for every human being has a self-image, somewhere near true or badly distorted — his personal picture of "what I really am." Part of this "self-image" is what is known as "body image." And to this body image the loss of physical integrity, the death of sight, may be a devastating blow.

An adult has spent many years in building up some sort of equilibrium which made it possible for him to live with his body image, to accept it and to believe it. Now he must drastically revise that image. His body is a blind and maimed body — a windowless, abnormal body. What happens to his equilibrium, to his whole method of action?

To make matters worse for the newly blinded person, our civilization tends to put a special emphasis on physical perfection. The spiritual emphasis of Judaism of old tended to make physical perfection of less than primary importance. The spreading of Christian civilization brought the same spiritual emphasis to a large segment of the Western world, and to that extent lessened the emphasis on physical qualities, and thus on the meaning of a physical deprivation.

Two factors in our day have tended to re-emphasize the importance of physical qualities and so have put added stress on the trauma of physical loss.

The first of these is the decreasing influence in our culture of the Judaeo-Christian philosophy. With the materialistic philosophy which has replaced it in our literature has come a natural emphasis on human environment — the things that surround us during the human life span: physical health, physical perfection, absence of pain, soundness of body, comfort, etc.

The second factor is advertising, with its careful analyses of human desires for the avowed purpose of exploiting them and its use of mass media to arouse in people all kinds of latent anxieties about themselves, their physical characteristics, and their social acceptability.

Our newly blinded man grew up in this atmosphere. He breathed it in from the conversation in his home, from the anxieties of parents and teachers about his physical health and physical appearance. It was a part of the preschool setting-up exercises and the afterschool cereal-serials. He heard it in a thousand slogans, read it in a million magazine and comic book advertisements. Dinned in by the age in which he grew up was the importance of physical perfection.

And now, whatever his previous physical perfection or imperfection, his is a blind body.

Another factor of great importance in this loss of physical integrity is the possibility that the newly blinded man may have a new insecurity about his manhood. If so, here is another dying.

There is something of the woman in the strongest and finest of men, and something of the man in the best and sweetest of women. But children do not know this! And the failure to know it causes insecurity in many a boy who finds in himself some of the "womanly" characteristics, and in many a girl who sees in herself something that is "manly."

If our newly blinded man is one of these people (even though the insecurity is so far back in childhood that he may think he has forgotten it, and even though he may be the most virile of men), he may have real trouble on this score. For, depth psychologists tell us (and the theory may be accepted or rejected without destroying the importance of the loss of physical integrity), any physical loss is taken by the unconscious to be an attack on the distinction between the sexes. And they note that the eye is, for some reason, connected more intimately than any of the other sense organs with these feelings about manhood and womanhood. The loss of an eye or the loss of the use of an eye is consequently in a special way a blow to the distinction that makes us man or woman — and thus a grave blow to our security about our very selves. This new blindling, this changeling, may, then, in the realm of his own feelings even be a gelding. This theory opens the way, perhaps, to a clearer understanding of the vague feelings of disquiet which blindness arouses in most people, of the fears involved when we connect blindness with ourselves.

Two more indications from the depth psychologists may help to put the importance of this chapter into focus. They tell us that in the unconscious the loss of one's eyes (and, to an extent, the loss of the use of one's eyes) is equated with death itself — that often enough nightmarish dreams about blindness are truly dreams of fear of death. And there seems to be a special difficulty for those who were brought up with the English language. In them, the unconscious often makes an attack on the "eye" an attack on the "I" which it symbolizes. Thus, in the feelings, the loss of physical integrity may well be the loss, the death, of *self*.

In conclusion, it is important to emphasize that the connotations of this loss of physical integrity seldom if ever appear in their full clarity to the blinded person. If they did, it would be ever so much easier to deal with them; the blinded person himself could, for the most part, handle them and reject them. Instead, they may show up in all manner of vague fears and symptoms which have no apparent connections with the feeling underneath. And unless something is done for these unrecognized feelings, all manner of physical, moral, and social symptoms may form themselves into one or another pattern of maladjustment or pseudo adjustment.

2. LOSS OF CONFIDENCE IN THE REMAINING SENSES

Perhaps more than any other of the losses which we list, loss of confidence in the remaining senses is one whose existence the public never suspects. On the contrary, the public is convinced that at the onset of blindness there occurs a phenomenon generally called "compensation." To some it appears as a "natural," to others a "divine" phenomenon. Seldom is the exact mechanism of it spelled out, but in general it is supposed to result in an acuteness of the remaining senses such as sighted people never know. Thus we hear talk of the "unusually keen sense of hearing" of persons who are blind, of their "extraordinary sense of touch," their "gifted sense" of smell or taste.

If we are to understand blindness and its effects on human beings, it is important that we disabuse ourselves of this notion very early (while at the same time recognizing that an increase in *sense efficiency* occurs in some blind persons and understanding the reason why).

Not only are the senses of blind persons no more acute than those of their sighted counterparts; in some cases they are less acute.

Sufficient testing has been done on the touch (the tactual sense) of blind and sighted persons to show that the sense of the former group is no keener than that of the latter. In our day, moreover, much blindness results from diabetic retinopathy, and in many such people certain tactual areas are "anesthetized" by the progress of the diabetes itself; as a result, the blinded diabetic may have a poorer sense of touch than many of the general public in his own age group.

Audiograms made of groups of blind and sighted subjects show that the former are subject to the same areas of hearing loss as the latter. But a certain few causes of blindness also affect the hearing to such an extent that the subject who is blind may also be hard of hearing, if not deaf. In this category are certain of the meningeal diseases, and apparently some of the familial forms of retinitis pigmentosa.* Furthermore, in our times, when the preponderance of blindness is found in the geriatric groups, the same hearing losses exist among blind persons in that age category as among sighted persons in the same age group (and as a result far more hearing loss exists in the over-all group of blind persons than in the over-all group of sighted persons of all ages).

There is no reason to believe that tests of the senses of smell and of taste would show us anything different. The fact is that a number of persons blinded from certain neurological causes or from certain types of injuries completely lack any sense of smell or of taste. And, generally speaking, the senses of smell and taste of the blind are no more acute than those of the sighted public.

Furthermore, the use of blindfolded subjects as control groups in

* See "Audiometric and Vestibular Examinations in Retinitis Pigmentosa" by J. Landau and M. Feinmesser, *British Journal of Ophthalmology*, January 1956.

certain experiments with blind people carried out by the psychologists C. E. Seashore, Karl M. Dallenbach and Philip Worchel would seem to indicate some sighted subjects show a better ability both in touch recognition and in sound localization than do their blind counterparts.

The distinction between sense *acuteness* and sense *efficiency* is a very important one here, both for the individual blind person and for the field of rehabilitation of the blind.

For it is true that many blind persons appear to hear things which we do not hear, to smell things which we do not smell, to taste differences which we do not taste, and to learn things through their sense of touch which are not discernible to us. But this does not prove the possession of "keener" senses, let alone any natural, divine, or magic "compensation."

The increase in sense efficiency, where it exists, has a twofold explanation. It is partly the result of concentration (the very reason why some people close their eyes in order to listen to a symphony more carefully, and why most of us "hear" more sounds after we turn out the lights at night). It is also the result of training (too often merely self-training) and of experience (like the ability which enables some people to tell the vintage of a wine by its taste and bouquet or the quality of cloth by its touch). Modern armies have trained specialists to read aerial photographs. Their training and experience allow them to see things in these photographs which we cannot see — supplies, stores, buildings that indicate a moving army. There is no special acuteness to their sense of sight; it is simply a question of trained observation. We do not endow such specialists with magic powers.

In the same way, over a period of time, many blind people do learn to interpret sound and smell and taste and touch better than the average person. But this is by no means universal among blind people, and so long as we believe that it is and cling to the notion of "compensation," we set blind persons apart in some magic supersensory area. And so long as work for the blind is influenced by this erroneous concept, we will neglect the important development of sense *training* in blind people and leave it to take place "naturally."

It is small wonder, then, that to the general public, fed by false notions of "compensation," it comes as a surprise to learn that new blindness can cause a loss of confidence in the remaining senses. This loss of confidence is not the result of that actual destruction of the sense or sense function which, as we have said, is caused by certain diseases or injuries. It is a condition, existing to a greater or lesser degree in many newly blinded persons (and lasting for a greater or lesser length of time), which makes it difficult or impossible for the blinded individual to believe what his remaining senses tell him. This loss does not occur with its full impact for every blinded person; for some, its duration is mercifully brief. But to the degree to which it prevails, the person newly deprived of sight is deprived of the use of his other senses as well.

To understand the reason for this loss, we must recognize the degree to which we depend on sight as a censor or tester of the information gathered by the other senses. True, to some extent we use each of our senses to add to the information brought by the others and to test and validate that information. But more than with any other sense we do this with sight.

When seeing is no longer possible, then for many people believing becomes difficult, if not impossible. They tend to doubt the information gathered by the other senses, to suspect its validity. This should not be thought of as an intellectual doubting but rather as a "sense doubting," probably due to some disturbance of the pattern of the "central sense," which lasts until some kind of reorganization of that sense can take place. This disturbance assumes major proportions when it escapes the control of the intellect, and the insecurity that it arouses builds up a state of panic.

Consider the way in which we use sight to test the information from some of the other senses.

The *sense of hearing* brings us a great deal of our information about the world around us. Yet time and again we test that information with the censor, sight. The quick turning of the head, the automatic gesture which turns our eyes toward the source of a sound, the accompanying question, "What was that?" — all these indicate how automatic is this tendency to test. Easily identifiable familiar sounds call us quickly to look and "make sure" if something causes them to assume importance.

The *sense of touch*. Our pocket or purse contains, we know, a quarter and a dime. Reaching in for the quarter, we have no difficulty in telling by touch what it is. Yet, as we take it out, we look at it automatically, unconsciously (even almost compulsively), just to "make sure." Or again, we gingerly touch the side of the boiling pot, quickly pull back knowing that it is hot; then we remove the cover and look for the familiar bubbles that will help us to "really know."

The *sense of smell*. "Close your eyes and smell these," someone says to us. We do. "Violets!" we are sure. We open our eyes, and "sure enough," they are violets.

The *sense of taste*. Not all cigarette smokers would do well with a blindfold test. Yet surely we can tell the taste of smoke from the taste of air. Why, then, the automatic reflex after the long inhalation which causes us to look to see if the cigarette is lighted? Simply that we are censoring with sight the positive or negative information given us by our sense of taste.

Besides the so-called "major senses," there is the long list of other senses much discussed in our day. Two of them seem to call for special mention.

The *sense of balance*. If our vestibular sensitivity is normal, our balance need not depend on sight. Yet in a completely dark room most people are capable of suddenly imagining that perhaps they are not erect, and their only answer lies in finding the light. Or, if we close our eyes for a period of time, it is possible for us to begin to lose our balance; to achieve it again we must open our eyes and orient ourselves by the use of sight. We check this sense, too, with the censor, sight.

The *sense of motor memory* (or "muscle memory") is also very important here. Using it rather than sight, almost anyone can go upstairs or down in his own home with no need to look for the top step or the bottom step. Yet turn out the lights and start him upstairs or down, and he is lost. Motor memory is completely overridden. The use of sight gone, our confidence in motor memory vanishes.

From such examples, it is easy to see that something might be expected to happen to confidence in the remaining senses when the sense of sight is gone.

Exactly what does happen differs from person to person and differs greatly according to the manner in which sight is lost. The person who loses sight slowly over a long period of time may actually go through a long period of reorientation of his way of censoring sense information. During this period, however, he may have occasional difficulties with this loss, and they will be so difficult to recognize for what they are that he may have grave misgivings about himself and his mental well-being unless the cause is made clear to him.

In sudden new blindness, this loss may be a serious factor in the shock stage, and over a long period of time it may contribute to the person's insecurity about himself. For some people, the experience may be so traumatic as even to lead to certain hallucinatory experiences, which will become more understandable as we study the next loss. With everyone, depreciation of trust in the information brought directly through his remaining senses can be a serious factor. It throws the newly blinded person back on two sources for trustworthy information: what he had learned before the loss of sight and the things that people tell him — on memory and on human trust. Here, then, is a serious area of dependence (and in this very dependence he is somehow cut off from the people upon whom he is dependent).

This loss, particularly during the shock stage of new blindness, is a shattering one, since it leaves a man so completely helpless. It removes him further from the world about him and makes more distant the possibility of rehabilitation.

3. LOSS OF REALITY CONTACT WITH ENVIRONMENT

The loss of contact with reality, of "reality contact" with the tangible world in which we live, is one that easily leads to panic, or that makes still more numb the numbness of the stage of shock. It is a further "death" to the world of things about us.

To the person who knows contact with reality to be a measure of sanity, this may seem to say that the blinded person loses sanity. No. Rather, the world of sanity is more difficult to hold on to. Reality contact is one of the differentiating notes between neurosis and psychosis. And in this loss, a major bond with reality is cut.

Perhaps the significance of this will be clearer if we look at some of the questions a psychiatrist is likely to put to a person suspected of being "disoriented": "Who are you?" "Who am I?" "Where are you?" "Who are these other people around you?" "What are you doing here?" "How long have you been here?"

Passing over the first question (with a recollection of the blows to "self" suffered by the newly blinded person), ask yourself what sense would be the most important to you in answering the other questions To answer with assurance at least four out of five of them, the average sighted person would depend heavily on sight.

In orientation to environment, kinesthesis and vestibular sensitivity both have a part. But it is sight above all which fixes me in my relationship to things around me. Sight relates me to the things to right and to left, to things above and below, to things in front of me and even in back of me. Sight not only identifies these things. It centers me among them.

Hearing is a help. But sounds are disembodied things. Sounds change; they move; they echo; they filter in without focus. They have not the sharp localization of sight. Smell and taste are of little use for orientation to the sighted man. They have no sharpness of location. They pervade and they become confused. Touch is more concrete; it is the sense of the "tangible." Yet touch can fail. Touch binds us only to a small segment of reality — a segment easily misidentified. And it is so easy for "touched" things to "move," for the whole solid world to seem adrift, if even for a moment I give up my grasp on reality.

Thus, for those who have grown up with the use of it, sight is the great sense for contact with the concrete world of things as they are. For sight, too, *touches*. It reaches out; it holds; it grasps; it binds; it embraces. Sight reaches to the environment my body cannot touch; sight extends my sense of touch; it extends *me*. And in so doing, it gives me a fixed and stable place, since it perceives all things in relation to my centric position. The other senses are too often nebulous. But sight is *real*; sight is concrete.

We can realize now what sight means for orientation to the environment.* And stability of orientation is of very great importance for security. Aside from the somatic factors, this may be a major reason for the disorientation involved in "senile cataract psychosis" (also known as "black mask psychosis").† Under operating conditions of the present day, this condition is seen less often than in former decades and is usually quickly cured.‡

The doctor has only to order the removal of the bandages from the eye and contact with the environment is restored. But with new blindness no such simple solution is possible. Herein lies the terrifying nature of this loss of reality contact with environment. This severing of a major bond with the reality world is a kind of dying to the things around us — and one of the most frightening aspects of the multiple trauma of blindness.

* Persons blinded long enough to be partly recovered from this loss may feel new panic in stepping onto scales to get weighed if they are not given something to take hold of. The unsteadiness of the platform removes their newly established reality contact through their feet, and anxiety arises very quickly. Usually the explanation of the reason for the anxiety is enough to allay it.

† See "Mental Disturbances Following Operation for Cataract" by Alan Greenwood, M.D., Transactions of the Section on Ophthalmology of the American Medical Association, 1928; "Psychosis Following Cataract Operations" by Ethel C. Russell, M.D., *Annals of Surgery*; and "Complications of Cataract Operations" by Conrad Berens, M.D., and Donald Bogart, M.D., 5 *Tr. Sect. Ophth.* A. M. A., 1938, pp. 238-283.

‡ Operation for cataract in the aged is now considered a routine procedure. There are instances of complication, but any worker for the blind will strongly recommend that whenever an ophthalmologist wishes to perform the operation, his recommendation should be followed. The procedure is so relatively simple and its results are so spectacular that thousands of octogenarians enthusiastically recommend it from their own experience.

4. LOSS OF VISUAL BACKGROUND

The loss discussed in the previous section was that of an object; now we shall consider the loss of the background in which that object exists. The former held the terror of looking for something which "is no longer there"; this one holds the emptiness, the loneliness of what might be called "visual silence."

To understand this loss we need to recognize how great a part visual background constantly plays in our lives, as a backdrop of peaceful or kaleidoscopic change, a sort of visual "orchestral accompaniment" to the events or the monotony of daily living. It is comparable to the auditory background of our lives, the loss of which leaves the deaf man in a monotony of stillness in which only silent things are seen.

We walk down a street; we ride in the subway; we sit in our living rooms; we stand talking in a crowded hotel. Supposedly we see nothing except the particular things on which we may happen to concentrate. Yet subconsciously our eyes and our minds are seeing; they are photographing and rejecting, photographing for memory, photographing for immediate need, taking in the world of color and contrast, of movement and rest, of light and shade, of people and things, of form and texture and shape which is all around us. We talk with someone, and as we do so we "concentrate out" the whole background in which we are seeing him. And yet within ourselves we are seeing him *in* that background.

Though it be as unconscious a reflex as the protective blinking of the eyelids, this photographic activity has the function of guarding us from danger. Even the sudden passing of a shadow can alert us quickly, put us on our guard against real or fancied hazards.

And it also has the function, mentioned in connection with the previous loss, but here carried out less consciously, of keeping us in contact with the world around us.

We are always at work not only placing others in a certain background but placing ourselves in the scene—orienting ourselves in our environment, though "totally unaware" that we are doing so. But if at any time we were to be so distracted that this unawareness became truly total, then our "coming to," our "snapping out of it," would be accompanied by a very real panic—so completely is this visual orientation a part of ourselves.

Again, while we are active about other things, this perception of visual background is a form of recreation for us, almost of unconscious recreation.

For example, there has been a changing visual background in my office during the day. When I began work the direct light of the sun was off at one side; now it falls half across my desk. In the course of the morning, the heat rising from the radiator behind me has given a gently rising motion to the sun's rays falling across the floor and table. The tree has thrown a moving shadow over the room, undulating until a steady wind held it still for a time. The shadows and the highlights of the room, its furniture, its paintings—these forms and colors have taken countless new relationships. Form and texture have gained new subtleties which have come and gone; colors have known innumerable nuances which have lasted momentarily. I "saw" all these things and yet did not actively "see."

Such is the changing visual world in which we live. Distraction, diversion, change—all these keep us from monotony, thus (as recreation does) refreshing our spirits and strength not merely after, but during, drabness and drudgery.

This perception of visual background can aid us, too, in experiencing a certain kinesthetic pleasure—again not a fully conscious activity—the pleasure not only of muscular motion and motion in space but of motion recognized visually, motion seen against a background of nonmotion.

There is also that wonder, to which the physicists give the cold name of "parallax," by which we lend motion to an earthbound world of lifeless objects, thus making the inanimate alive. Seen from a moving train, far objects move in the same direction you are going and near objects move off behind you—and a thousand different relationships of speed and urgency are set up among the many lifeless objects in between. But you need no train; the process is happening all the time. Hold an object — a cigarette, a pencil — a foot before your eyes. Now look at the far wall, and move your head first to the right and then to the left. The object has moved away from your movement and the far wall has moved with you. This constantly occurs as you move, and constantly you take it in as a part of the perception of visual background.

These are some of the values which perception of visual background gives to us. Their loss leaves the newly blinded man in a visual vacuum, a void in which he is dead to the change, the color, the moving forms, the visual background where the world of people lives.

5. LOSS OF LIGHT SECURITY

To speak of blindness as the "loss of light" is inaccurate and it is harmful to blind people. Yet there is every reason to believe that there is a loss of "light security" which in many cases is part of the trauma of blindness. To evaluate this loss, we must first understand the error involved in thinking of blindness as loss of light and the harm which this concept has done and is doing to the blind.

In one way or another the general public applies (and is encouraged to apply) analogies of light and darkness to the conditions of sight and blindness. It continually speaks of the "darkened lives" of blind persons; it refers to bringing "light" to the blind; it speaks of the blind as "sitting in darkness"; it calls its agencies for the blind "lighthouses." Yet this analogy can be a serious barrier to both the understanding of blindness and the acceptance of blind persons in society.

That sighted people should draw such an analogy is very easy to understand. When light is absent we are unable to see; we are, in a sense, blind. This kind of "blindness" is within our experience, and so we generalize from it about the unknown experience of real blindness. We have also had the opposite experience of being momentarily "blinded" by *too much* light. Yet we never make this analogy. We never think of blindness in terms of being overwhelmed by light — only as being without light. Why?

Light is the medium for sight. It is not sight itself. If the medium is absent, or if it is present in too great quantity, we are unable to make use of it; we are unable to see. But the medium is not the sense; light is not sight.

From the viewpoint of the science of optics, the analogy between darkness and blindness might not be too bad — since one certainly cannot see without light. But from the broader standpoint of ophthalmology, and from the outlook of psychology and sociology as well, this comparison can only do grave harm to an understanding of what blindness means.

Let us first see why the analogy is *inaccurate*. The vast majority of people who are "blind" according to the definition of blindness now almost universal in the United States* see light quite clearly; some of them can read newspaper headlines and some can even identify distant objects by sight. Therefore, the great majority of those who are clients of our "light" agencies for the blind actually see light. Some of them see so much light they don't know what to do with it; they are overwhelmed with light. There are no statistics to give the exact number, but it would be surprising if more than one in thirty of our blind population were so blind as to be unable to see any light (ten thousand out of more than three hundred thousand).

Furthermore, even according to the most restricted popular definition of a blind person as someone who "can't see," many of those who are blind would still be able to distinguish light from dark. These people are clearly blind, yet they are not without light. The person with light perception or even light projection, and certainly

* Definitions of blindness vary throughout the world. The definition most commonly accepted in the United States is an equivalent of the following: A person shall be considered blind whose central acuity does not exceed 20/200 in the better eye with correcting lenses or whose visual acuity is greater than 20/200 but is accompanied by a limitation in the fields of vision such that the widest diameter of the visual field subtends an angle of no greater than 20 degrees.

the person able to distinguish vaguely among moving forms, is not deprived of *light*. And yet any one of these is "blind" under any common-sense definition of the term.

Again, people with no light perception whatsoever often have a great deal of color vision — not the reception of colors from outside the eye (which is also possible for some "blind" people), but the floating colors which come from changes inside the eye or of the optic system. This phenomenon is not so rare as to be considered only an exceptional case.

Thus many people who cannot receive any light whatsoever through their optical system (even, in fact, people who have had both eyes removed) often see color, even kaleidoscopic colors, through a great part of their waking day. This is not a hallucinatory symptom, but something very real which is seen. To understand this phenomenon, we need only recall the fact that stimulation of the optic nerve, as by a blow on the head, can cause us to "see stars." And in some forms of blindness this stimulation occurs sufficiently often to cause the blinded person to live in a world of light and color.

We are certainly not trying to give the impression that such color and light experience is constantly and universally pleasant. On the contrary, it can be very disturbing, especially to the individual who does not understand it. But in any case, it provides many blind people with a world of color and light quite different from the popular notion of the lightless world in which all the blind are supposed to live.

This still leaves that group of blind persons who are totally deprived of any incoming light and who experience nothing of the color or light sensations of which we have spoken. Is their condition one which can be adequately described as lack of light? Above all, are we to think of them as living "in darkness"? To both questions, the answer is *no*.

They are deprived of sight, and in this their blindness consists. They also are deprived of light, but they are not in darkness in the popular sense of something with positive qualities: "It was a black night"; "The darkness was so thick you could cut it with a knife," and so on.

Cutsforth* and Chevigny,† the two blind writers who have contributed most to this subject, emphasize the fact that absence of light does not mean an awareness of darkness. They point out the error of writers on blindness who make darkness almost a positive thing, a tangible reality. Both of them call attention to the phenomenon known to physics as "dark adaptation." Sighted or blind, we can and do become "dark-adapted." After a period in the dark, darkness does not mean blackness as it does in the first sharp cutting off of light, but rather a neutral gray. Geldard ‡ says: ". . . the experience of looking at physical 'blackness' is not black, nor is black the lack of sensation. Perhaps due to autonomous processes working in the brain one gets, in the dark room, not black but gray or purplish gray. This is sometimes called 'brain gray' or the *self-light of the retina.* It appears that gray may be a constant background process and that all stimulation must 'break through' it, or perhaps 'modulate' it, for visual quality to be experienced."

All of us have had the experience of awakening in the middle of the night in a room from which light was completely shut off, and gradually gaining the feeling that we could see shapes in the graying dark. Experiments in lightless caves have shown that with "dark adaptation" there is a loss of the sense of positive darkness with which one begins the experience. Cutsforth speaks of a "visual field so free of dark experience that it seemed as though objects should be distinguishable."

We might say that after dark adaptation the experience is not one of *darkness* so much as a certain recognition of *lightlessness,* the first being a quality of pervasive gloom, the second a physical reality.

Clearly, then, the analogy which makes sight and light the same

* *The Blind in School and Society* by Thomas D. Cutsforth, Ph.D., American Foundation for the Blind, 1951.

† *The Adjustment of the Blind* by Hector Chevigny and Sydell Braverman, Yale University Press, 1950.

‡ *The Human Senses* by Frank A. Geldard, John Wiley & Sons, 1953, p. 52.

thing, or obversely blindness and darkness the same thing, is positively untrue and, moreover, *seriously harmful* to the blind, a barrier to their acceptance in society. It uses as symbols of sight and blindness two symbols which are basic to mankind, and in so doing gives blindness a symbolic meaning which it should not have (and which workers with the blind should be the last to accept).

Light, in the thinking of mankind, both primitive and civilized, is connected with ideas of truth, beauty, and goodness; it is a "physical transcendental." It is knowledge, hope, and love. Christian theology and worship, particularly among the great Eastern theologians but also in the West, have a vast "literature of light," using the term analogically not alone for goodness and grace and Heaven, but for the glory of God Himself.

Darkness, on the other hand, the negation of light, has become the symbol of ignorance and error, of ugliness, evil, despair, hate. Darkness becomes gloom, blackness, unending night, the "shadow of death" and even death itself. The time of darkness, the period of night, has traditionally been thought of as the time of conspiracy, of hatred, of crime, of sin. Darkness is mysterious and horrendous, and Satanic power is known as the "power of darkness."

These are the meanings of light and darkness in the emotions of man — not primitive man only or civilized man only, but in varying degrees, tones, shadings, and understanding, mankind itself. Not of sighted men alone, either, but of blind men as well. Consequently, as long as we equate blindness with darkness, we equate it not alone with physical darkness (the absence or negation of physical light), but with all the connotations of "darkness." And doing this cannot help raising an insurmountable barrier to the full acceptance of the blind into their proper position in sighted society.

Since this analogy is so harmful to the understanding of blindness and blind people, is it not paradoxical, even ironic, that it has been stamped into the public consciousness both by people who have given their lives to the assistance of the blind and by blind people themselves? Cutsforth and Chevigny have pointed out the degree to which agencies for the blind either directly or indirectly implement the concept. They point to the number of agencies which include in their titles the words "light" or "sunshine" or some derivative, which use in their mottoes some similar term or thought, which call their publications something which refers to the same concept, which speak in their advertising or their public relations media with one or another extension of the same thought, or which directly or indirectly do or say things which propagate the notion of blindness as a "dark world" of dread and despair.

Personally, I recall rather guiltily the readiness with which I took up the idea when I first came into work with the blind, and my own readiness to spread it until other people showed me its falseness. In the field, the idea still persists very strongly. Two serious examples appeared recently in fund-raising material, one from a large private agency for the blind and one from a very large organization of blind persons. The first appeal enclosed a "coloring book" supposedly belonging to some blind child; its cover was bright with colors and pictures that would appeal to childhood. When the potential donor opened it, he found inside a completely black page representing how the coloring book would look to the blind child. The second appeal, somewhat similar, had a black page to show how the world looks to the blind adult. Both of these may have been very effective in raising funds, but no amount of money could be worth the damage that such things do to blind people.

But this building up of the darkness concept is not the work of agencies or organizations alone. Cutsforth and Chevigny, themselves blind, point out the degree to which blind individuals are responsible for the general persistence in equating blindness and darkness. They note particularly the titles of books by blind persons which refer to emergence from or continuance in "darkness." And anyone who has listened to many blind people (with or without light perception) speaking to sighted groups has heard more than once the notion that they "live in darkness." Small wonder, then, that the great mass of the general public continues to equate blindness with darkness and with all the dank ideas and fetid feelings which "darkness" has for them.

Since there is no positive darkness, no loss of light in the ordinary sense, what is this *loss of light security* which we noted above? We have already considered something very similar to it in the loss of visual background — of light and change. But the loss of light security is distinct from this other loss. And since it is painful for a number of blinded people, it needs to be clearly understood and carefully handled.

A small proportion of blind people, as we said above, do not receive any light; "lightlessness" describes their condition better than "darkness." And these people suffer in two ways from a loss in "light security."

First, many of them are impressed and harmed by the public concept that they "live in darkness." If you have been pitied long enough and steadily enough for living in darkness you may actually come to believe it, unless you re-evaluate the situation. If you have been totally blind from birth, you have no knowledge of light and darkness and must take the word of sighted people who tell you that you are in darkness. And many blinded persons have so long feared the final loss of sight in terms of darkness that when it comes they never reevaluate their experience to see if they really *are* in darkness. The total meaning of the concept, with all its gloomy connotations, may and often does overwhelm them.

Second, even for that larger group who reject the public concept, lightlessness may have meanings which are upsetting. Usually these meanings are the result of the personal associations which night and lightlessness have for the individual. Perhaps often in his childhood, especially his early childhood, the coming of night was associated with separation from love. "Lights out" meant lonesomeness, being placed in a room alone with his own insecurity, cut off from mother and father and all who might have given him love. The lightless time was a loveless time — when love was downstairs with the grownups and he was shut off behind a closed door unable to feel or know it. Such fears and feelings of insecurity may have been successfully repressed through the years, yet the lightless time may still have meant for him a time in which he has been liable to quick risings of anxiety.

Now he finds himself in a constant lightless time. If
means also lovelessness, then the irreversible nature
blindness may make feelings of lonesomeness partic
the feelings appear to have no end. The resulting insec
very difficult to handle. Once again, then, we find in one of the los
which constitute blindness not alone the important reality factor, but also all the meanings and associations which add to the loss itself.

To sum up: *although* the actual loss of light does not affect every person who is blind, *although* it is never to be thought of as if it were the whole of blindness, and *although*, further, it must never be taken in the full emotional context given to it by the public at large, yet some *do* lose light, and a consequence of this in some instances is the loss of light security.

A BREATHING SPACE

This is a place where the reader may need an opportunity to come up for air.

From its opening paragraphs this book has plunged into depths of emotion and has moved in murky places of human psychology. Death. Blindness. Mutilation. Body image fears. Enucleation. Panic. Disorientation. Psychosis. Neurosis. Shock. Mourning. Darkness. Insecurity. Magic. Horror. The Eye and the I.

Even in our psychologically sophisticated day, not too many people give themselves over to this kind of reading. Readers who feel in themselves a vague disquietude as a result of these chapters are probably experiencing a very normal reaction. If we are to understand blindness as something other than a mere mechanical loss, we must study blindness in its effects on human nature. And perhaps, in going through this book, some readers may have gone deeper into human nature than they ever did before. But human nature is our own nature, and every time we look into its depths to some degree, we are uncovering recesses in ourselves. It is this, rather than blindness, which is the cause of our discomfort.

Other readers may have felt even greater disquietude because of their own close identification with blindness — their own sight is weakening; someone they knew in childhood was blind; someone close to them now is blind; they have worked for a time with blind persons. These readers may by now have strong feelings that this book is tending to mark blind people off as "different," as somehow "abnormal." But the very reason these readers are more than ordinarily disturbed by an analysis of what blindness does to people is the fact that blind people are in their psychology, in their human nature, like all the rest of us; and so we take what is said about them and apply it intimately to ourselves. Herein is the disturbance and fright.

For the first kind of reader, I suggest that now is the time to take a breathing space — not a long period of introversion, but a quiet review of what he has learned about human nature, with a recognition of how human we all are.

To the second kind of reader, I repeat the suggestion made in the introduction. Instead of proceeding directly through this long first section, which analyzes the losses suffered by the person who is blind, move into the section on rehabilitation; read first a section on a particular loss and then move to the part of the book which tells what is to be done about it.

Otherwise, to gain some insight into the total impact of the loss of sight, it is well to go directly forward through the remaining losses — seeing and feeling something of what they do to the blind individual, to those who are near to him, and to so many things which were most important in his life.

3

Losses in Basic Skills

6. LOSS OF MOBILITY

THE PERSON who suddenly loses sight (and only by considering a sudden and total loss can we see how complete this blow can be) is immobilized. He is fixed, rooted, confined to the spot on which he stands. He has lost one of the first marks of his infant development — the power to walk. And he stands held by panic and fear — yawning openings around him, threatening protuberances. Alone, he is being watched. Surrounded, he is cut off. He is without security, without maturity, without ability — a terribly dependent being.

This is an exaggerated picture, putting together all the worst. Yet even though the coming of blindness be gradual, even though its results be not so complete or so terrifying, something of this feeling comes to every blinded person. In some cases, these added fears may come only after early attempts at locomotion. In others, the panic may be very slight. But for every normally active adult who is blinded, the loss of mobility is a major loss. For mobility means more than walking. It means getting from place to place, by all the normal means which human beings regularly take advantage of, both in small spaces such as the room or home in which we live or work and in local or extensive geographical areas. It means going somewhere for the sake of getting there, for the sake of getting away from where we are, and even just for the sake of "getting."

We have all seen blind persons moving from place to place by one method or another. We know that the complete immobility of the blind man as pictured above is not a continuing fact. Actually, spaces do not always yawn nor obstacles always protrude to block the way. In fact, a blind person walking around his own house soon after losing his sight seems in much the same situation as the rest of us when, as often happens, we walk about our own houses after turning out the lights.

Yet there is a great difference. For the blinded person there is either a terrible finality to his condition or the suddenly recognized possibility that there may be that terrible finality. He either knows that he will never see again or he lives with the fear that such will be the doctor's verdict. Sighted people are certain that sooner or later darkness will be lifted and so are usually able to control the neurotic elements of their fear. Yet even so, when we are in darkness, unusual circumstances can bring all manner of neurotic panic to the surface.

The newly blind person certainly may have the same kind of neurotic fears, but it would be a grave error to think that his only fears are neurotic. Many have a very realistic basis. And his fear of travel (including the fear of walking, even in his own house) may very well include both neurotic and real fear.

When he believes (or *feels*) that the floor of his own living room may suddenly have changed its shape or its form, when he feels that perhaps there is an opening — perhaps the flooring is not complete, when he fears that perhaps someone has removed the railing from the stairwell — these are neurotic fears. But in contrast, when he believes that perhaps a chair will be in his way and that he may injure his shins or stub his toe, when he knows that he may walk into the edge of a table and knock his wind out or otherwise cause himself physical injury, when he fears that someone may have left the door partly open with the sharp edge of it toward him and that he may bump into it and cause his face to cut and bleed — these are reality fears, and very normal for a normal human being.

This distinction is extremely important. A few examples: Shopping crowds as a rule involve no danger; the person who feels a vague unreasoning terror in the midst of such a crowd is in the grip of a neurotic fear. On the other hand, a crowd that is about to get out of control, to trample, and become a mob presents a real threat. The crowd that is pushing us inevitably toward the edge of a subway pit is a real threat to our security, our safety and our life. To feel fear in such circumstances is to have a real fear and a very normal one. Again, the person who is afraid of high places in themselves, afraid to sit on balconies or to go above the second story in a building, is possessed by a neurotic fear. But the person who finds himself in a high spot — on the edge of a cliff, for instance — and is in real danger of falling to his death, whether from pressure from behind or from the insecurity of his footing, feels a real and normal fear of losing his life.

On this reality level — without any inclusion of the neurotic whatsoever — the blind person has many things to fear if he intends to walk about or to travel. A later chapter will describe the kind of training in mobility which will eliminate many of the dangers; trial and error will help to lessen some others. But there will always be more danger for a blind person in getting about than for the rest of us. There will always be the furniture and the small obstacles in the house. There will be the stairways, the kiddie carts, the baby carriages, the hydrants, the animals, the backing trucks, the low awnings, the spiked edges of low-hanging signs, and the impervious pedestrians along the sidewalk. There will be ice and snow, oil and slick, excavations and manholes. And there will be automobiles — with drivers obeying the lights and the speed laws and drivers disobeying both, drivers with coated windshields and drivers with the sun in their eyes, drivers backing out of alleys and drivers cutting across the corners of sidewalks. And with all these there will be danger — real danger — of minor physical injury, of major injury, of death itself, or only of embarrassment.

On this reality level alone, then, the blind person needs greater motivation to cause him to travel than do the rest of us.

Exercise and enjoyment are sufficient motives for many persons to walk. But this is seldom true for the untrained blind person. The motivation is not strong enough to overcome the inconvenience; it does not outweigh the strong deterrents of tension and of danger of personal injury.

Weariness with the place we are in, boredom, nervousness, the need for a change of scene may be motivation for us to get up and walk somewhere (or even just pace the floor). But the boredom, the nervousness, the need for a change of place would have to be much stronger for the blind person because of the difficulties which attend his walking.

Or the place we want to get to — our business, a club, a movie, a dance, church, a lecture, a bar, a friend's house — may provide the motivation that causes us to move, to walk, to travel across town. In every instance the degree of motivation will have to be stronger for the person who is blind in proportion to the added degree of difficulty which traveling causes him.

And if overlying all these real difficulties are the neurotic fears discussed earlier, then only the strongest motivations of terrible need will cause the blind person to move. In this case he is truly immobile. This neurotic type of immobility may well be denied by the individual afflicted by it. His unconscious may rationalize his fears by believing that he is "not interested in going," that "those things don't mean anything any more," or that he is "perfectly happy and contented" to sit still and relax with the radio. But tensions within him may be causing terrible conflicts and unhappiness.

Later chapters will discuss other factors which must be kept in mind in connection with this loss of mobility: its relationship to career, to recreation, to social adequacy, for example. Nor have we as yet more than mentioned the very important factors of the embarrassment of being different, of making mistakes in front of people, of being watched while bumping a lamp post, of being pitied, and all the shattering implications of dependence. But even without any of these, the loss of mobility is obviously a major loss — one of the greatest of the reality losses which follow the loss of sight. It is a dying to adult independence — a return to the immobility or creeping dependence of childhood or a forced entrance into the slow, shuffling dependence of old age.

7. LOSS OF TECHNIQUES OF DAILY LIVING

There is nothing subtle about this loss. It is made up of the thousand repeated frustrations in the daily life of the blinded person which remind him that he is blind — and never let him forget that he is blind. The little things — maddening in their inconvenience, embarrassing, painful — which drive home the helplessness and the dependence of blindness.

"He's really quite amazing. He just laughs at those things. I saw him the other day and I was really embarrassed at the mistake he made, but he just made a wisecrack out of it." You wonder if the people who say such things about a blind man have any understanding of human nature. Can they have any idea of just how unfunny the situation was to the person who laughed? That laughing was the only possible way of handling the situation?

Eating and drinking. Caring for bowel and bladder functions. Keeping oneself clean and neat. Undressing at night and dressing in the morning. Even in these simple basic functions, the blind person is hampered. In his growing-up process, these were some of the earliest things he learned. They were among the earliest actions whose success won him praise and a display of affection: "My, he's really getting to be a big boy." And now! Even in these things he is hampered, frustrated, embarrassed. So far has he sunk. So far has he regressed.

To catalogue all the difficulties involved in this loss would take a book. And in fact, many of the books written by blind persons relate endless anecdotes about such little frustrations and good-humoredly tell how individuals have met them.

Eating can cause so many difficulties that a few blind people give up the fight to eat normally and revert to bib and spoon. Try it yourself some time — the blindfold dinner technique. It won't teach you about blindness, but it will teach you about this one phase of blindness. Your hand wanders out to seek the first dish put before you, gropes for it, finds it, explores it, trying to find out what it is just so you will know how to handle it. Is it fruit cup, shrimp cocktail, grapefruit, tomato juice in a tall glass, tomato juice in a short glass, tomato juice in a glass buried in a bowl of ice, jellied consommé, hot soup? What? Do you eat it, sip it, drink it? Do table tools come into this? Where are they? What glasses or goblets are around as you start to explore? That is only the first course. As you go on, there will be the little booby traps, perhaps even that awful little paper cup of sauce or dressing for you to stab with the fork and try to eat. Every main course will be a mélange for you. No more choosing a forkful of this and then a forkful of that; you lower the fork each time resigned to take whatever is on it, hoping only that it won't come up empty, or with the whole main course hanging from it. You won't have to worry about buttering your bread, because if you are like most blind persons you will have decided by now that it isn't worth the struggle and you didn't really care for butter anyhow — besides, it's fattening.

The adult losing his sight certainly needs no course in "toilet training" in the commonly accepted sense of the term. But if he brings to his blindness the same embarrassment about bowel and bladder functions which an elder generation dinned into many of us and which the multiple American bathroom has fortified, if he brings the same anxiety about germs and dirt, if cleanliness is not merely an aim but is in any degree a compulsion for him — then, especially in a strange bathroom, and more particularly in a public washroom, his lack of sight is going to cause him grave disturbance. For the man there is the added humiliation of being compelled to squat each time he empties his bladder. And in general there are the problems of personal hygiene, both for men and women.

Not only cleanliness but ordinary neatness is a problem for the person who is blind. Chances of spotting clothing, whether by spilling or by bumping against something soiled, have markedly increased, while the opportunity for noticing a slight spot or soiling of clothing has disappeared. Wrinkled clothing and a generally unkempt appearance may result not merely from a neurotic disinterest in appearance, as with the sighted, but from the visual nonawareness of them

Undressing certainly is no major problem; it is merely another occasion to remind a man of his blindness as he tries to hang his things in such a way that they will be neat and place them so that he can find them and distinguish them from other things on the following morning. Dressing is more of a problem — choosing the tie that goes with the shirt, the socks that make a pair, and for the blind woman of course there is a far greater degree of choice as to what combination of clothes and accessories to wear each day or on special occasions.

The choice of new clothes is also a part of this. The ability to choose one's clothes according to one's own taste is of great importance to many people. The blinded woman deprived of the opportunity to go out and purchase a new hat in accordance with her own ideas and feelings may find it particularly frustrating — along with the loss of the psychological lift that the new hat gives to so many.

Take also the twin rituals of shaving or make-up. Even if you choose a shaving instrument that cuts the beard without cutting the face, you have the problem of making sure that every spot is smooth shaven, and the particular problem of keeping hairline and/or sideburns regular and even. Choosing the right jars and soaps and the order of their application must be difficult enough for the sighted woman without the complication of not being able to see the jars and to tell one from another. Make-up can become an ugly blotch and lipstick a more than ordinarily ugly scar if you are unable to view your application of it or the results. And even if you have made certain that it is tooth paste, not shaving cream or that new shampoo, contained in the tube you are holding, you now have the minor nuisance-value problem of making sure that it goes onto the tooth-brush and not onto you or the floor or the sink.

This should be enough to show why the loss of the techniques of daily living is a major loss — because of its multiplication of a thousand little inconveniences and nuisances. Imagine yourself trying, without your sight, to run the house, keep your accounts, sign checks, count the money in your wallet, find the telephone, dial it, locate the key you dropped on the floor, find the hat you thought you left on the shelf, keep your living quarters attractive, light your cigarette, empty the ash tray, clean in the corners, purchase for the household or your own needs, eat in the self-service restaurant, cook supper, breakfast or anything else, pick a can of food out of the well-stocked food closet, etc., etc., etc.

The loss of techniques of daily living forces dependence; and it is in this dependence and the embarrassment it engenders, as well as in the constant repetitious reminders of blindness itself, that most of its pain consists. With this loss, the blinded person dies to self-sufficiency, to adult responsibility.

4

Losses in Communication

8. LOSS OF EASE OF WRITTEN COMMUNICATION

THIS LOSS — one of the most widely known of the losses due to blindness — includes mainly, of course, the writing and reading of language symbols, but takes in also signs, cartoons, pictures, etc., and might therefore be called the loss of graphic communication.

If the loss of reading were merely that of the power to read books, this loss would not be a very widespread one, or at least would not seriously affect the great majority of blinded persons. The percentage of people who spend any considerable amount of time reading books is smaller than is generally realized, and therefore the deprivation of this particular power is important to fewer people than is sometimes thought.

But this does not mean that this loss is not a most painful one to many persons. Despite the fact that we are hardly a literary people, the reading of books plays an important part in many lives. When blindness takes this power away, the loss is a very keen one. However, for the non-book-reader the loss of the ability to read books is merely a meaningless phrase.

But there are innumerable readers who never open the pages of a book. Among these are people who spend a major part of their available time reading magazines. Whatever the value of the material they read, the loss of the ability to read it is of great importance to them.

Then there are the readers of journals, trade publications, professional magazines, economic and business reviews, all of which may be very important to a person's work in life. The loss of the ability to read this particular type of material may have a direct bearing on his ability to earn a living or to keep his position in his profession. Here again, then, the loss is a severe one.

Many others read only the daily papers. Among them are the avid readers whose whole morning is spoiled without the breakfast paper, and those who cannot see an evening through without the latest edition. Take the power to read newspapers from these people and you have caused them a real loss.

And so with all kinds of reading. It may be comic books or comic strips (and incidentally many intelligent blind persons lose all patience with adults who find time for Little Orphan Annie, Dick Tracy or any of the rest). It may be advertisements, billboards perhaps; it may be the reading of weather signs and symbols. Whatever it be, the loss of it is greater or smaller depending on its value to the person. Watching television is another form of reading, a form to be considered more in connection with the loss of recreation. And, of course, there are such simple forms of reading as finding numbers in a telephone book.

But the greatest loss in this connection is the loss of the ability to read one's own mail, with the corresponding loss of the ability to write one's own letters, to keep up one's personal correspondence without the intrusion of another party. These losses may be very painful, because they involve not only independence but personal privacy.

And one grave loss here may be the loss of the ability to write one's own signature. It is legally possible to sign with an "X," but it is a definite blow to pride and self-esteem. And so with the ability to write out checks and, to a lesser degree, to scribble the grocery list, the girl's telephone number, the personal notations of things to remember, the social notes, the message on a Christmas card.

Only the author, the editor, the news writer and those in similar occupations feel very seriously the loss of the ability to do manuscript work. But there are also the accountants, the draftsmen, the typists, the printers and all the rest whose lifework is bound up with written communication.

This whole loss of ease of written communication is far more serious in our day than it ever was in the past. Not only is literacy widespread, but the inability to read and write is widely (although falsely) equated with ignorance and stupidity. The blind man, unable to read and write, becomes in a sense "illiterate." Thus, in one more sphere of important and normal activity, he is not only disabled, but set aside with the ignorant and the witless.

Since the reading and writing public in our country includes every normal sighted person above the age of seven or eight, the loss of written communication is far graver than might appear at first glance. Many technical advances of our day have been working to ease this particular loss (although the advance of television seems once more to be emphasizing it). Nevertheless, this loss remains a major handicap — a dying to our ability to communicate and to receive communication by means of the written word.

9. LOSS OF EASE OF SPOKEN COMMUNICATION

This loss affects not only actual listening and speaking, but also gestures, posture, mannerisms, pantomime, and facial expression — all the unspoken elements of "spoken" communication. Yet, unlike the previous one, this loss is seldom spoken of and apparently seldom recognized. The glib distinction is often made that deafness cuts its victim off from a world of people, whereas blindness cuts him off from a world of things. But the loss of ease in spoken communication is one aspect of blindness which (even apart from the psychological barriers it raises) tends to cut the blind person off from the world of people as well.

Even in the vocal element of speech, the blind person has suffered a handicap. Everyone of us — whether he realizes it or not — is to some degree a lip reader. When we listen, we perceive some words entirely with our ears; other words we partly see. If the speaker's lips are hidden from us, we must concentrate more in order to catch his words.

But words are only one element of speech. The facial expression which accompanies any statement is capable of changing its whole meaning. As a smile may make a gross insult into a compliment, a sneer can turn the compliment into a slur. The person who cannot see the changes of facial expression may completely miss the meaning of the speaker; and thus ordinary communication, "vocal" communication, has failed him.

The gestures that accompany "over there" or "so big" or "as tall as this" are frequently used, day in and day out, in ordinary talk. The jutting jaw with which the storyteller accompanies his description of the aggressive individual is not an essential part of the story, but it belongs to the total conversation, and the blind person misses it. More important are the shrug of the shoulders, the arching of the eyebrows, the tossing of the head, which in themselves are words, phrases or sentences — and sometimes are more important than many-worded speeches.

Uncertainty as to the source of a voice, as to where the one is who is speaking, may make identification of the speaker difficult, and thus in another way hinder conversation. Even more difficult is the uncertainty as to where the voice is directed. "Is he speaking to me?" is a question continually in the mind of the blind man, for time and again he has no way of knowing whether or not he is the one addressed.

Or again, conversation, and especially conversation among friends, is often made up in great part of silences. But the blind person lacks his former ability to judge the meaning of the silences; he cannot see the mood or the expression accompanying them. Instead of the calm, relaxed meditation which may be indicated, he may find himself nervously wondering if he is expected to say something. Has he embarrassed or insulted anyone by his silence? And there is always the possibility that the silence indicates that the sighted party to the conversation has quietly left the room, with nothing but a visual indication of his departure.

Worst of all is the awful and unpardonable possibility that there is another conversation going on around him in which he is not supposed to have a part — that by nods and gestures, sighted persons are "conversing" about his blindness. This is seldom done except by way of sympathy; it is done at times even by the families of the blind and, worse still, people in the field of work with the blind. But whatever the motives, it implies a total lack of confidence in the blind person and indicates how little he may trust the frankness and sincerity of those around him.

And his own speaking is similarly interfered with, although nothing has happened to his voice. Many of the elements referred to above obviously play a part here. The blind man is not always certain that the person he is about to address is still in the room, or in just what part of it he may be. The blind person, therefore, may well develop what Cutsforth refers to as the "broadcast voice," the voice which instead of being directed to a particular person attempts (like the radio speaker) to fill the room with sound in order to catch the person addressed, wherever he may be.

A strong element in our speaking is the reaction to what we are saying. In ordinary speaking, we never know, when we begin on a topic, what words we may bring into it, let alone what vocal or facial emphasis we may give them. The total conversation develops according to the reaction which we perceive as we continue. If that reaction is hidden from us because we cannot see it, our speaking is greatly interfered with.

Again, gestures are a part of conversation (even in a nation which considers that foreigners are the only ones who gesticulate), and blind persons, even persons blinded in adult life, often fail not only to perceive but to use many of the natural hand and body movements which accompany everyday speech. Using them may mean the embarrassment of bumping a nearby table or lamp; moreover, the blind person naturally puts a greater emphasis on the verbal side of speech than the visual. Thus the gestures blinded persons do still use tend to become self-conscious, and self-conscious gestures, even more than the lack of gestures, interfere with spoken communication.

This loss of gestures is not something that the average sighted person specifically notices. What he does notice is that there is something intangibly "different" about the way in which the blind person speaks. He will go away with a sense of "something missing," and its very mysteriousness will make more serious the interference with normal communication and so make this particular loss more important.

Even more disturbing to normal communication is the loss of facial expression and the substitution of the "bland" look or the fixed smile. This change results in part from the failure to see other people's facial expressions, causing a lack of visual memory as to nuances of expression. It seems that much of our facial expression is a mirroring of the expressions of those around us, and so it is not surprising that when the mirror is gone there is no "mirroring." Perhaps, too, this change is due in part to the fact that our facial expressions vary according to the reactions of others to what we are saying. Since the blind person is not able to get this reaction while he is actually speaking, he may unconsciously set his face into the familiar "dead pan" until he knows whether the tide is flowing toward acceptance or rejection.

There is also some reason to believe that the fixed smile is a mask, a "poker face" unconsciously adopted to hide the true feelings which are underneath. (Anyone who has seen the improvement in the facial expression and the posture of a blind person when he gets at the roots of some of his own feelings in, for example, a course of analysis must give credence to this as a possibility.) Some sort of mask is almost necessary for the type of blind person who is often far away from a conversation, daydreaming about his own personal problems.

These and the other expressions, habits, mannerisms which go under the title of "blindisms" interfere with normal social intercourse and cause a real barrier to communication. This is especially true of failure of the eyes to focus, or of a tendency of the eyeballs to wander back into the head so that the rolling whites show what is, to many people, a hideous appearance.

These difficulties can become more magnified for the blinded man who addresses an audience. He may, for example, half turn away from his audience, not knowing just where they are, and by so doing completely snap the bond between him and them, putting an insurmountable obstacle in the way of his getting his message across.

A further problem for the platform speaker is the difficulty of speaking while reading his notes. Relatively few blind speakers are such fluent braille readers as to be able to read rapidly and gracefully on a platform. The problem was solved in part by a Canadian blind speaker at an international meeting in Paris, whose wife remained off stage in a place where she could read his typed notes into a microphone with a long cord leading to a "hearing aid" in his ear. But any auditory cue interferes with the speaker's concentration on the auditory reactions from his audience.

Thus loss of ease of spoken communication is the one loss in blindness which resembles the loss of personal communication induced by deafness. In fact, the blind person speaking is, in a sense, "deaf" to his own voice, since he is deaf to the reaction of others to it.

Most serious of all, and underlying all the other problems, is the very great loss in the communication of "affect"—of the extra something over and above the words used which communicates from person to person, almost from soul to soul. Words are heard and spoken by the blinded person, but all too often the personality which gives them life, the "enfleshment" of the words, is gone.

Here again, then, is a major loss in the multiple handicap of blindness. It is a further dying to the world in which the blinded person has lived, a dying to his friends and acquaintances.

10. LOSS OF INFORMATIONAL PROGRESS

This loss might be given various names; loss of *awareness of the social scene*, loss of *growth in information*, loss of *ability to keep up with the times*, or loss of *contact with the present day*. It is a loss of progress when other things are moving on, a standing still while the world goes by, in fact a moving backward, since it puts the blinded person far behind his previous position.

This loss is the result of the fact that the blinded person is severely hampered in means for obtaining that scope of information expected of him before he lost his sight, for gaining the current knowledge which helped to keep him up to a certain level in the circle of friends, neighbors, and associates who make up his "intellectual environment."

The content of this loss varies greatly with individuals. In one group it may concern current comment on the social attitude of a newly discovered composer or the mannerisms of a salon philosopher. In another it may be a newspaper biography of a leading sports figure or the results of the Grand National. Professionally it may concern new discoveries in atomic energy, the state of the stock market, or the search for some unfiltrable virus; or it may pertain to higher wages and greater security through a new union, or the availability of jobs at a newly constructed industrial plant.

Informational progress may be concerned only with such matters as comic strips, the activities of movie stars, the batting averages of ball players, the characters in a trunk murder, scandals in private or public life, the relative merits of various cosmetics, the design of the latest highway or the newest automobile.

To each group, the content is different. But for the blinded man in each group, the means and the opportunity for progress in it, for keeping up with what is happening, are definitely cut down. And this does not mean merely standing still. It means going backward. For it is standing still while the world goes on. The blinded person may still obtain new information, but his visual progress is stunted, and as a result his progress in information is terribly limited. For progress here depends in great part on two things — on *reading* and on the *observation* of people and of things.

The kind of reading involved may be any of the varieties discussed in the chapter on written communication; in any case, it is clear how much more difficult, if not impossible, any kind of reading has become. The observation of people involved is not necessarily completely visual; yet those of us who have grown up with sight realize how large a part seeing plays in our observation of people. The visual emphasis is even more pronounced in our observation of things. And with mobility gone, chances to observe are restricted to a small geographical area.

The blinded man who still wears the sideburns of another day and who always gets a 1910 haircut may well do so because of this failure in informational progress, or, for the same reason, a blinded woman may not share with all her neighbors the knowledge that a house in the next block has been torn down — so pervasive in daily life is the blinded person's difficulty in observing ordinary people and ordinary things.

And he also suffers a decrease in his opportunities for gaining new experiences and information about scheduled or predicted events — the line-up of the coming ball game, the announcement of a lecture, the weights of the boxers in tonight's match, the scheduling of a concert or an opera, the calling of an air raid test, or the imminence of a storm. Lack of information along these lines may cost the blinded person dearly in one or another area of life.

But lack of the means for obtaining current information affects most of all his status in his own mind and in his circle of friends and acquaintances. What will happen to his status in his circle as he has (or feels that he has) less and less to give to it? Information is the stuff out of which knowledge is made, and people have a way of confusing lack of knowledge with lack of intelligence. Soon his acquaintances may begin to think of the blinded person's lack of current information as stupidity. And from that it may not be far to the time when he thinks of himself as stupid.

It is easy to see some of the effects on the blinded man as he realizes what has resulted from this "dying to the world in which he lives." He may surrender and live in a world of the past; he may become an "expert" on some subject and pontificate upon it as often as someone will lend him an ear; he may take the floor and hold it on things he knows nothing about; he may stop completely in intellectual growth, close his mind to all new opinions and hold only to the things he knew about — unless something is done to restore his loss in this vital area of keeping up with the changing world.

5

Losses in Appreciation

11. LOSS OF THE VISUAL PERCEPTION OF THE PLEASURABLE

IN STUDYING this loss, a striking difference should be noted between the attitude, or at least the verbalized attitude, of sighted people toward these aspects of blindness and that of those who have become blind. When sighted people talk or write about blindness, they very frequently mention something like: "Never again to gaze on his mother's face — never to see his own home nestled among the trees." Yet blinded persons seldom mention anything of the kind.

There are many possible interpretations of the failure of blinded persons to discuss this loss at length. But if anyone is tempted to think that this is because it is not a major loss, let him look at the statements of those who have regained their sight after years of blindness. Time and again they have said in one way or another: "The most wonderful thing was to see my wife and my children again," or "The greatest moment of it all was when we turned the corner into my own street, and for the first time in years I saw the house I have lived in so long." Does this suggest a minor loss? On the contrary, it suggests a loss so great that it has been impossible to speak of it.

The loss we are analyzing here is the loss of the visual reception (intake, embrace) of an object which the blinded man formerly found pleasing. This object might be a painting in his living room that no stretch of anyone else's imagination could call "beautiful," or some completely ugly piece of "religious art" — completely ugly except that to him it symbolizes something which he loves. Again, it might be the "smile on his own mother's face," though the face may happen to be the homeliest as well as the finest on the block, or "his own home nestled among the trees," for although the house may be an architectural monstrosity, to him it is the most homey of all the houses in the neighborhood. The goodness symbolized by these things is what pleased him when he once looked at them — and this is the special pleasure that is now lost.

The pleasurable object in this sense might also be, for example, a traffic pattern in a city, the speedy passing of the newest car, people going by on a nearby road, sheep wandering, the color of a display window, the running of a rabbit or of a fine horse. In any case, the loss of pleasure is great in proportion to the pleasure the individual once found in looking at such an object.

This lost pleasure may also be the very normal kind in which "sensible" and "spiritual" * pleasure to a degree overlap: the sight of a handsome man to a woman, or the sight of a beautiful woman to a man, or it may be in the field of sinful and of abnormal pleasures, where erotic satisfaction runs wild.†

Or — back to the normal and generally sinless — the pleasurable object may be one's own self. The harmless (and somewhat foolish)

* "Erotic" and "artistic" might be other terms for what we are referring to here, but these words lead to real semantic difficulties. There is a pleasure which the total human being enjoys in meeting and seeing another human being; it is a pleasure partly of his material side and partly of his spiritual side; it is a "human" pleasure. This must be sharply distinguished from the sinful pleasure in which one aspect of the human being takes over, and the pleasure is sensual or carnal. The normal young man or the normal young woman should normally be pleased upon meeting one of the opposite sex. Part of that normal pleasure lies in the *seeing* of that person. The loss of this normal pleasure along with the loss of sight is sufficiently important to be stressed. On the other hand, it is perfectly possible that without mention of the distinction, seriously false inferences might be gained from the text.

† Obviously I am not suggesting that the loss of the ability to sin is something to be grieved over. Loss of a sense does not take away the ability to sin. The loss of the visual perception of these things will not in itself do anything to make the blind person less sinful or more normal in his pleasures. Sin will still be possible — this type of sin through visual fantasies still remaining in the mind. In this case, the loss of a pleasurable object is the loss of a sinful one. Pain results. Our job is to remove the pain without the restoring of the sin.

pleasure which many people take in looking in a mirror is gone. The further pleasure — even without the mirror — of a visual awareness of one's own body, an awareness that for the most part we are almost entirely unconscious of, yet have probably had with us from the day when we first made the great discovery that those toes at the foot of our cradle were our own — this visual awareness and the subconscious pleasure which accompanied it are gone, and the loss may be included in this loss of the visual perception of a pleasurable object.

Some would include here also the loss of pleasure in the sight receptor, but I do not believe that any such pleasure exists in the senses of sight or of hearing.

Yet we should consider here the loss of direct sense pleasure which comes to us all at times in the presence of color, form or movement. This particular aspect of pleasure concerns not simply natural emotional reactions but associated emotions — emotions associated from the days of our earliest memory with form, color and motion, but most especially with color, and emotions associated with our training to evaluate and appreciate them or with our "conditioning" to avoid and evade them.

12. LOSS OF THE VISUAL PERCEPTION OF THE BEAUTIFUL

This is the loss of the visual embrace of the beautiful object, the loss of the visual reception, the "visual drinking" of the beautiful. Not every blinded person feels this particular loss; some people cannot "die" to visual beauty, for they have never been alive to it. But those who do feel it must experience the pain of this particular dying as one of the most severe of all the dyings caused by blindness.

Now, all the beauty that they once experienced through the sense of sight, all the pleasure that burned and pained at the sight of true beauty, is cut off. To stand now in the presence of a delicately or majestically beautiful object, to know that it is there in front of one, and yet to be unable to contemplate it, is a different pain, a pain without pleasure but with only terrible frustration. And to stand by impotently while someone ineptly tries to describe something beautiful, tries to capture and communicate it in stupid words — here can be a source of sorrow indeed.

Sighted people almost invariably mention this loss — even more often than the preceding one. "Never again to see the blush of a rose, the glory of a sunset." Blinded persons mention it but rarely.

This is a striking difference, and one that is difficult to evaluate. Perhaps sighted people find this loss easier to speak of than some others; perhaps it saves them from contemplating other aspects of blindness which they would not like to think about. Or perhaps this loss has been so stressed in literature that sighted people have learned that they "should" advert to it. But why do blind persons mention it so seldom? Is the loss unimportant to them? Perhaps they feel it is so obvious as not to need mentioning. Perhaps it is so outweighed by other losses that these others take precedence. Possibly it is too serious a loss to bear. But even more likely is the possibility that the true bitterness of this loss is felt only by those people who actually have a strong love of the beautiful, that they feel it less at some times than at others, and also that it is a loss so keen and close to the heart that to speak of it in the wrong words to the wrong people would cheapen and sully its meaning and would be worse than nothing.

But, whatever the reason may be, there is no doubt that this loss is grave in proportion to the person's individual perception and appreciation of visual beauty prior to blindness — and that for some persons it can be a very grave loss indeed.

6

Losses Concerning Occupation and Financial Status

13. LOSS OF RECREATION

RECREATION is refreshment, reanimation, the giving of fresh life, especially after wearying toil or anxiety. In one or another form it is important to everybody and most of all to those under serious stress. Yet in the midst of new blindness, with all the stresses and strains it brings about, the blinded man has lost recreation also. From any standpoint this is a major loss.

Recreation varies so much with individual needs, individual temperaments and habits, that it would be impossible to catalogue all its forms. But it may be helpful if we run through those most common in our culture to see how many are seriously interfered with by the loss of sight.

Recreation, for most people, is either intellectual or physical, or a combination of both. For some, recreational reading is foremost, or discussing things that have been read. For others, movie-going, play-going, or cards, the stimulation of checkers or chess. To others, recreation means the whole range of conversation and people. It may be watching television or attending one or another type of sports event, eating out — new people — new places — new foods, pleasure driving or pleasure riding, hobbies, the collecting of stamps or useless items, the workbench in the cellar, amateur painting. Then there is the recreation that calls for more physical effort: the "constitutional," the tramp through the woods, the "fast workout" at handball, boxing, or tennis, the round of golf, hunting and fishing and sailing, horseback riding, the various activities that make a person "feel like a new man." Sudden blindness interferes with, takes the pleasure from, or puts an end to all these.

Music is commonly thought of as a universal form of recreation for the blind. Yet the blinded music-maker — pianist, horn player, stringed instrument player — now finds his enjoyment diminished or entirely gone if he depended partly or wholly upon printed music. True enough, the person who found his pleasure simply in listening to music can continue this recreation almost as before, but if his listening took place away from home in places where he now cannot go or cannot feel at ease, then this too is interfered with.

Whatever the blinded person's forms of recreation may have been, and whether they were formal or informal, whether they occupied a major portion of his life or only the weekly holiday or annual vacation, their loss can be completely disturbing to the whole pattern of his life, and also to his emotional life and his physical well-being.

If participation in a sport is important for a man of his age group, then standing by, unable to participate, he may have strong feelings of frustration, even awakened feelings of misgiving regarding his manhood. He is even denied what is so important to some of those who take part in sport for its own sake — the reward of applause for a job well done.

Recreation may have meant many different things to the blinded man. It may have been his only escape from the drabness and drudgery of life, and now certainly the drabness if not the drudgery of life has greatly increased and there is no escape. It may have been his only means of working off feelings (perhaps of hostility and aggression), and now there is nothing to do with those feelings except to work them off on those around him or to keep them bottled up inside him. It may have been his one method of protection from wandering daydreams and erotic phantasies — and now the protection is gone. It may have been his one opportunity for equal-footed competition, for feeling real and whole and adequate — and now when he needs these things most they have disappeared.

The loss of recreation is a grave loss — a "death" in which there is no opportunity for "refreshment," for "new life."

14. LOSS OF CAREER, VOCATIONAL GOAL, JOB OPPORTUNITY

All those who lose their sight do not necessarily find their careers thereby ended. About 50 per cent of them are over sixty-five years old when they become blind, and their careers are already over or are so well established that they can continue. Some of those who become blind early in, or in the midst of, their careers are able, because of the nature of their work, to go back to it with little or no interruption — for example, lawyers, judges, business executives, personnel workers and the like.

Yet the loss of a career, of a vocational goal, of job opportunity is an important loss for most persons and a most serious one for some. And in our day there is at least some recognition of this fact, although the question of employment is often confused with the question of income and financial security or with the notion of "busy work."

To lose a job, especially the particular job on which a person has set his heart or on which his career seems to depend, can often be a tragedy in itself — without blindness. Newspaper stories of the depressed person who went off the bridge or out of the window often indicate that the loss of a job or the breakup of a business or professional career occasioned the tragedy.

Certainly the loss of a job, the closing out of a career, the blocking off of a vocational goal can constitute a very severe blow, its nature and severity depending on the meaning of the career or goal to the individual. For over and above the need of the financial income from a job, over and above the need for keeping busy, a career, vocational goal, and job opportunities have a deep meaning and a deep importance.* And these are bound up with the dignity of the indi-

* The type of forced retirement we are discussing must be distinguished from retirement because of age when a career has been completed. There is widespread knowledge of the bad effect on some elderly persons forced to retire because of age. Yet recent scientific studies have showed that retirement because of age can

vidual, the dignity of the job or position involved, the dignity of work itself, the social pressures, the external and internal need of doing what is expected or demanded of us according to our age, ability, training and environment.

What is most important to us here is that the impact of this loss on each individual varies in accordance with all these factors. But for every person who would normally be working, the loss of job opportunity, of vocational goal, the closing out of a career is in itself a severe loss and should be recognized as such. The "death" here is to usefulness, to a life of productivity and worth.

15. LOSS OF FINANCIAL SECURITY

Although loss of a job and loss of financial security are not necessarily the same thing, for the average person the loss of a job does mean the loss of income, and few have sufficient savings to cushion the quick drop to financial need and financial dependence.* Moreover, besides the loss of income through loss of employment, blindness can cause financial difficulties by *increasing expenses.*

The increased expenses which blindness brings may be divided into two types: sickness expenses and expenses incident to blindness.

Sickness expenses are easily recognized — cost of hospitalization, drugs, medicines, surgery, nursing care. Even after a final verdict of permanent incurable blindness, these expenses sometimes run on much longer than they should. The rumor of a doctor somewhere else who has cured "just your type of blindness." The hope-lifted trip (perhaps to a distant place) to consult with him. The despair-laden return. Or perhaps the whispered story of some new treatment. The weeks or months of paying for it. And again disappointment. These

---

be of benefit to the person prepared for it and can increase rather than decrease the life span.

* Nevertheless, it is never necessary in the United States for a blind person to resort to begging as a means of gaining subsistence. The presence of blind beggars on the streets is bitterly resented by most blind persons. In various parts of the country, organizations of blind persons and others are trying to outlaw this practice, and it is already forbidden in many cities and states.

things do not happen to every blind person, but they happen often enough.

Expenses incident to blindness are chiefly incident to the loss of mobility, the loss of written communication, and the loss of the techniques of daily living.

The person whose mobility has been hampered or lost is quickly involved in new expenses when he tries to get from place to place. Where previously he might walk, he now finds that he must ride. Where formerly he would have gone by streetcar, bus or subway, he now finds that he must go by taxi. Where hitherto he would have gone alone, he now finds that he must bring a guide (and whether he pays the guide or merely pays the guide's fare, expenses soar).

The loss of written communication leaves the possibility of paying for a reader — and also the expense.

It is the same with the techniques of daily living: The blind person has to buy service. He has to "buy sight," and the oftener he buys, the heavier the cost. The person who used to eat in the self-service cafeteria is forced into the more expensive restaurant where he will get (and pay for) service. The shopper who sought out bargains or made purchases in the self-service stores now orders by phone and gets (and pays for) delivery of goods. Cleaning bills mount as the person more easily spots his clothing, or at least must have his things cleaned more frequently since he cannot otherwise be sure they are clean. The person who lived alone now seeks a housekeeper. Messenger service becomes a necessity in situations where once it was a luxury.

If he can afford it and if the opportunity exists, the blind person may purchase sight to make up for more of his losses as well. He may, for example, try to restore his job or career by contracting to purchase sight regularly — the sight of the chauffeur, the observer, the reader, the secretary he needs. Here, obviously, the expense is great.

There are, it is true, some persons whose expenses are actually *decreased* by blindness. These are non-wage-earners, whom blindness makes into "sitters." They never leave the house, they do not need many new clothes, they cease to be interested in anything which would involve expense. But when rehabilitation gets them off their chairs, it increases their expenses to "normal"—and beyond. They begin to take streetcars, they begin to get interested in doing things—and so, inevitably, they begin to buy and spend.

Whether the expenses in each case are great or small, there are always some of these expenses incident to blindness. And these, together with the sickness expenses, mean outgo is increased while income is decreased or completely cut off. Thus, to many people, this loss of financial security implies a death to freedom.

7

Resulting Losses to the Whole Personality

16. LOSS OF PERSONAL INDEPENDENCE

VERY FEW reality situations can be a greater blow to personal independence than becoming blind. To the public at large, the "helpless blind man" is a symbol of utter dependence. Every loss that we have been considering involves a loss of independence — even the loss of physical integrity, for one of the first feelings it brings with it is that of being a dependent person, and the very fact of being "different," in the sense described under that particular loss (page 14), makes dependency more difficult to accept.

But individuals react differently to this forced dependence. If we are to help blinded people in the various ways that they need help, we need to understand that from our dependent infancy through the growing independence of youth and adult life to our dependent old age, two forces are at work: the desire for independence with its freedom and the desire for dependence and its protection.

Seldom are we aware of the degree to which these two divergent drives are operating in our lives, but the fact that these two forces exist in us side by side leads to some very real and startling paradoxes. Generally speaking, the persons who are labeled "very independent" are extremely dependent persons, and the stronger the symptoms of what seems like independence, the greater the dependence within. On the other hand, the truly independent, those who have an inner independence, have no difficulty with the occasional situations — illness, unforeseen calamities — in which all of us have to be dependent.

When we hear about someone that "He is very independent. He won't accept help from anybody," time and again we discover that the "he" in question is an innerly dependent person — so dependent, and so bitterly anxious to be rid of his dependence, that he cannot accept help. Help of any kind will show how dependent he is — and that he cannot accept. We see the same thing in the person who can never let another "pick up the tab" in a restaurant. We see it in people who are forcing others to become dependent on them; they must do this lest their own real dependence come to the surface. We see it in people who must rebel against authority, against customs, protocol, morals, inhibitions, and taboos.

Yet when a sufficient excuse allows such a person to indulge in dependence, he "goes all out." When he is sick, he can be dependent — openly, childishly, utterly dependent — and if he is sick enough, he does so and enjoys it. No one now can accuse him. Of course he is dependent, but it is only, he is sure, because of the severity of his sickness.

In such an excessively dependent person, strong bitterness often burns, usually at a level below consciousness. This bitterness is directed not alone at self, nor yet at "circumstances," but very often (most often, in fact) at the person or persons upon whom he is dependent. And strangely enough it is often masked by something that appears to be "loyalty" or even "love."

But the measure of true maturity and of true independence is the degree to which we can accept dependence when it is forced on us. The person who has achieved something of the balanced maturity of true independence can readily accept the dependent situations which come in every life. He may fight rules, customs, prohibitions, but he is able to do so on a reasonable basis. He can agree with authority or disagree with it, but his disagreements will not be like those of a rebellious child fighting what reminds him of the fact that he is a child. He can pay his way or accept the help that friendship offers, and in neither case is he disturbed about it. He has no need to force others to be dependent on him, because he has nothing special that he must prove about himself.

Yet people are not divided into two groups, the dependent and the independent. In each of us both forces are at work. In each of us there are large areas of emotional dependence. This may mean that there are certain people upon whom we cannot allow ourselves to become dependent: they bring out all the feelings of dependence against which we fight; in their presence our excessive dependence "shows" — sometimes as a weak leaning on them, sometimes as an angry "independence." Certain things or certain situations may bring out the same reaction. But the extent of our true inner independence determines how much additional stress we can bear in the way of forced dependence.

Thus persons who before blindness were quite able to handle the normal degree of dependence involved in living, are now tested in a new way. Dependence really burdens and hampers them. They are unable to escape from it. For the person who has strong inner dependence feelings, there are only two possibilities: either to surrender completely and luxuriate in dependence or to fight bitterly to escape. These are expressed in two extreme attitudes (or verbalizations): "Blindness is an insurmountable and hopeless handicap." "Blindness is nothing but a minor inconvenience."

The normal reaction of the emotionally mature person, in contrast, is made up of recognition of the dependence forced on him, a strong wish that it were not there, and an ability to accept it when necessary, while not seeking it when it is not. But few of us are fully mature emotionally, and the reactions of the majority of blinded persons are somewhere in between. These possible reactions to the forced dependence of blindness explain the different answers given by blinded persons to many questions: guide or no guide, cane or no cane, dog or no dog, braille or no braille, reader or no reader, job or no job, rehabilitation or no rehabilitation.

The dependence which blindness necessarily brings is bad enough. But when the blinded persons finds himself dependent and discovers in himself feelings of bitterness towards those upon whom he is dependent, he may cover up his feelings by becoming even more dependent than he need.

Or, not the blinded man himself, but those around him, those to whom he is tied by a bond of affection, may quite unconsciously increase his dependency. They may enjoy the new position they have found in relation to him. Without any realization of it, a wife may enjoy having her husband suddenly dependent on her. A child may be pleased to have a parent dependent on him. Neighbors and friends find that having this blind person dependent on them gives some new and pleasant feeling of strength, and so they unconsciously try to increase his dependence.

The terrible loss of personal independence is, then, one of the most significant losses which the multiple handicap of blindness entails — since death to independence means an end to adult living.

17. LOSS OF SOCIAL ADEQUACY

The loss we are going to analyze now is one of the most serious blows which blindness deals to the average person (with few, though sharp exceptions): the loss of personal acceptance, of human dignity, almost of individuality and personality.* And yet this loss, like the one following it in our analysis, is unnecessary. It is forced on the blind man not by his blindness but by the supposedly kindly and sympathetic people who surround him!

We, the sighted public, add this extra loss to the multiple handicap of blindness because we are afraid of blindness. We are afraid of all the connotations of blindness — all the dark, evil, ignorance, and mystery involved in shadow and gloom.

We are afraid of all the *effects* of blindness: of the loss of reality contact, of being cut off from people, of the loss of our jobs, of financial insecurity and of loss of our normal mode of adjustment to living. We are afraid of ourselves and of our weaknesses. We fear im-

* When the Blinded Veterans Association in its charter set itself up so that its members, blinded in the service of the United States, might take their "rightful place in the community of their fellows," it was against this particular loss especially that they were struggling.

mobility and we fear dependence. Above all we fear mutilation and the unknown. And we hate to face or admit our fears. In consequence, we (or at least the great majority of sighted people) will not look at our own attitude to blindness, nor will we look at blindness rationally. Many of us approach blindness and blind persons with our reason so hampered by conflicting emotions that it is almost impossible for it to function.

Fears bring about revulsion — and we do not wish to admit this either. For while we would admit to a revulsion toward a handicap — there is nothing wrong in this, we feel — revulsion toward a handicapped person is, we know, very wrong, and so is any resulting desire to obliterate him from our sight or even from our thought. If any of these feelings exist in us, then, we cannot let them come to light. Instead, we quickly cover them over by "pitying" the person handicapped — thus separating him from ourselves while at the same time easing our conscience. Our feelings may be assuaged yet more if we give him something — money perhaps, or insistence that the organizations we support should give him money. Or we may go further and give him something which we call service — but again from a motive of pity. And this "pity" is rooted in our fear or horror.

Perhaps the emotions roused by blindness are too much for us. Then we pity the blind person from afar. We shudder with feeling and admire people who can work with "them." Or, at the other extreme, we associate very closely with blind persons and "own" them. We force them into some kind of dependence on us, and then rankle at their supposed ingratitude if they still seek to exercise their own will.

And, whether from far or near, we do to them what we do to all minority groups — we separate them from society. This is the source of all the false generalizations, each of which is a caricature: the blind beggar, the blind musician, the blind man who smiles but underneath hates society, the happy blind man ("It's amazing how happy they are!").

This is the reason why people endow the blind with extraordinary virtues or preternatural powers ("They are all so good" or "Isn't it amazing how they can tell colors just by the feel of them?"), and then proceed to deprive them of reason, even of common sense ("You really can't expect him to make that decision for himself, you know" or "How will he be sure it's his wife?"). Any number of times, otherwise intelligent persons confuse deafness with blindness: they say, for instance, "If you're in work for the blind you must know the sign language," or they address a blind person through a third party ("Ask him if he wants sugar?"), or they speak to him in loud tones so that he will be sure to hear.

Nor are sighted workers for the blind free from these same faults. Usually they will not think, as the public does, that the blind are bitter and ungrateful. Instead they may well consider all blind persons "sweet and lovely." These are the sighted "owners" of the blind, the sighted agency workers who discuss and report on "our blind" and what they do and how they think. "Our blind are just the same as anybody else, I always say—but just between ourselves, don't you think they are different?"

It is out of just such a social context that the newly blinded man has come; out of it he has brought all his own attitudes and feelings about the blind people that he pitied in other days. Now blind, it is into just such a society that he moves. And, as if the other problem of blindness were not enough, now he finds that he is no longer accepted for himself.

In the community at large he is tagged as a blind man. People who never noticed him before or never thought of him in terms of any special adjective have now a new description for him; now he is that *blind* lawyer or *blind* tailor, and the emphasis is on his blindness. Perhaps a stranger stops him on the street to ask him if he attended Oshkosh College—"I sat next to a blind fellow in class all through Oshkosh, and I thought you were him. Nice fellow he was too." Nice fellow he may have been, but apparently the only important note about him was his blindness. Our newly blinded man realizes that he is typed. He is placed in a category and he is expected to fit into it.

His friends stay loyal—"After all, you don't give up on a friend just because he's blind." But soon he notices that something is strained. They come and they are kind. But they go and they talk to each other: "Poor Joe. He's certainly taking it wonderfully. It's awful hard to go and see him that way, though. But he certainly is cheerful about the whole thing." And Joe gradually realizes that he isn't Joe, but "Blind Joe."

Gradually he has lost his place in the community (although it is possible that he has assumed a new one and likes the role of "Cheerful Joe, the poor blind man"). In the wider circle of the community, and even in the narrower circle of his own friends and neighbors, he has lost his original place — the place which his own personality, character, habits, and accomplishments, his own self had found. He has lost social adequacy. If he meets strangers, if he moves into new circles, it is now not as a man, but as a blind man, that he must make his way.

Most serious of all, he has lost his position in his own family circle. No longer the breadwinner (or the homemaker), he is now a lesser person. The thoughts and feelings of the community move into the home. And here, either pity will not survive or the home will be destroyed. The blind man is dependent; in his dependence he feels or is felt to be a burden. (And those who feel this hasten to cover it up, to bury it deep inside themselves in one way or another.) All too often his dependence is increased because others in his own household unconsciously enjoy the feeling of power and superiority which it gives them. More and more, decisions in the family are turned over to others, as more and more he is made inadequate in his own family circle. And his revolt against it is laid to the new character which blindness has given to him ("Poor thing. I guess they're all that way.")

We fear blindness, we sighted people. And we cannot meet the emotions and feelings it arouses within us sufficiently to give the blind person his *personal* place among us. We cannot, that is, until we are willing to face ourselves and our feelings, and to treat blind men like other men, according to their individual worth and their human dignity.

And this loss is a two-way street. It is not alone the attitude of the sighted public, but the attitude of the blinded man himself that counts. If he himself feels he has not become "adequate" after his blindness, if he harbors feelings of resentment or remains in his grief, there is every reason why he will in fact not be *socially* adequate. If within himself he is not able and ready to assume his earlier role, to live in his former status, then by his whole attitude he will increase the difficulty and the importance of this loss.

Whatever the source, the loss of social adequacy, the loss of acceptance by one's friends and family, the loss of individuality will prove one of the most severe, probably *the* most severe loss in the whole multiple handicap. For man is a social being, and here is death to society.

18. LOSS OF OBSCURITY

The previous loss was, in a sense, that of the ability to be "big," to measure up to one's previous status in the community. The loss we are to discuss now is that of the ability to be "little," to be lost in the crowd, to be obscure, anonymous, to be just another man in the street. It is, essentially, the loss of the ability to fit in among one's fellows without being marked out as strangely different.

The blinded man loses his privacy; he becomes a public figure. BLIND MAN BEATS WIFE; BLIND MAN MAKES PHI BETA KAPPA make headlines when the fact that a sighted man had done the same thing would scarcely make the police column or the "personals." Social psychology is showing us something of the problems involved in being in an "out-group," and particularly of being marked with the sign of the out-group. But this is exactly the position into which the blinded man is forced. He is subject to the glaring light in which public figures must live, but unlike so many public figures, he has not sought it; he has been forced into it by the fact of his blindness. Not only is he living in a show window (with a glass through which he is seen but cannot see), but he is expected to "conform" to a degree not demanded of the average person.

Some handicaps do not publicly mark those
— for example, a deaf person or one with
easily pass unnoticed in the crowd. Other han
crippling, mark their victims so that they ar
they move down the street. This is true of bli
individuals it is one of the major problems of bli

With this stigma go all the questions about
— to attempt to "pass." This is one of the reaso
persons can never allow themselves to wear dark glasses, to carry a cane, or to use a guide dog. And sometimes the people who fall into the grossest "blindisms" and obvious signs of blindness, such as shuffling and insecurity, and the people who have the most embarrassing experiences, are those who cannot use cane or dog because they dread so much the idea of any badge which would mark them with the out-group.

This pressure from without and from within can build up inside a blinded person and can drive him into a segregated situation, where at least for a time he is a part of an in-group. It can become so strong that he wants to get off the street, out of the crowd, somewhere where the spotlight is off him for the moment. And night after night he can remember and long for the day when he had his social freedom, when he could mingle as one with his fellows.

This loss of obscurity, in which is interwoven a loss of individuality, is a severe and continuing trauma for the individual who loses sight — a trauma in which his privacy dies.

19. LOSS OF SELF-ESTEEM

The loss of self-esteem has two distinct phases: loss in *objective* self-estimate and loss in *subjective* self-estimate (self-image). Ideally, these two estimates should coincide in a self-evaluation that would take into account our total selves, with all our God-given native ability, our present degree of development, our potential for future contributions to and acceptance in society. Such a self-estimate would be neither self-deprecatory nor self-laudatory — it would be a com-

...ssay. But few of us are honest enough with ourselves not ...eive ourselves by way of overestimation or underestimation. ...of us have sufficient humility to be able to admit even to our-...elves the gifts that God has given us and the shortcomings with which He has left us. Within us, then, are two different estimates of self: the intellectual evaluation, or objective self-estimate, which comes closer to being correct; and the reflection of all the thinking and feeling we did about ourselves as children and whatever growth has come to it since: our "feeling self-evaluation" or self-image.

The existence of these two different estimates is seen clearly in mildly neurotic persons for whom a constant very real feeling of their own worthlessness is part of their self-image. When people value them at something more, these persons become upset; they feel like hypocrites for accepting some of the good estimation which the public has given to them. Yet often enough, given an objective analytical written self-examination, these people are able to score themselves high in point after point. When they have finished taking the examination, they feel that it is wrong, that it overstates their true value — yet they cannot in honesty change a single answer. Such an experience may be upsetting to the person examined, since his objective self-evaluation and his subjective one are brought into open conflict. (This is not meant to suggest that the self-image is always lower than the factual evaluation; it may be equally exaggerated in the other direction.)

Objective self-estimate, then, is like a ticker tape, showing a person his own worth. With the onset of blindness, that ticker tape reflects a sudden terrible drop in the stock. The bottom has fallen out of the market. He was a whole person; now he is maimed. He was sure of his manhood; now he has gnawing doubts. Not only is his sight gone, but he cannot trust his remaining senses. Sure of his orientation throughout his life, he now has no sure reality contact. He is without the relief, the "color" of visual background. In a life of lightlessness, he is alone and not sure of love. He can no longer see beautiful things or even things which would give him pleasure. Formerly free in his coming and going, now he is immobilized; he has moved back toward childhood. He cannot even read or write, and his face-to-face communication with people is hampered. So difficult is it for him to keep abreast of things that the world is passing him by. His opportunities for the recreation that he now needs more than ever before in his life have vanished. A thousand things that he could always do with ease, even without thinking of them, now cause him trouble, frustration, and pain. His job is gone and the well-planned career is shattered. It costs him more to live and yet his income is cut or gone. In one thing after another which he once did for himself he is now completely dependent and helpless. He has dropped in his status in the community, has had a secondary role forced on him in his family; he has almost lost his individuality and is no longer accepted for himself alone.

His objective self-evaluation has received a shattering blow. To accept this blow may well mean that he must begin his life again from the start.

And what happens to his self-image — his subjective self-estimate? Much work still needs to be done in studying the effects of a serious handicap on self-image. In its origins in our early childhood, self-image was the product of our limited knowledge of self and of the things that people (our parents, brothers, sisters, and others) said about us, or that we thought they were saying. Our adolescent and adult successes and failures also had their effect, but by the time they came along, a basic "hard core" in our self-image was already formed, a core which is sometimes almost impervious to change.

But it can be said with certainty that in a sense everyone's balance in life consists in his establishing an equilibrium with his self-image. Under the series of traumatic blows which blindness deals, that equilibrium may be seriously upset. The new burdens may be too much for the previous self-image to bear, and the result is a very severe disordering of total personality organization — and the death of the image of self.

20. LOSS OF TOTAL PERSONALITY ORGANIZATION

In conclusion, we come to consider what happens to the total personality under these multiple blows. Each person brings to his blindness a different set of feelings as well as a different personality; certainly blindness itself casts people into no common mold. Yet blindness has a common power to upset and undermine lifelong personality organization. It has this power, not because of anything peculiar about blindness, but because, like every major handicap, it is a blow — made up, as we have seen, of a series of blows, each severe in itself — at a whole life pattern.

We live in a civilization in which apparently few of us have any strong defenses against trauma or shock. Medicine is learning something about physical shock, the still mysterious reaction of our physical apparatus to physical trauma; psychiatry is attempting to learn more about psychic shock and to understand better the results of psychic trauma. Persons who have been apparently strong and adjusted to life suddenly lose their whole psychic adjustment, become disorganized in personality and sometimes completely so — and the occasion of it (if not the cause) is some simple and single blow, such as the loss of a job. Or persons may succumb without a single apparent major cause, and on examination a series of minor traumas may be found to have occasioned the break.

Whatever the explanation, it seems generally agreed that all of us are potential material for some sort of upset, some sort of emotional difficulty. Perhaps never in our lives will we actually suffer this upset, yet we stand ready for some severe blow (possibly a very minor one, but severe to us) to cause us difficulty. We often discern signs in those around us of a tension we never suspected before and that perhaps they themselves are not aware of, signs which remind us how many people in our time live as bundles of emotions, unrecognized and still under control, but awaiting only some static spark to throw them out of order and set off some real personality problem.

It is out of this background of tension and insecurity that the blind person comes face to face with his blindness. The personality that he brings to it, his strengths and weaknesses, are very important now. His philosophies and his goals in living are going to make a difference in the nature and the force of the blows which he suffers. But it is his personality, his self, that suffers these multiple blows.

For many people, if not for most, blindness is, consequently, capable of triggering some neurotic response. For practically everyone, there is a period of severe "reality depression" with at least some neurotic overtones. And when the depression period ends, the personality reorganizes itself or organizes itself into new patterns.

Some escape rapidly or gradually from facing the problems which blindness brings by telling themselves and the world that these problems are inconsequential and that blindness is "not so much a handicap as a minor inconvenience." Some escape facing the problems for years or throughout their whole lives by telling themselves, in the face of repeated medical advice to the contrary, that their blindness is not permanent: the condition is going to improve naturally, or some new research is about to find the answer, or else God is going to grant them a miracle (with the assurance not of faith but of presumption, almost as if God owed them one).

Still others escape from facing the weaknesses in themselves which blindness has brought out by placing all the blame on their blindness. To them blindness is an insurmountable tragedy and there is no use trying any longer.

Others escape into blindness: for example, the type of person who needs only some excuse in order that at long last he may luxuriate in dependence. The opportunity to be waited on, perhaps gradually to enslave into dependence those who wait on them, is actually an opportunity long sought by these people. They talk about the difficulties they undergo, perhaps even make a brave show of attempting to overcome them (a show sufficiently good to convince themselves). But in reality it is much easier for them to be dependent with a good excuse for dependence than it ever was to feel dependent with no sign of an excuse outside their own nature.

Here blindness has not given the person any new personality structure, but has merely emphasized the one he brought to it. The same thing seems to be true in most cases (although not in all): no new personality structure is set up but the old one becomes more set than ever in its basic channels.

This does not mean that the personality will necessarily *seem* the same after blindness. Currents that have long flowed underneath may come flooding to the surface. The person who has long held his hostility submerged may no longer be able to keep it under control; his hostility and hatreds may become apparent to those around him. The radical, who out of inner needs revolted against parents, society, morals, the church, or whatever, with seeming reasonableness, may continue to show this particular symptom, but now it will appear more clearly as revolt.

Anxiety may arise in many newly blinded persons when it has never been a problem before; it may be with them until they die unless with psychiatric help they are able to bring it under control. This anxiety may, in blind persons as in sighted, show itself in one or another physical symptom: gastric ulcers, severe headaches unconnected with the physical blindness itself, serious palpitations, sweating palms, long-term low-grade infections, rheumatism, arthritis, loss of voice, or (worst of all to the blind person) loss of hearing. Other sense functions may be interfered with: the blind person may be unable to learn braille because he cannot "feel it," whereas the loss of sensitivity in the fingers may be only a direct result of his psychological difficulties; he may develop an awkwardness in walking which will keep him from doing the very thing that he thinks he wants most to do — move about freely again. These and a thousand other minor variances of physical symptoms may appear, all as results of his blindness, and all of them a great challenge to psychosomatic medicine.*

* Cutsforth offers the very interesting observation that people who show somatic symptoms of anxiety before blindness often lose these completely when blindness comes. Apparently the unconscious masochistic need is satisfied by the blindness response. Cutsforth further notes the possibility that when rehabilitation makes blindness less burdensome, the somatic anxiety symptoms may return. In this connection one is led to think of persons blinded in suicide attempts. The author is unaware of any broad study on this subject, but offers the suggestion that blindness perhaps completely satisfies the masochistic aspect of the suicidal urge, and

Again, hostility may arise where it has never shown itself before, as may an apparent acceptance of suffering, a false martyrdom which does not seek to submit but to punish. Boasting and looking for praise may go together as a sign of inner insecurity and need for love. And the blinded person who doubts his manhood (or her womanhood) may go about showing the doubt more clearly by "proving" his manhood by sexual affairs or his "independence" by an ill-advised marriage or a series of them.

The clue to the blind person's inner disorganization may well be his attitude to and his relations with other blind persons. He may constantly choose his company from among the handicapped, or he may separate himself almost completely from other persons who are blind and even show jealousy of them or other feelings of distrust.

Again, we can tell a great deal (but here we must be very careful of our own rationalizing) from the attitude of blind persons toward organizations for the blind. We can see whether they seek dependence on the organization, whether they seek out organizations which will allow them to be dependent, or whether they rather seek out those which will help to increase their independence. We can see occasional signs of resentment and hostility against organizations of both kinds, and from the resentment and the circumstances surrounding it, we can gather a great deal about the attitude and the adjustment of the individual to his blindness. (Here we must be very careful that we are not rationalizing, that we are not defending our own agencies by blaming any criticism of them on the hostility of the individual and his dependence.)

The last great blow of blindness is the blow which this multiple traumatic experience exercises upon the total personality organization. Putting the pieces back together, mending this blow, is the greatest challenge to agencies for the blind. For here, the very personality has suffered a death.

---

that the second attempt is therefore seldom made. The question arises as to the possible return of the "need," in cases where total rehabilitation reduces the burden and thus the "punishment" of blindness.

8

Further Considerations

1. CONCOMITANT LOSSES

As WAS noted in the Introduction, however we analyze the losses of blindness, they overlap and interweave with one another. After our analysis is finished, then, it is quite possible that other losses may seem to one reader or another to have not been covered. We should at least briefly discuss three which have been mentioned often enough by newly blinded persons, and with enough feeling, to call for some clarification: the loss of decision, the loss of sleep (or of sleep at the proper time), and the loss of physical tone (and as a result a constant feeling of fatigue).

The people who speak of the *loss of decision* seem to have two aspects in mind: the fact that many decisions which were formerly made by them for the family are taken over by others, and that they themselves find difficulty in making decisions.

This condition appears to be rather widespread among newly blinded persons. The reason for the first aspect of it was discussed in part under the loss of social adequacy; one or more members of the blinded man's family may enjoy the new role held out to them of being leaders in the family, those who make the decisions. This is then, in great measure, a loss of role, and it finds easy entrance into families in which the various stereotypes about blindness are accepted. To overcome it, it is most important that much direct work of a casework nature be done with the family. It should be recognized, also, however, that one of the reasons the family is willing to take on the new role is because the blinded individual is, at least unconsciously, willing to relinquish it.

The second aspect of this loss, inability to make decisions, is not something in any way peculiar to blindness. Indecisiveness is a symptom. Very often it is a symptom of insecurity or of a neurotic period in a person's life. Since blindness is a repetitive multiple trauma, it almost necessarily places a person in an extremely insecure emotional state for a period.

When the blinded individual is sufficiently reorganized to want once more to make the kind of decisions he used to make, a real difficulty may arise if the person who has assumed the decision-making role is happy in it and not completely willing to relinquish it. At a time when the blinded person should be gradually "supported into" making decisions again, he may find instead that he is encountering resistance, either openly or unconsciously. Obviously we have here a problem which calls for some highly expert family casework.

The second loss noted by many newly blinded people is the *loss of sleep*. Others modify it to say the "loss of sleep at the right time." The primary factor here seems to be emotional strain. Anyone who has had any extensive dealings with emotional problems or with "nervous" people is aware of the different ways in which sleeping problems often enter into their difficulties, whether as inability to sleep or as inability to find rest while sleeping.

Under the great emotional stresses of new blindness, many people have difficulties with their sleep habits. Often too tense to sleep when they retire, they are also inclined to become so weary during what should be the waking hours that they become drowsy. Add to this the complete disruption of schedule for people who have put in a regular working day prior to blindness, only to have long periods of unoccupied time after blindness, and it is easy to understand how their sleeping habits might be completely disrupted and sleeping become a problem, particularly sleeping at the right time.

Over and above this, for the totally blind person, there is the loss of the distinction between daylight and dark. This is not the major factor in the sleeping problem, since human nature is readily capable of changing sleeping habits from regular nighttime sleep. But particularly for people who are disoriented as to the time of day, this is a contributing factor.

This particular problem of sleeping is quite easily solved in the course of a good rehabilitation program. If the blinded person is completely reorganized, there is no reason why his sleeping habits should not be reorganized also.

The third additional loss suggested, the loss of physical tone,* is, like the other two, symptomatic of the tension under which the newly blinded person is placed. Part of the explanation, also, in many cases, lies in the loss of the normal amount of exercise to which the individual has been accustomed. This, however, does not seem to be the primary cause. Not only psychiatrists but all general practitioners of medicine know that few factors more readily and commonly cause general fatigue or loss of physical tone than does emotional strain. Such a loss is, in fact, one of the most obvious symptoms of anxiety. The newly blinded person, therefore, weighed down with all the emotional problems of adjusting to his handicap, suffering under the repetitive multiple trauma which we have outlined, is almost bound to show loss of physical tone.

As he moves through the phases of rehabilitation, there is a still further strain of a different kind as it becomes necessary for him to be constantly alert to a thousand new stimuli coming to him from the environment around him. This is particularly true of his learning period, during which all his sense activity must be brought very definitely to a conscious level, interpreted consciously and acted on consciously. When much of this activity has become habitual, much of the strain of conscious alertness wears off, although there is a degree to which the blinded person must always remain more alert than the sighted person, particularly in strange circumstances.

* Tonus in its modern physiological meaning, the normal tension or response as to stimuli, is not what is meant here, but rather tone in the medical sense: that state of a body or any of its organs in which the animal functions are healthy and performed with due vigor.

But the temporary and symptomatic loss of physical tone should, generally speaking, be confined almost entirely to the period before rehabilitation is completed. The process of rehabilitation should work on it in a double way. It should deal so directly and expertly with the person's emotional problems as to lighten their burden on him, and it should decrease the strain of the necessary alertness by making complete sensory activity a part of his "second nature."

Undoubtedly there are other losses suffered by individuals who lose their sight. Experience has shown, however, that most of these can be understood in the light of the twenty losses found to be more or less common to most persons who become blind.

2. SUPPOSED GAINS RESULTING FROM BLINDNESS

Among the many people who have studied the analysis of the losses resulting from blindness given in this book, not a few have suggested that there are gains as well as losses from blindness and that these too should be listed. I am convinced that the supposed gains are accidental, that they are not by any means universal, and that when they exist they are occasioned by blindness rather than caused by it. But since some people do believe that certain gains can exist, it would perhaps be well to examine them.

What might be called *vocational gains* among people who have lost their sight are certainly not infrequent. Among men blinded in the service, in particular, there are many who had supposedly finished their education, perhaps at grade school level, whose whole vocational goal had been thought of in terms of unskilled or semiskilled trades, and who, after blindness, have re-evaluated their goals and gone on to higher education and to work in professional or semi-professional areas. In civilian life also, in families in which all the other children leave school early for some kind of job, the blind member often goes on to receive education at a much higher level and finds his vocation much further up the professional scale.

This clearly could be thought of as a "gain" from blindness on the vocational level. In my experience, however, it is more than offset by the number of cases in which there is a complete disruption of vocational goal. One of the reasons why families educate the blind member is that so many job opportunities on the unskilled and skilled labor level are closed to blind people. But often the educated blind person meets new frustration by finding even fewer opportunities at the white-collar level.

What might be called a *thinking gain* also exists. It is certainly true that blindness gives to many people an opportunity for more abstract thought. The very freedom from concrete, visualized objects and from the many distractions which are visual affords some people the opportunity to do a kind of thinking for which they otherwise might not have had the energy or inclination. On the other hand, there are many distractions in blindness itself, and the very confusion of weighty emotional problems may keep the individual from other than introverted thinking and block any abstract thought. I have seen altogether too many persons who made no gains whatsoever in this area, and too many others who tended rather to more talking and less thinking, to consider this in any sense a universal gain.

Now and again, what might be thought of as *self-image gains* can be noticed: people who had a very low estimate of themselves and their place in society appear to gain in feelings of personal stature as a result of their blindness. Involved in this is, apparently, some assuming of the hero or the martyr role. Such cases are not rare. The person who never was anything before is now as a blinded person at least someone different in his community. He has certain skills, certain sense capacities, which other people have not developed, and as a result he may find a certain amount of admiration turned his way which is new for him.

Possibly this amounts to a gain for some people, but it is always difficult to tell how important the gain is and to what extent it is accepted and used as a substitute for facing the realities of the situation. In any case, it is certainly not a universal gain that could be thought of as part of the pattern of results from blindness.

Insight gains should also be mentioned here, but these are usually the result of rehabilitation rather than of blindness. In coming to understand his own reactions to the multiple trauma of blindness, the blinded individual may have a much clearer understanding of his reactions to other things in his life and to his whole make-up. This may be of great advantage to him in his relations with other people and in his whole inner security, and may make him able to assist other people along these lines as he could not have done otherwise. Any gain here, however, obviously does not result from the blindness itself but from the insights derived during the rehabilitation process.

People sometimes speak of a gain which might be called the *recognition-of-the-good-in-the-world gain.* They say that blindness brings some people for the first time to a recognition of how much good there is in the world, a realization of the number of people ready to assist, to go out of their way to help others, etc. Undoubtedly it is true that many people do lead such self-centered lives that ordinarily they are not aware of the goodness or the charitable acts of others, and some of these people do experience an awakening when they find themselves helped by the love of others.

But this experience, again, is not universal. Many people are already aware of the existence of goodness and helpfulness; many people who were unaware of them before blindness continue to be unaware afterward.

And some blinded people who say that they have now come to appreciate the kindness in the world do so with a certain subservience indicating that while they think they should voice such sentiments, they are actually feeling guilty because they are filled with resentment rather than gratitude. Such a gain, where it exists, cannot, therefore, be thought of as a gain intrinsic to blindness.

Others speak of the *friendship gain.* This is not entirely distinct from the previous one, but it is far more particularized. A number of people are able to say that but for their blindness, they would not have met this or that very good friend. Even more, there are many cases in which blindness was the occasion for the person's meeting his or her marriage partner. Many blinded servicemen, for example, met wonderful girls who have since become their wives, whom they would never have met if their blindness had not brought them to a particular hospital. And in civilian life also, blindness has not infrequently provided the occasion for a blinded man to meet his future wife or a blinded woman her future husband.

No one will deny that to make a good marriage and to make good friends is a gain. But there are also many cases in which blindness and its resultant tensions have placed great strain on existing marital relationships, where it has even been the occasion for the disruption of marriage, and many cases also in which once good friends have somehow drifted away. It is difficult, then, to see any pattern here which indicates anything like a universal gain.

Some people mention a gain in the *blotting out of the ugliness in the world.* But is this supposed gain really a gain at all? Is it not, as usually expressed, rather an escape from truth? If the fact of blindness brings an individual to a better recognition of "how much good there is in the worst of us," then it may be valuable in balancing his scale of values. Too often, however, the statement is meant to indicate satisfaction in the fact that a person no longer has to see the evil that exists — physical evil and moral evil. Yet the world as it is *does* contain evil and ugliness, moral and physical. The fact that a person can no longer see physical ugliness does not give him the right to close his other senses and his mind to reality and escape into some dream world that does not exist. While the world exists as it is, we do well to live in it as it is — doing our part to improve it certainly, but not denying the truth to ourselves or to anyone else, not trying to fashion some world of our own.

This "gain" is actually, then, no gain at all. Moreover, it is very dangerous because of the damage it can do to a person's psychological make-up and because it can seem to allow him to run away from his responsibilities.

There is also the gain of *discovery of unknown strength.* I believe that some persons actually experience this gain at the end of the rehabilitation process. It is not unlike what happens to many people under combat in wartime. All their adult lives they feared that they would collapse in the face of serious trouble. Experiencing the trouble and finding themselves capable of undergoing it, they find for the first time real confidence in themselves. This does not happen to all the people who need new strength, nor do all people need to undergo disaster to experience it. But for those to whom it happens, it might be thought of as a gain — though resulting from recovery from the blow of blindness rather than from the blow itself.

Finally, there is a possible gain to be found in the *reorientation of temporal and eternal values.* Some people who lose their sight gain a recognition that the merely temporal goals on which their whole lives were based do not have the value they once gave them. They see, for the first time, something of the need for working for values that last.

Undoubtedly a gain when it takes place, this new vision of values certainly does not come to everyone who loses his sight — and many people who lose their sight were aware of this truth before they became blind. Gain for some, it is not so universal that it should be thought of as a part of any pattern of gains resulting from loss of sight.

Nobody wishes to deny the silver lining which exists behind many dark clouds, but it is an unhealthy attitude which persists in looking for such a lining instead of getting a raincoat. Blindness is severe, devastating, even disastrous. Pollyanna attitudes may allow one to deny it, but never to conquer it.

Some people are able to use the most difficult circumstances — even blindness — to make themselves better. But for most people there is nothing in the nature of blindness itself which brings gains. For most it cannot help but be a series of serious losses.

3. THE PARTING OF THE WAYS IN WORK WITH THE BLIND

Throughout the first part of this book we have been trying to analyze the handicap of blindness. With a constant attempt at objectivity, we have been studying the meaning of blindness and what it does to human beings.

Now, before moving on to consider what should be done about

it, the reader needs to realize that in the past as well as at present there have been two widely different sets of principles operating in the field of work for the blind. These principles have not always been clearly defined, and sometimes both are apparently operative at the same time in the same agency, or even in the same worker.

Whatever the verbalizations in this work (and the platitudes are many), the whole field seems to be torn between a hope that the blind person can operate normally and a despair that anything can make this possible. Yet this conflict goes on below the surface and is not even perceived by those in whom it exists. Sincere people say that blind persons are "perfectly normal," etc., while at the same time operating programs which accept blind people as lifelong dependents and tend to make them such.

This does not mean that either attitude is impossible as a working basis. I believe that it is possible for some people to work on the basis that adjustment to blindness is hopeless and for others to base their activities on the hope of adjustment.* But it is vitally important to the field of work with the blind that each worker should come to an explicit realization of what he believes and should operate on it openly — that he should be honest with himself and honest with the world.

If the analysis of blindness given in the preceding chapters is correct, or anywhere near correct, it is obvious that at least one conclusion must be agreed upon — blindness is indeed a most severe handicap. It is awesome in its multiple effects. It touches on practically all normal external activities. It reaches close to the innermost core of personality. It is devastating and almost catastrophic.

If we can all agree on this much, the disagreement must begin after this point.

Having completed an analysis of blindness, it is quite possible to come to the conclusion that it is so complete a tragedy that it cannot be overcome; that it so shatters personality that there is no mending; that its losses are so many and so severe that it is useless

* Obviously unless workers identify themselves with agencies which hold the same philosophy, the agencies themselves will be "schizophrenic."

to try true rehabilitation; that it so differentiates a person from normal sighted persons that no attempt should be made to restore the blinded person to a place in sighted society.

Everyone concerned with work for the blind should thoroughly examine this proposition. For, if it is correct, those agencies which act in a paternalistic manner toward the blind are completely right, and those who criticize their paternalism are guilty of an error which is doing great harm to blind people.

If this proposition is true, the segregation of blind people is a logically inevitable consequence. Parties, recreation, dances for the blind, feasts for the blind, common entertainment — all follow, and all make sense.

Segregated working conditions, sheltered shops with special privileges not accorded to sighted people, and a general air of kindness not to be found in ordinary working conditions — all these are then seen as simply the workings of ordinary human decency.

Homes for blind people where they will get consideration that people do not ordinarily get in their living circumstances would also follow. And into these homes would necessarily come the kind entertainers and the good people of the community eager to ease the lot of the blind.

If this proposition is correct, we can find nothing wrong with class legislation for the blind, giving them free rides on buses and streetcars, for example, and free fishing licenses, and free rights to hawk and peddle.

If this proposition is true, agencies for the blind should deal with all the problems of blind persons, whether the problems are concerned with their blindness or not. They should handle all these problems because they are those of blind people, and it is too much to expect that they can solve their own problems or that general agencies could handle them knowingly and sympathetically.

If blind persons do not possess the capacity to exercise full adult citizenship, no one has a right to criticize those agencies for the blind which coddle them, wheedle them, occasionally punish them lightly, and generally treat them as children.

agrance gardens will bring some little surcease to these poor only the very harsh would criticize them.

If this proposition of the hopelessness of trying to rehabilitate the blind is true, what is really needed is not a professional approach toward work for the blind but the proper use of sympathetic people who will give them friendly support and will understand their problems as if they were their own.

If the blind cannot be responsible adults, it becomes clear that the criticized "ownership of the blind" by certain supposedly "overprotective" people is but a kindly and firm guardianship called for under the circumstances.

To summarize: If you believe in this proposition, then you expect no real happiness for the blind person in this life and you act to protect him from competition with a sighted world, to support him in every way possible, and thus make him as "happy" as possible under the circumstances.

I am convinced on the basis of experience that this proposition is utterly and completely wrong, and it is on this basis that I criticize the conclusions which logically follow from it.

I agree that blindness is a devastating handicap, with multiple complex consequences. I do not believe that I have minimized or avoided any of them. But I believe that it is the other path that is to be chosen — that of dedicating ourselves to returning the blinded person to the society from which he came.

It is that path which we take in the second section of this book, when we come to consider "what to do about it."

PART TWO

Rehabilitation and Restoration

9

Helping the Blinded Man Gain His New Life

THIS SECTION is concerned with helping persons who have been deprived of sight in their adult years but are otherwise normally capable.

The rehabilitation process should begin at the hospital bedside during the "shock" period that results from the first realization of the fact of permanent blindness. No attempt should be made to cut this period short or to inhibit the depth of mourning in the "bereavement" period that follows.* Rather, the hope of normal functioning as a human being should be substituted for the hope of normal sight, and the blinded person should be helped to begin to regain simple skills — eating, dressing himself, lighting a cigarette.

It is of the utmost importance here that neither the person giving such help nor any other should hold out to the blinded person any false hopes regarding the restoration of sight.† He will cling to such hopes anyway; it is only human to do so, and he will take as utter

* See "Psychoanalysis and Blindness" by H. Robert Blank, M.D., *Psychoanalytic Quarterly*, January 1957.

† We are concerned here with persons whose sight, according to competent medical authority, has been irretrievably lost. But in any general population of blind persons, there are a few who might be aided medically — whether by some new medical or surgical technique invented since they last saw an eye doctor, or because they mistakenly thought themselves too old for an operation, or because new optical aids might benefit them to some small but important degree. The person interested in blindness is careful never to arouse any false hopes, but he also makes certain that all blind persons are encouraged and enabled to have the best in ophthalmological care and information.

truth any words that go to build them up. But these hopes may not only delay his decision to begin rehabilitation; they may also badly disturb his whole psychological adjustment. The real friend of the newly blinded person is not the one who hides the truth from him but the one (eye doctor or layman) who, undelayed by fear, at the proper time tells him the full truth. In the same way, the outcome of rehabilitation should not be exaggerated but presented realistically.

The twofold process of arousing realistic hopes of rehabilitation and of helping the blinded person to regain lost skills should be carried on at home during the first weeks of the bereavement period.

In these early stages, aid toward rehabilitation is in the hands of near relatives and friends, the attending physicians, and any experts they may call in. It is of the utmost importance that these persons and anyone else closely associated with the patient at this time be convinced both of the seriousness of his handicap and of the real possibilities for rehabilitation.

Formerly, the home teacher — when one was available — was expected to undertake the task of further rehabilitation by teaching skills and the use of devices, with whatever financial or other aid might be furnished by local, state or private agencies. These home teachers usually worked alone and against tremendous odds; they did a remarkable job under very difficult circumstances. Now their work can be increasingly concentrated on that geriatric group for whom total rehabilitation is out of the question, since for the group we are considering here another possibility exists: the training given at a "total" rehabilitation center.

Many people still fasten on the idea of one or another *single* restoration — of financial security, of employment, of mobility, of reading material, of recreation — as the whole answer to a blinded person's problem. Certainly, braille is a help, a dog guide is a help; so is a job and so is psychiatric counseling. Any restoration is good. But obviously, making up for one loss, or two or three, cannot be a satisfactory solution to the problems of a handicap made up of twenty losses. Blindness is a multiple handicap; true rehabilitation must be multiphased and at the same time form an integrated whole.

A "total" rehabilitation center, consequently, provides not only the best but the only reasonably adequate answer. Blinded persons have, it is true, made wonderful adjustments in the past without the aid of total rehabilitation training. But the rare possibility of making a true adjustment to blindness unaided should not deter the blinded person from enrolling at a total rehabilitation center which will provide him with the most effective and efficient aid now available.

The Veterans Administration runs such a center for newly blinded veterans at Hines, Illinois. St. Paul's Rehabilitation Center in Newton, Massachusetts, similarly serves the general population; another is being established by the Greater Pittsburgh Guild for the Blind. (A number of other centers have been set up in various parts of the United States, a few of which are of high quality; but these are not directed exclusively toward meeting the needs of the newly blinded. Many shops and other facilities are now beginning to be called rehabilitation centers, but this book considers rehabilitation centers in the strict sense of the term and directs itself to those set up precisely and exclusively for the purpose of helping newly blinded persons.)

A center of this kind takes from the physiatric "rehab" center the idea of the multidisciplinary approach, of bringing together the experience of many different branches of knowledge to focus on the multiple problems of each individual. But the physiatric center has a basically medical orientation; its main purpose is to restore atrophied muscles and the like. The orientation of the total rehabilitation center for newly blinded persons is basically psychosocial; its goal is the total adjustment of the person to his new situation, including the necessary attitudes and skills, and his reintegration into his society.

This need for psychosocial orientation does not imply that blinded persons are abnormal, that there is "anything wrong" with them mentally. On the contrary, it implies that they are (to quote a phrase used in a slightly different context by Dr. William Menninger) "normal people under abnormal circumstances." Because they are normal people, accustomed to more or less normal circumstances, they react strongly, each according to his individual temperament, to the strange circumstances of blindness. These reactions, emotional in nature, have a wide and deep effect on the person's reactions to other people, on his attitude toward rehabilitation, on the learning process itself, on his very attitude toward himself. A rehabilitation center that will really meet his needs, consequently, needs a staff aware of all these emotional factors and able to assist him in the process of personality reorganization.

"Total" rehabilitation, then, is the process whereby adults in varying stages of helplessness, emotional disturbance and dependence, come to gain new understanding of themselves and their handicap, the new skills necessary for their new state, and a new control of their emotions and their environment.

This is no simple learning process, but one of pain and recurrent crises — a process of accepting the implications of the many "deaths" to sighted life in order to go forward and gain the new life ahead. It must, in consequence, be a process that makes full use of group strength and group support but is ultimately tailored to the unique personality and problems of each individual (trainee) undergoing the process. At St. Paul's, for example, sixteen trainees go through the sixteen-week program as a group. But since the staff includes some twenty-five experts in various disciplines, the many phases of the program can be adjusted to the special needs of each trainee.

Such a process makes heavy demands on the staff. It is both a science and an art, calling for breadth of knowledge and experience as well as the ability to give mature love. It requires the ability to give support and to withdraw it at the right time in the right way; all support must be "support toward independence." The total rehabilitation program is a delicately woven pattern of skills and attitudes for the benefit of the total person.

Rehabilitation in this modern sense is very young. Our knowledge of the over-all pattern and of all the elements involved is still very small in comparison with the vastness of the problem. Yet the modern approach to rehabilitation has already been carried out for a sufficient length of time and for a large enough number of persons for us to know that it is a real answer — and one with unlimited possibilities of development.

In this part of the book, we shall take up in turn the twenty restorations required by the twenty losses already analyzed, building up to the total rehabilitation which returns the blinded person to his or her society. The core of our discussion in each case will be the work to be done in the rehabilitation center.

However, all those closely associated with the blinded person have an important role to play in helping him resume his normal place and function at home and in his society. This role — both before and after the rehabilitation training period — will be indicated in connection with some of the restorations.

Again, "restoration" has wider implications than "rehabilitation." The completely rehabilitated individual will always need special services in some areas to restore what he has lost. He may need "substitute eyes," for example, to carry on his particular type of work. He will also always need special devices, such as the braille watch or reading and writing aids, while further research and the development of new devices may make more complete restoration possible in some areas. Discussion of these needs and possibilities enters into many of the questions we shall be concerned with here, although it goes beyond the scope of the work of the rehabilitation center as such.

Finally, reintegrating the blinded person into his society — the goal of rehabilitation training — involves not only his own attitudes and capabilities, but also his society's acceptance of him. The work of the center here is to aid him to understand and not unduly resent the still prevailing attitude, while helping him toward the total adjustment which will do more than anything else to change that attitude. But the work of educating the public is the responsibility of all agencies and institutions for the blind, of everyone interested in some one blind person and in the problems of the handicapped. Ultimately it is the responsibility of all of us who go to make up society. These wider problems need to be discussed in connection with several of the restorations.

It is also true that many blinded persons will not receive training at a rehabilitation center. This does not mean that nothing can be done to help them; any restoration is a gain. But it does mean that workers with the blind and other specialists who wish to assist them in one particular phase of restoration, as well as relatives and friends, should be aware of the whole picture, so as to make their help as effective as possible and yet not offer it as the whole answer.

This part of the book is designed, therefore, to open out to the reader, whatever his interest in blindness, both the real possibilities and the many-sided task of total rehabilitation.

Rehabilitation has four main phases, involved in varying proportions in each of the twenty restorations we need to consider: training the other senses to take over the role of sight; training in skills and the use of devices; restoring psychological security; influencing the attitude of his society to him and assisting him to meet the prevailing attitude.

The first is the basic "reality restoration" making up for the basic "reality loss" of a major means of perception. Since it is so vital to all the particular restorations and since any intelligent person can help with this training when full training is not available, it will be discussed separately in the next chapter. Training in skills and in the use of devices will be considered in connection with the various restorations, as will the attitude of society.

But the problems of psychological restoration are ones which, so far as active assistance is concerned, must be left entirely to experts — to the *trained* psychiatrists, psychologists and caseworkers who are professionally equipped to handle them. No "knowledge of people," no "understanding the blind" can substitute here for professional knowledge and skill. It is vitally important that the worker with the blind — and the relative or friend who knows a little psychology and wants to be helpful — be aware of this necessity for "hands off" and the reasons for it. Otherwise, with the best intentions, he may do grave and irreparable harm.

Integral to the theory of rehabilitation outlined in this book is the belief that no person can overcome the problems of blindness without an honest confrontation of them. The blinded person must be assisted to face his blindness in its totality and finality, to accept "death" to sighted life, if he is to go forward to gain a new life. If we understand the full meaning of this necessity, the prospect is a frightening one — a fright that is felt rather than understood by the vast number of persons who try to convince the blinded person that his condition really isn't so bad.

The danger is that what are called the "delicate defenses" might be destroyed, and the personality with them. In the development of the human personality, the individual builds up various means of protection from internal and external problems that might overwhelm the self. Basically, the strongest form of self-protection is the strengthening of the ego; the stronger the ego, the less the need for protection. (This does not mean that the egocentric person is the strongest, but rather the "secure" person.)

But few personalities are so strong as not to have found a need for other means of defense and unconsciously to have developed them over a period of time. These "delicate defenses" vary in their nature according to the individual. At times they become so involved in personality structure as to form what has been called a "complex." Various forms of overcompensation, of overactivity, and of involvement in distraction can also be considered as forms of defense. But especially important from our standpoint is the defense of escape by denial, the most common one in blinded persons.

In psychosis this defense becomes a denial of reality itself; but here we mean only some degree of failure to admit to oneself the reality of the insult (using the word in its medical sense) to the personality dealt by blindness. This denial, or failure to admit, is not a conscious act or one meant to fool other people; it is an unconscious reaction by which the person fools himself.

Denial in this sense may be manifested in a refusal to admit as permanent a condition that obviously is so; it may show itself in an inability to admit that a painful condition hurts; or it may take the form of seeking out and exaggerating minor compensatory gains. What is really happening is that the ego is face to face with a problem which it fears will overwhelm it, and, in one way or another, it refuses to look at the problem honestly. The gravity of the situation lies in the likelihood that the personality would indeed be overwhelmed if it attempted (or were able) so to confront the problem.

The basic question in rehabilitation is, then, how to assist the blinded person (and note that it is "*assist* him") to face his blindness without overwhelming his personality.

The answer does not consist in an assault on the delicate defenses. It involves many factors, not the least of which might be described as building a bridge of love and confidence from one personality to another. There must be no destruction without a prior or concomitant buttressing of the ego. While the problem is being presented in a manner in which it can be accepted and understood, the ego must be strengthened to some degree. The controlled use of group dynamics can be of great assistance here; the individual finds certain strengths in the group which he could not find in himself. Meanwhile, professional interpretation to the individual of some of the frightening reactions which he finds in himself may be most important in removing his fears that he is losing his mind or otherwise behaving in an abnormal fashion.

The problem of the delicate defenses is one of the reasons why rehabilitation should be undertaken soon after the loss of sight, before a pattern of denial has become ingrained. After maladjustment or apparent adjustment has become habitual the problem is greatly magnified.

With the person who has been blind from birth or early childhood, there is not only the problem of the length of time during which the denial mechanism has become set, but the even greater problem of its having been formed during the developmental period of the personality structure. But with the person blinded in adult life, we must sharply distinguish between the needs of someone who has always reacted to the problems of life by escaping from them and those of the person who had a normal capacity for solving his problems honestly but finds that of blindness too massive to bear. The latter case is much more easily handled, but the former must also be assisted to whatever extent is possible.

The capable practitioner will know almost instinctively the degree to which he can go with each individual in bringing him to face the totality and finality of his blindness. In some instances he will recognize that the "operation" is too dangerous to be undertaken; in others he will see that the defenses are so strong as to be almost impenetrable. But he will always face the fact that the problem of the delicate defenses is a very real one, the solution of which demands his highest skill.

This is the reason why the need for professionalism must be so strongly emphasized. No one has the right to put another's personality in jeopardy by forcing his defenses without proper professional knowledge and assistance. What the nonprofessional can and should do here is to work on his own attitude to blindness and to the blind persons he is in contact with. And it is hoped that the following discussions of the reality and psychological restorations which must go along together in true rehabilitation will help him to do so.

10

Training the Other Senses

FOR OUR purposes, the senses of a human being may be thought of as so many channels or cables of communication, the external senses conveying various kinds of information about the outside world and the internal about the condition and operation of the body itself. All this information goes to a kind of central intelligence station (located, according to some authorities, in the central cortex of the brain) which correlates it for use in thinking and acting.

Among these many channels, sight is unique. Anatomically, the eye receptor is capable of taking in and transmitting a vast amount of information at one time. The other channels are far more selective and less capable of carrying a great deal of information all at once. As a result, sight conveys by far the greater amount of all the sense information received, especially during the early learning years and in new situations. Hence, every sighted child instinctively organizes the information furnished by the other senses mainly in reference to that conveyed by sight. The sense of sight is, then, not only the main *source* of information, but also the main *censor or tester* of all sense knowledge.

The blinded person, consequently, needs to develop much more than a single substitute for sight. He needs to develop his use of all the remaining "cables," and to reorganize his central sense so that without sight it can take in and order these multiple cues into a usable pattern. He must learn how to do all this at first very con-

sciously and then, at least under ordinary circums
below the level of conscious awareness and effort.

This task is not easy. Yet, while no one sense c
of sight, all of them together can convey a gre
information adding up to a reasonably adequate k
environment for ordinary purposes. And adults ca
ences of their whole lives, their storehouse of memories and particularly of visual memories, to fill out and interpret the information furnished by the other senses.

The first step in such training is to make the person aware of some of the knowledge he is already receiving through these other senses and of the source from which he is receiving this knowledge. This quality of "awareness" is of very great importance to his further development. It means that he can ask himself and answer the questions: "How did I know that?" (or "How did I guess that?"); "What sense cues entered into it?"; "What was significant, what was different about that experience?"; "What sense told it to me?"

Persons who have been blind for years, as well as those newly blinded, have been able to increase greatly their ability in "orientation," in contact with the world around them, by the simple method of beginning to answer questions like these, analyzing their sense experiences of the world and becoming alert to the clues these are offering them. For, despite all the onslaughts which modern civilization has made on our use of our sense knowledge, our senses still have much to tell us. They have not been atrophied by our airtight, soundproof houses, by our scent-killing and scent-masking chemicals, by air conditioning or any other of the "sense reducers"; these only make it more difficult for us to use our senses to full advantage.* Nor is age any barrier to the development of the senses, unless it has to some degree actually diminished sense power, or unless senility has begun to destroy reasoning power.

It might be thought that "nature" would automatically carry out

* Yet the fact that such devices do make sense perception more difficult for the blind person might well be taken into consideration in planning his home, or in planning rehabilitation centers, etc.

ask of sense-development for the blinded person. But it does not. ew people are aware of the full range of their sense equipment or alert to the information it is giving them, and the onset of blindness does not of itself open out these possibilities.

Furthermore, the unaided blinded person cannot provide himself with anything like the amount of checking or "feedback" needed to develop his use of his senses to the full. He can go and touch the trunk of a tree to test the accuracy of what he has perceived about it through hearing and smelling — exactly where it is located, for instance, and its approximate size. But obtaining feedback in ways like this is impossible in many cases and would be extremely hazardous in many others. At best, the training he can give himself by his own unaided checking is haphazard, time-consuming and incomplete.

He can be greatly aided by any intelligent person who will help him become conscious of his various sense powers and provide him with feedback as he begins to exercise them. But he can be most effectively helped by a whole program which provides feedback effectively and scientifically and is oriented toward the final correlation and use-in-action of all his developing powers.

Such a program in relation to mobility, for example, gradually brings the trainee to an awareness of all the information his senses convey about the terrain on which he is walking. It gives him practice with feedback in testing the accuracy of his interpretations of this information. When he has gained a reasonable amount of accuracy, using his various senses first separately and then together, he is given practice in traffic, at first with protection. After complete training, he can safely take a walk by himself on busy city streets — something he should never attempt without this truly professional preparation.

Sensory training is concerned with arousing awareness of various kinds of information formerly not adverted to, and with its correct correlation and interpretation. (This includes awareness of absence: to smell no smoke, to hear no sound may be very significant in a given situation.) No one kind of information is important by itself. It is the whole picture and the correct filling in and interpretation of the picture that keeps the blinded person in complete contact with his environment.

Scientific studies of the last century have demonstrated that the number of human senses is far more than the classical five. No listing now seems possible which would be satisfactory for every branch of study; the number in each case depends on the particular emphasis and purpose of the study. Here we are concerned, not so much with the separate senses from the physiological point of view, as with the sense *activities* that appear to be particularly important when sight is gone. We shall discuss the use of these in orientation to environment and to mobility, and the general means by which they may be developed.

Activities of the Sense of Hearing

Six activities of hearing seem to be particularly important when sight is gone: three concerned with sounds coming directly from objects, three with sounds reflected from objects.

Recognition and identification of sounds. All of us can recognize and identify the sound of a dripping tap, a creaking chair, different voices. The blinded person needs to develop this ability to a greater degree than the rest of us, so that he will be informed about his environment and, when he is moving about, can identify places by their characteristic sounds: the crunching of gravel on a driveway, the noise of a manhole cover being stepped on, the squeak of a door, the lapping of water, the croaking of frogs.

Training is given by repeatedly asking the blind person: "What was that sound?" and by giving him feedback to confirm his identifications and help him correct his mistakes. In the rehabilitation center, a planned series of exercises, using not only the normal sounds in the immediate environment, but also a much wider range made available on high-fidelity recordings, greatly speeds up the development of skill.

The discrimination of sounds is a further step and a very necessary one. All of us can, for example, pick out the sound of a policeman's whistle from other traffic noises; the blinded person needs to develop this ability so that he can pick out one or more important sounds from among many and recognize the particular sounds that go to make up a jumble of noises. Some sounds, like that made by a pneumatic hammer, actually mask other sounds, making identification impossible. But on many occasions there is no true masking, and in our noisy world it is extremely useful to be able to pick out one or two meaningful sounds from among many.

Here again, high-fidelity recordings of actual sound situations — many people talking, various combinations of traffic noises — with the constant furnishing of feedback can be used to give the trainee experience in distinguishing among sounds, without the inhibiting effects of embarrassment or fear, before he is taken into actual social or street situations for further practice.

Localization of sound. The ability to determine where a sound is coming from is useful in locating oneself, even in a small room or apartment, and vitally important in mobility. Many authorities recommend, for instance, that a ticking clock be part of the furnishings of the home of a blind child or any blind person to provide a fixed and constant sound source by which he can always orient himself. The noise of a refrigerator, the squeaking of a floor board, the noise of a stove or a radio in a fixed position can serve the same purpose. Similarly, in moving around outside, the blind person can learn to orient himself by recognizing characteristic sounds — the rustling branches of a particular tree, the traffic roar from a highway — as coming from one or another direction.

This ability is also most useful in giving information about one's environment: where the approaching person or car is coming from, and a great deal more besides. For example, by following the location of the sounds that someone else makes in entering and crossing a room, the route of that person can be determined and, as a result, something of the layout of the room itself — the location of the doors and of some of the furniture, where there are rugs or bare floor, etc. Both positive and negative information is involved: there must be a piece of furniture here to have caused the person to turn, and no furniture there since he came straight across.

Training in this ability is given first by means of synthetic sounds (buzzers and the like), by exercises such as locating dropped coins, and later on by practice — always with feedback — in locating ordinary sounds in social and traffic situations.

In connection with this particular ability, the trainer needs to remember the importance of binaural hearing. The cup shape of the human ear helps somewhat to determine the direction of a sound, although not enough to determine whether a sound is coming from behind or in front. The fact that we have two ears with approximately equal hearing power is of primary importance in determining both direction and distance of sounds: we recognize the difference between what we hear with the ear nearer to the sound and what we hear with the ear farther from it.

Trainees should therefore be encouraged to follow the normal tendency to turn their heads from side to side to help determine the distance from which a faint noise is coming on the horizontal plane. And they should be shown that to determine the direction and the distance on the vertical plane it is useful to turn the head so that one ear is above the other, even if this means almost lying down.

It should be noted also that most of us think we are localizing sounds when we already know from the nature of the sound where it must be coming from. We look for an airplane overhead, not because we have localized the sound accurately, but because we have recognized it as the sound of a plane. The blinded person needs to develop the power of localization itself, as well as this power of inference.

The trainer also needs to remember that the human ear appears to have two independent mechanisms, one for high-frequency ranges and one for low (with the greatest error range in the area of 3000 cycles per second). Thus a person with a hearing loss affecting one of these mechanisms can still be trained to become highly expert with the other.

Reflection detection, type* A is the ability to determine the dis-

* This term is used to avoid the misunderstandings and overlappings caused by such terms as "obstacle detection," "echo perception," "facial vision." For further information about research in this area, see *Books about the Blind* by Helga Lende, American Foundation for the Blind, 1953.

tance and direction of an object and something of its nature by hearing a sound and its echo from that object, with a distinct interval between the two sounds.

A dramatic method of convincing a blinded person that he possesses this ability is to take him into a large open field, with a single building on it which he is to locate, and instruct him to clap his hands sharply at intervals, while pivoting. The sound of his handclap comes back to him from the building with the sharpness and force of a gunshot; he immediately knows which direction the building must be in. With practice, he can begin to know how far away from him it is, and even something of its nature — its size, material, etc.

This ability can make use of other less obvious sounds caused by the blind person himself, such as those he makes by walking with metal heelplates or leather heels or by snapping his fingers. (What seems like a nervous habit of finger-snapping in many blind people is actually done on purpose to set up echoes.)

Sounds coming from sources other than the blind person himself may also be used. Outdoors, for example, the echo of traffic sounds indicates where there are buildings; the absence of such echoes indicates an open space. Indoors, the way in which noises made by people entering an empty hall echo from its walls can tell the trained blind person something about the size and shape of the hall. When the lecturer begins to speak, the reverberations of his voice indicate still more about the size, height, and shape of the hall and whether it is packed, partially full, or nearly empty.

Training in this power is given by practice with feedback, both with self-originated and other sounds.

Reflection detection, type B is the ability to gather information by perceiving the change in quality when a sound becomes reflected from an object. Here there is no recognizable interval between the original sound and its reflection. For example, a person who is talking as he walks across a room toward a flat wall can, without the use of sight, detect the wall before he bumps into it by hearing the change in the sound as his voice becomes reflected from the wall. Even a completely untrained person wearing metal heelplates or leather heels can walk down an empty business block and, if there are no extraneous noises, tell from the reflected sounds where the doors are set back from the street, whether they are open or closed, where the plate-glass windows come out to the edge of the sidewalk.

With training, the blinded person can make the same deductions even when there are heavy traffic noises. And he can be shown how to attend to the sound signals he sends off by walking with metal heelplates or leather heels, hearing these sounds quickly diffused when there are no objects nearby and reflected when there are, in differing pitch and timbre according to the nearness, size, and texture of the objects. He can also be shown further possibilities of acquiring information by this means, such as, for example, dropping a hard package or a coin on the table when he enters an office or conference room so that the reverberations can give him clues as to its size, shape and furnishings.

This is the type of reflection detection most used by blind persons in mobility. Like the other powers, it can be trained by exercise and practice with feedback. In the early stages, synthetic sounds may be used like that made by the "Twersky Tweeter"—a bell-shaped metallic cup developed by Professor Victor Twersky, which sends out a high-pitched signal when the rubber bulb at its neck is squeezed. Later on, the trainees are shown how to make use of ordinary sounds, like those described above.

Reflection detection, type C is distinct from the other two types since it is not recognizable as a form of hearing. It is the ability publicized as "facial vision," an ability in no way peculiar to blind persons, but one awaiting development in anyone who possesses normal hearing. It is a means of perceiving nearby obstacles by what has been described as "feeling something like a cloud on my face" or "feeling pressure on my cheekbones and forehead." But research has conclusively shown that this ability is connected not with the touch senses but with hearing; deaf people or those with their ears stopped do not possess it. The explanation seems to be that some change is perceived as the background sounds, the "noise level" of the immediate environment, become reflected from the obstacle, but that these sounds are not recognized as "heard," or that the changes in ambient sound are so slight as to be at the threshold of auditory perceptibility, thus triggering an instinctive rather than a conscious response.

A method of demonstrating the existence of this ability is to hold a large flat book near the face of a blinded person or of a sighted person whose eyes are closed so as to exclude light. The book is held first at an angle to the face, then with the flat side toward it. Almost anyone can tell immediately when the book comes near his face and whether it comes at an angle or flat. If the experiment is repeated several times, with feedback when an error is made, the ability develops.

It can be further trained by presenting objects of various sizes and shapes and at various angles and distances from the body in situations where the amount of noise is controlled. A device like a clothes reel, from the arms of which objects can be suspended on ropes running over pulleys, has proved very useful.

This ability is an important adjunct to general orientation and to mobility. Considerable research has been done on it already and should be utilized in work for the blind; here is one more source of information, and the use of *every* source is important for blinded persons. In the meantime, the mobility therapist in particular should repeatedly call attention to the existence of this ability and give his trainees some informal practice in its use.

Smell

Because of its long range, second only to that of hearing when sight is gone, the sense of smell is particularly important to the blinded person. It can contribute a great deal to the interest and variety of life (see page 183), and it can be extremely useful in conveying information about places and things, and also about people. The scent of shaving soap, tobacco, perfume can help to identify and characterize different persons — and, while our culture tries to do away with ordinary human smells, they do exist.

This sense is consequently useful in orientation and even more useful in mobility. Places can be identified by characteristic smells —

sea and lake shores, pine woods, hayfields. A pharmacy, a grocery, a leather-goods store, a gas station, a restaurant — each has its special single smell or combination of smells by which the blind person can identify it as he walks down a street. Again, if the trained blind person catches the scent of coffee from the coffee district of a city, notes its intensity and the direction of the wind, he can orient himself anew by the compass.

Training in developing the use of this sense is given along the same lines as with hearing: by exercises giving practice with feedback in identifying various smells, their intensity and the direction they are coming from, in distinguishing between them, and in becoming alert to the inferences that can be drawn from them.

Taste

Taste is so closely connected with smell that, for example, one both tastes and smells a sea breeze. Developing one of these senses thus helps, at least to some extent, to develop the other. The sense of taste is important to the blinded person for what might be called "contact with the reality world of food and drink." Unless he is alerted to discriminate between and to appreciate tastes, eating may become merely a tedious chore which he tends to neglect — the reason apparently being that most people in our culture appreciate what they eat by the way it looks rather than by how it tastes. This sense, consequently, although not useful in mobility, can be important for health and for the enjoyment of many social situations, as well as for increasing the pleasure and variety in life.

Training can be given by practice with feedback in recognizing and identifying the taste sensations (sweet, sour, salt and bitter) separately and in combination in various foods and drinks.

Activities of the Labyrinthine or Vestibular ("Equilibrium") Sense

A great deal of research on this sense, the organ of which is located in the labyrinthine canals, or vestibule, of the ear, is being carried out by the armed services, by civilian airlines, and by all agencies interested in outer space; this research, again, needs to be utilized in work for the blind. The first activity of this sense, the *perception of balance,* is closely bound up with a general feeling of security: "Stability of orientation is generally regarded as necessary to feelings of security, and vestibular disturbances or vestibular stimulation lead to feelings of insecurity, anxiety, fear or panic." *

At the beginning of the program, each trainee should be tested to ascertain the degree, if any, to which this power has been impaired. The usual causes of loss of sight do not cause labyrinthine damage, but laboratory experiments indicate that sight can inhibit or reinforce this sense's response to stimuli. The loss of sight, therefore, may affect the *use* of this power.

The main work to be done here is to reassure the blinded person that the sense itself is not impaired and to build up confidence in the information it gives — a confidence which will grow as he regains security in moving about and confidence in his muscular reactions. Many persons who begin a rehabilitation course with an apparent deficit in this sense are able at the end of ten or twelve weeks to operate with no apparent labyrinthine loss or a lessened one. How much this may be due to improvement in general physical tone and how much to present methods of testing cannot be calculated, but there is no doubt that the use of this power affects the general sense of security and vice versa.

The *sense of turn,* the second activity of the labyrinthine sense, works with kinesthesis, to tell us when and how far we have turned in one direction or another on a horizontal plane. As yet very little is known about its operation, but it undoubtedly is a factor in what is commonly called the "sense of direction." All that can be done at present is to test this power in each trainee, correlating the results with his skill in mobility. Then we can attempt some experimental training and test again to see what results have been achieved.

* Chapter on "Vestibular Functions" by G. R. Wendt in *Handbook of Experimental Psychology,* edited by S. S. Stevens, John Wiley & Sons, New York, 1951.

Activities of the Touch Senses

One of the commonest delusions about blind persons is that they are gifted with an exceptionally keen or "superhuman" sense of touch. Fortunately or unfortunately, comparative measurements do not bear out this belief; neither the touch senses nor any others are automatically sharpened by blindness. But these senses, like the others, can be developed by training. The importance of these senses to the blinded person for information, orientation and mobility is second only to that of hearing.

In actual use, the external or cutaneous touch senses blend and work together with the internal or kinesthetic touch sense (and, in many cases, with the labyrinthine sense also). Training is given, consequently, mainly in connection with the various skills — in shop and kitchen courses, modeling, braille, typing, mobility. But the trainee needs first to be alerted to the existence and working of these various kinds of touch and to be given some practice in the use of each as a distinct mode of feeling. We shall therefore discuss them first separately and then in combination.

Perception of pressure and pain. Two different sets of nerves are involved here, but the two kinds of sensation can be treated together for our purposes. The blinded person needs to be shown that he can perceive pressures on the tiny hairs of the skin without direct contact with the skin itself. Each hair acts like a lever, spreading to the surrounding area of skin the sensation aroused by the lightest pressure.

The use of this means of perception can keep a blind person from knocking over small objects when he reaches for them. It is used in working with moving machinery. It aids in perceiving the direction of a gentle breeze, which in turn indicates the door or window through which the breeze is coming or the opening between two buildings. It is also useful in gaining information by brushing by an object — a chair, a door — without seeming to touch it. Moreover, information can be gathered not only from pressure on the exposed surfaces of the body, but also from that exerted by clothing as the person moves about.

These sense activities should be tested at the beginning of the program, and the pressure sense trained by exercises given under laboratory conditions, which develop awareness of lighter and lighter pressures, and by various skill courses as noted above.

Perception of warmth and coolness (*"temperature sense"*) is obviously necessary for anyone working with hot and cold objects, for example in various types of repair work and in cooking. But its use in orientation and mobility should especially be pointed out and developed. The heat coming from a stove or radiator can serve as a landmark for orientation without the necessity for touching the object. Awareness of the warmth of the sun coming through a pane of glass or open window aids in locating the window, and so does awareness of a sun-warmed area of the floor, even when the sun is no longer shining in directly. In the same way, landmarks for orientation may be given by an awareness of cold from a refrigerator or coming through a pane of glass, a thin wall, a crack or a window.

Use of this sense helps in mobility. On a sunny day, alertness to warmth and coolness can help the blind person tell when he is passing under the shade of trees or buildings and out again or when he is going under an awning. From the difference between warm and cool breezes he can tell when he has come to the corner of a building and when he is passing a break between buildings. Changes in the temperature of air currents tell him when he is passing a blast of hot air from one open doorway or of cool air from another, or going past the mouth of a subway structure.

These sense activities, again, should be tested, and training should be given mainly by arousing the trainee's awareness of the information they give, as well as by encouraging his use of them in kitchen and shop work and above all in mobility. They will not give fine discriminations, but it is possible that they can help a person recognize the proximity of a 98.6° object in a 60° room.

Kinesthesis has been defined as that "set of sensations comprising the mass of feeling generated by movements of the body itself";* that is, according to present usage, feelings aroused by muscles, tendons

* Geldard, *op. cit.*

and joints.* This is the sense that makes us aware of our own position and movements, telling us when we are standing, walking or running, sitting upright or slouched, how far we are reaching for an object and how heavy it is when we hold it (except for those light objects whose "lack of weight" is determined by the sense of pressure). Kinesthesis works with the labyrinthine sense and the external touch senses to tell us whether we are walking up or down a sloping grade, bearing to the right or left, etc. And when we extend the reach of our touch senses with a cane or other tool, kinesthesis is brought very much into play in bringing back communications from the other end of the tool.

Normal life and activity would be impossible without this sense, and yet many people are unaware that they possess it. The blinded person needs, therefore, to be informed about its workings and about the reliance that he can place upon it. Asking him such questions as "Where is your left leg?" "What is the position of the knee joint, the ankle joint?" shows him that he does not need sight to know the position of his own body; the body itself tells him, and finding out that it does gives him great reassurance.

Training is given by a special course in "kinesthetic awareness," which includes exercises to improve posture, balance, locomotion, direction and timing of movement, relaxation, freedom of movement and general co-ordination. Kinesthetic awareness is also developed in connection with all skill courses and particularly with mobility.

Stereognosis (knowledge of three-dimensional form) is a touch activity using the external touch senses and kinesthesis for the tactile discrimination of shape and form. It is trained by exercises with feedback in recognizing and discriminating between objects by handling and feeling them, and also through many of the courses noted above.

A term with a somewhat wider meaning has come into use particularly among the blinded veterans of World War II: *to braille,*

* It is essential that the worker for the blind be aware that blind persons (blinded adults and especially the congenitally blind) are often unable to point with the arm or finger to an exact spot, although they may be localizing correctly with their other senses. The pointing error is the result of the structural angles of the body. Close your eyes; point to a specific location; open your eyes and check. By repeating this, you are likely to discover a considerable angle of error.

used not in the usual sense of "to transcribe material into braille," but as meaning "to handle, to feel, to explore tactually, to gain all the information that can be obtained about something by touch." This term arouses much feeling among workers for the blind, some holding that "to see" or "to feel" are adequate words and that using "to braille" means setting up a special "blind" vocabulary, others insisting that this term fills a real need, and that even if a verb could be formed from "stereognosis," it would not cover the complex activity described by "to braille." In any case, the spontaneous adoption of this term emphasizes the importance to blinded persons of tactual means of acquiring information.*

Somesthesis is a term covering the use of all these body sensibilities: the external touch senses, the kinesthetic and the labyrinthine sense. No one touch sense but several working together are needed to determine whether objects are wet, dry, hard, rough, smooth, soft, blunt, sharp, slick, greasy. The ability to determine these various qualities is, again, trained by practice with feedback, both on fine objects for information about the immediate environment and on large ones for mobility.

The trainer should keep in mind the importance of movement in the exercise of the touch senses — to determine roughness, for example. In reading braille, not only is pressure needed, but movement of the fingers over the object; a space-time pattern must come into the determination if the dots are to be recognized.

The trainer should also remember that it is not only the touch of the hands which needs to be developed from a grope into an assured, trained receptiveness. The touch of the feet, involving the kinesthetic and labyrinthine senses as well as the pressure sense, needs to be developed so that carpets, rugs, worn places on the floor, sloping sidewalks, curbings, gravel, and trimmed lawn edges all become recognizable to the discriminating "foot touch" of the blinded person.

* See *T.K.G., Studies in the Art and Skill of Form and Space Perception,* No. I, by Robert Amendola, American Foundation for the Blind, 1961.

Co-ordinating Sense Activities

Motor memory (*muscle memory*) is "the memory of the living body in motion. When certain movements have been repeated often enough in a fixed sequence, they become automatic; they are executed without volition and with a minimum of attention. Motor memory accumulates and conserves the many skills which every man or animal needs for everyday life, walking, talking, writing, reading, using tools are different manifestations of motor memory." * Without it, we could not develop any skills; we would have to give full attention to all the habitual activities of daily life. The blind person needs to be able to rely on it even more than the sighted, so that, for example, he does not need to count the number of steps to the door or to the corner; so that the blind man can move with assurance around his office and the blind woman around her kitchen. (It is this ability which, incidentally, is the answer to the particularly stupid question "How does a blind person find his mouth with a spoon?")

It cannot be said that we can train this ability directly, so that when the trainee seeks to use a learned set of actions in a new pattern, it will work effectively with less need of conscious repetition than before. But the blinded person should be made aware of his possession of this faculty and of the reliance that he can safely place upon it. He should also be shown that once a pattern of movement has been fixed by conscious effort, motor memory works best when it is not adverted to. Sighted persons use this faculty with confidence to go up or down familiar stairs, but if the lights go out, they may get panicky and, by trying to force motor memory to operate, inhibit its workings entirely. So with the blind person in other situations; he needs to learn to take his attention away from this power so as to allow it to work.

In addition, the rehabilitation center should provide sufficient drill in the activities which the trainees will need to repeat in daily life

* *Philosophical Psychology* by M. F. Donceel, S.J., Sheed & Ward, New York City, 1955.

to make sure that such patterns will become deeply fixed in the motor memory.

The sense (or "perception" or "faculty of judgment") of spatial relations is the "sense" of pattern discrimination and of space discrimination, telling us where we are on some mental map of our surroundings. It seems to involve many sensory activities, including the labyrinthine sense, kinesthesis and motor memory. (A significant number of tests indicate a correlation between the patterns a blinded person draws and those he walks. Trainees who draw a circle on the blackboard with a bulge at the nine o'clock segment tend to walk a circle with a similar bulge; trainees whose blackboard triangle leaves an opening rather than a closed angle will walk a triangle and arrive wide of the starting point.)

Giving special attention to the making of such a mental map and to keeping one's place on it as one moves along is certainly of great importance. Women were once thought to have practically no sense of direction, whereas nowadays they are found to possess it. The reason seems to be that the women tested in the past were accustomed to being escorted or driven. Now that they are used to going about on their own, they find it necessary to keep track of where they are and where they are going, and so have become accustomed to giving the kind of attention to their surroundings and their motion that a sense of direction requires.

While the workings of this sense are by no means clear, it can be trained by something like a course in navigation. Trainees are given a series of graded exercises in which the information from the various senses is co-ordinated and cross-checked in connection with a technique of quick mental mapping, so that they can at any given instant answer the questions: "Where am I?" "In what direction am I facing?" "In what direction am I moving?"

The central sense, the general headquarters of the whole sensory system, "(1) makes the animal (and man on the sense level) aware of the activity and the objects of its external senses . . . (2) enables the animal to distinguish between the different sensations deriving from the various senses . . . and (3) . . . integrates the data of the external senses and refers them to their common object." * also be remembered that in man there is the great powei and that this cogitative power also aids the "internal sense a judgment on a given situation.

Unless this sense is working effectively, normal living is impossible. We would never get anything done if we needed continually to attend to all the various kinds of data conveyed by our senses and to sort them out consciously. For the blinded trainee whose sense activities are being developed, life is consequently very difficult and confused until his central sense has reorganized so that it can correlate all this new information into an intelligible pattern, and can do so under ordinary circumstances somewhere below the level of conscious effort.

Separate training for each sense activity trains the central sense to handle a particular kind of information, and the use of these activities in skill courses and in mobility aids the central sense to readjust. But its final reorganization for effective operation under the new conditions of blindness cannot be hurried or forced. The trainee needs to have it explained to him again and again during the program that his central sense is now working overtime to take in and co-ordinate consciously information which it either rejected or handled unconsciously in the past. He needs frequently to be reassured that the time will come when he will not have to give conscious attention to so many details and can go about the business of living with a minimum of attention to the operations of his various senses. The sense training must be given with support and understanding, and at the rate at which each individual can take it fruitfully.

Visualization. But we can do still more. As was said earlier, because sight conveys so large a part of all sense knowledge, the person who has grown up with the use of sight instinctively correlates all the data furnished by the other senses in reference to it. His sense knowledge is ordered in a primarily visual framework; his sense experiences are

* Donceel, *op. cit.* In this terminology, "external senses" refers not only to the exteroceptors but also to the proprioceptors and interoceptors; the "internal senses" are the central sense, imagination, memory, and the estimative power.

cast mainly into terms of visual experience. The blinded adult is, consequently, a sighted person in his whole psychological make-up, and he will suffer the complete disruption of his ingrained way of learning about and experiencing reality unless he can continue to operate according to such a visual pattern. The congenitally blind person, with no visual experience, co-ordinates his learning, his sense experiences, by some substitute method, the nature of which is not clearly known, although it is probably some developed sense of spatial relations. The person who has grown up with sight cannot find his adjustment by this other method.

But the once sighted person still possesses the power of visualization. He can therefore be trained to use this power so that all his sensory activity can continue to be visually oriented. People who have grown up with the use of sight possess a vast storehouse of visual images, a collection of "slides" of things they have seen. And these can be not only recalled but combined to make new images. The person who once saw a Model T Ford can bring back the picture of that Model T. The one he saw may have been the familiar combination of brass and black, and he can recall it thus. But if he has also seen lavender and silver, he can combine all these images and visualize a Model T with lavender body and silver trim.

Our visual images vary in their strength, their concreteness. Strongest of all is the visual image of the thing now seen before us, the "sight image," almost the retinal image. We pass over the hallucinatory image, when, in a waking state, the thing is "seen" as existing outside the person. Next come the visual images of the dream state, which though greatly distorted, can have a very colorful "concreteness." Next come the images recalled as we saw them, among which scenes and objects of our early lives or scenes of great emotional meaning seem to have the greatest verisimilitude, the greatest "reality." And finally, there are the composed images, put together by an effort of imagination and memory and, like the simply recalled images, "seen" in the mind's eye, visualized. It is with the visualization of this last type of image that we are concerned here.

People certainly vary in their power to visualize, yet everyone who has had the use of sight possesses it to some degree, and it can be stimulated and developed. Thus in every use of his remaining senses, the blinded person should be encouraged to make the effort not only to know the thing which becomes apparent to him through these senses, but also to "see" it in his mind's eye. (Such an effort should *never*, of course, be even suggested, let alone urged, to the congenitally blind person.) Thus the song of a robin should not be only a disembodied sound in the blinded person's mind; with it should come into his mind's eye the picture of the robin, and not by itself but on the ground or on a branch.

Moreover, he should try to visualize what would be within his normal field of vision if he could see. When he comes into a new room, every bit of information coming to him through his various senses should go together to elicit a picture of the room as he would see it from where he stands, and then as he would see it from another angle when he has crossed it and sat down. With training and practice, he can thus learn to use all the information furnished by his other senses to evoke the appropriate images (realistic, if not completely factual images), making him constantly aware of how things around him look, centralizing him in a seen world.

If he does not use this power of visualization, after a time he will be living in a visual vacuum; the power will gradually atrophy so that he cannot easily or accurately recall visual images, especially color images, even for purposes of pleasurable memory. But if he does use it and develop it, he will continue to live visually in the three-dimensional colored world he has always known, filling indoor spaces with their furnishings and people, outdoor spaces with their hills, valleys, buildings, trees, clouds, distances. And obviously such visual awareness of his environment is not only in harmony with the requirements of his psychophysical make-up, but is of immediate practical value in orientation and mobility.

Training in visualization can be given in all the courses at the rehabilitation center, by constantly calling for its use. St. Paul's also gives two special courses. "Imagery stimulation" is designed to keep the visual memory alive, to make it active and responsive to the will.

"The art of visualizing" trains the imagination to respond visually to the intake from the senses and to focus the flow of imagery on that part of the environment which the trainee is facing, so that his physical responses are normal and appropriate to whatever he is thus imaginatively looking at. He is not, of course, trained in any way to make believe that he is actually seeing what is in front of him. The aim of the training is simply to restore to him, as far as possible, his visual pattern of experiencing and reacting to his environment.

Accurate measurement of the effects of this training has up to the present time seemed out of the question, but certain research ideas are now being considered which may make this a real possibility. In any case, the practical results seem to indicate that this training is being given along the right lines and that development of the power of visualization is the keystone in training the senses of the blinded person to take over the role of sight.

Co-ordination through fencing. Various special courses and skill courses for developing the blinded person's remaining senses have already been indicated. But by far the most important single course is that in *fencing* in the classic French style. This course is invaluable for general sense development and physical education, improving posture, poise, rapid motor memory response, discrimination and alertness, while the suppleness of wrist and alertness to information conveyed by the foil as an extension of the touch senses are particularly applicable to the use of the long cane in mobility. No rehabilitation program can be considered adequate without such a course.

11

Restoration of Psychological Security

1. THE SENSE OF PHYSICAL INTEGRITY

THE LOSS of the sense of physical integrity, as we saw earlier (page 14), is due mainly to psychological factors. A blinded person, although he has lost his sight and perhaps the organ of sight as well, is still basically whole and healthy. He must come to realize, deeply and sincerely, that this is true.

He will be greatly aided here by the whole rehabilitation program, particularly by regaining mobility and the techniques of daily living. The fact that he is once more functioning as a normal, healthy human being shows him that he is one.

Dealing directly with the feelings about himself and his blindness that are the essence of this loss is part of the work of the psychiatrist, the clinical psychologist, and the trained caseworker at the rehabilitation center. These feelings are bound up with the personality structure of the blinded person; to interpret them and change them involves rebuilding his body image and his self-concept (see page 73). Group psychotherapy may aid here, but in any case this is a task for experts.

The average worker in the field needs to have a complete understanding of the meaning of this loss, and to know that it can be overcome. He needs also to realize that unless it is overcome, it can stand in the way of a complete adjustment to blindness.

In addition, a great deal can be done to give the blinded person the assurance that he presents a normal, healthy appearance to others.

And if he does in fact look unobtrusively normal, other people will more easily accept him as such, and this acceptance will reinforce his own sense of physical integrity. One factor here in the prevention or overcoming of "blindisms"—peculiarities of posture, gait, expression (see page 161). Another may be cosmetic aid to give a more normal appearance to disfigured eyes, which can cause a feeling of revulsion in sighted people.

Such cosmetic aid is neither needed nor possible in every case, but in some it is extremely important. This fact may easily be overlooked by the worker who has become so accustomed to unsightly eyes that he no longer realizes how strongly they may affect the people around the blind man and, through their feelings, the blind man himself. In many cases, such a condition can be cured by the substitution of a prosthetic eye (glass or plastic) or by the use of a plastic shell which covers the eye.

Yet here again, only the expert psychiatrist or psychologist, working with the ophthalmologist, can safely decide whether to mention the possibility of cosmetic restoration to a particular blind person, still less to urge it upon him. Untold damage can be done by even the right advice wrongly given or by any advice given to a person not in a condition to receive it. The unsightly eye that a well-meaning worker wishes to have covered with a plastic shell may be receiving a little light, which means a great deal to the blinded person. Or again, a disfigured eye and eye socket may be in such a condition that they could not tolerate a prosthetic shell. In either of these cases, no matter how gently the worker may broach the subject, he manages only to arouse fears and feelings of insecurity where perhaps no such fears and feelings existed before, or to stir up dormant ones. And there is no telling how far-reaching the resulting damage may be.

Even harder to handle properly is the case in which enucleation seems indicated, not because of the medical or surgical condition of the patient, but because the one remaining eye is useless, there is no hope that any sight can be restored, and the eye is so distorted as to cause revulsion in other people. A well-meaning adviser might easily forget to take into consideration how much hope the blinded person was attaching to such an eye and how much protection that hope was giving him against facing the terrible finality of his blindness. Or the adviser might overlook the possibility that the thought of enucleation might have inner meanings to the blinded person which he would be unable to face.

Such situations call for the trained expert, working in co-operation with the ophthalmologist and the maker of prosthetic eyes. But the effects of their combined work may be extremely helpful to the blinded person's acceptance of himself and to his being accepted by others. A case in point is that of an intelligent young woman who had allowed an unsightly and useless eye to ruin her appearance for many years. Well-meaning people had urged her to have the eye enucleated, but this advice only aroused a genuine neurotic anxiety, which attached itself to many different things and made her life difficult in many ways. Eventually she sought psychiatric aid for these difficulties and within two months, without any urging on the part of the psychiatrist, she herself made the decision to have the operation, having come to see something of the reasons why the idea of enucleation had disturbed her. Social pressure from her family or from workers with the blind might have succeeded in forcing her to have the operation without previous psychiatric help, but this would only have brought about a long-term disturbance, with postoperative misgivings about the course taken. Instead, she is thoroughly satisfied with her decision and with the very beneficial effects of the operation on her appearance.

To summarize: rehabilitation in other areas, the avoidance or cure of blindisms, and cosmetic aid in some cases all help toward the restoration of the sense of physical integrity. Direct work on the feelings involved is the task of the trained personnel at the rehabilitation center.

2. CONFIDENCE IN THE REMAINING SENSES

Loss of confidence in the remaining senses is due, as was noted earlier (page 18), to the loss of sight as the chief tester of all sense information, the loss of this tester apparently causing some disturbance in the working of the central sense. Confidence is restored as this work of testing is taken over by the other senses, a process which in most cases, though not in all, takes place naturally over a period of time. Sight had formerly been the *chief* tester but not the *only* one — each sense had always been called on to some extent to test the workings of the others. Calling upon the remaining senses to take over *all* this work does not, therefore, require any major change in the make-up of the blinded person.

In fact, the initial lack of confidence seems to hasten this process of redistribution. The more a person doubts what his ears tell him, the more he is driven to check this information by his other senses, until he comes to recognize the validity of what each sense tells him and to trust the working of his sensory equipment as he did before blindness.

In most cases, this restoration begins even in the early days of the shock period and usually is so nearly completed by the time that a person comes into contact with an agency that workers with the blind have little experience with this loss. Occasionally, however, the person is so panicked by his blindness that he does not give his other senses the opportunity to go to work. He remains in the shock stage, his only means of contact with reality being the senses of others, so that he asks again and again for reassurance and assistance from those around him. Such a person will almost certainly need psychiatric help. But even with such help, it is important that he have close to him someone whom he can recognize and trust, who will give him constant support until his senses begin to function again. And it is important that this person should gradually assist him in interpreting sense data and help him begin to realize how much trustworthy information he is receiving from his various senses. Regaining simple skills and learning new ones may help also.

Among those whom this loss does not affect so severely, there are some persons who also may find that the process of regaining confidence in their remaining senses is speeded up by mastering various hand skills: making belts, lacing wallets, simple weaving and the like.

But mastering such skills may well be a positive barrier rather than an aid to other persons. Activities of this kind have unfortunately become linked to an unpleasant stereotype of the blind man who has nothing to do but make belts or wallets. And it is a sorry day when a man who before he became blind ruled an industrial kingdom finds himself being complimented because he can fashion a woolly dog (and an even sorrier one when he is childishly gratified by such compliments). Instruction in any crafts like these should, therefore, be offered only as affording purposeful manipulative exercises, a means to further rehabilitation, and offered only to those blinded persons who will accept it as such a means, not as a dead end.

For the same reasons, those who are helping a newly blinded person to train his senses and regain confidence in them should avoid setting up situations that resemble children's guessing games in identifying smells, sounds, touches. Only very small children are unresentful about games that teach, and the blinded person's adult dignity is already under too severe a strain to be subjected to the further indignity of being put into a childish recreational situation.

But the blinded person needs not only to regain the confidence he had before blindness; he needs to gain a *greater* degree of confidence in his remaining senses than he ever had before. In the rehabilitation center, therefore, the testing of the trainee's various sense powers preliminary to training builds up confidence in the fact that they have not been essentially impaired by the loss of sight. This confidence is further built up by the training program described in Chapter 9, including the maturing of such skills as braille, typing, mobility, and in particular the skills that take the trainee through progressively more dangerous situations. For example, in shop work the trainee begins by learning how to hammer nails without damaging himself and, before he completes the course, to use power tools. This course is given to both men and women trainees, since its object is not to turn all blinded persons into handy men or cabinetmakers, but to enable them to put confidence in their senses and physical reactions with complete physical safety and to prove to them that they can do so.

3. REALITY CONTACT WITH ENVIRONMENT

The problem here is to restore strong, sure, direct contact with the real environment to the person who has lost it in whole or in part because of the loss of sight. Solving this problem is not easy, but it is most important, since in its solution lies security for many blinded persons.

On some persons the impact of the loss of reality contact is most severe. In such cases, it is strongly indicated that some member of the family remain with the blinded person and repeatedly give an assurance which will act as a tie with reality. Ophthalmologists frequently urge this in the case of older patients for whom there is reason to fear the possibility of "cataract psychosis" (see page 25). It is equally necessary in cases of new blindness, and certainly when the loss of reality contact is unusually severe or prolonged.

Others must continue to "fight for reality" during a period of indefinite length. And still others occasionally suffer from a sudden panic that renews the problem, especially in travel situations which cause them even for a few moments to become physically disoriented.

Prolonged and continued suffering from this loss indicates grave emotional disturbance. Here again, professional help is needed. But in the course of the psychiatric treatment and as a part of it, the psychiatrist will insist that between treatments some personal bond be established to keep the blinded person in touch with a human being in whom there is love and trust.

But the majority of blinded persons do not suffer for more than a short time from the full impact of this loss. Reality contact is in most cases restored together with confidence in the remaining senses. As was said earlier (page 103), the person should be helped to take the first step toward this twofold restoration in the early days of blindness, to ask himself "How did I know that?" or "How did I guess that?" "What sense cues entered into it?" "What was different, what was significant about that experience?" Thus he begins to forge a

bond of consciously received and correctly interpreted
between himself and reality.

The problem still remains of giving him an increasingly
with that reality. The solution lies in the further training c
and the help toward emotional reorganization given by the total rehabilitation program. Complete sense training orients him securely in the world of external reality; emotional reorganization rebuilds the complementary emotional security; and both are needed if this loss is to be completely overcome.

4. BACKGROUND

With the loss of visual background, as we saw earlier, blinded persons easily lose their awareness of the living, three-dimensional world, and lose also that continuous screening of information which takes place below the level of consciousness and contributes a constant "sight background" to daily living.

While this sight background cannot be restored, the blinded person can learn to substitute first an auditory background, then, as a further step, an omnisensory one, and finally, a visualized background which will to a considerable extent at least, take the place of the visual one.

The degree to which an auditory background can be developed naturally, without any training, and some of its quality can be ascertained from our own experience. At night, when the last light has been turned out, we often become far more aware of the noises around us than we were during the day — not only the special "night noises" of nature, but the ordinary sounds that have been going on all the time. We can recognize some of these sounds, but others can be quite disturbing because we cannot identify them or tell what they mean.

In the same way, the newly blinded person may be far more aware of noises than he was before he lost his sight. But because of the emotional strain under which the blinded person is laboring, many of the sounds can be disturbing and even frightening to a far greater degree than in the case of the sighted person at night, especially if he has no way of finding out what caused them. In this stage, then, the auditory background becomes a foreground, and an anxiety-laden one.

Moreover, many of the sounds will seem raucous, mechanical, monotonous; they become nerve-racking. Much of this is because they have no meaning; they elicit no good or pleasant associations; they remind him of his blindness. When he was sighted, not all the sights that made up his visual background were necessarily beautiful or pleasing to look at. But because they were meaningful and associated with experience, they went to make up a total visual background that was ordinarily a pleasing one.

Thus the development of a true auditory *back*ground for the blinded person requires systematic training of the sense of hearing already described. He also needs to be shown how much of the difference between "sounds" and "noises" is in the associations he has with them; that the reason why some sounds bother him lies in him rather than in the sounds themselves. And therefore, "noises" will become "sounds" and go to make up an auditory background for him when they come to have intelligibility, meaning, associations for him.

Ticking clocks and dripping faucets, gurgling pipes, creaking floors, whirring motors do not give music, but they do give an auditory background to life. And so do human sounds, work sounds, animal sounds, city and country sounds — sounds near and far, loud and soft, sharp and gentle, high and low, angry and friendly. All these can move in to give an auditory background once the blinded person is trained to identify them, to appreciate their qualities, to build up meaningful associations with them. But this is no magic "compensation"; it means training and learning.

In the same way, and even more so with the development of an omnisensory background, training and effort are necessary. Sound is not enough to substitute for the lost visual background — every sense experience needs to be brought in to bring to the blinded person the totality of the environment in which he is living. Not only auditory images, but also olfactory, gustatory, tactual and kinesthetic images are needed.

Together with the training of the senses, then, the blinded person needs to have the meaning of the loss of visual background explained to him; he needs to be shown how the development of all his other sense powers can help to substitute for it. And he needs also to be reassured that in time his central sense will be able to handle all this information below the level of consciousness and form it into a *back*ground to life, not a continually obtruding foreground.

We have already discussed the development of the power of visualization as the keystone in the process of training the blinded person's remaining senses. It is the keystone also in the process of substituting for the lost visual background. When the ability to visualize has been sufficiently cultivated and practiced, this activity also will take place somewhere below the level of consciousness. The sounds, smells, tastes, "feels" coming to him from his environment will elicit the appropriate visual images and thus form a visualized background to daily life.

The impression should never be given, of course, that the substitution of an omnisensory and visualized background will completely and satisfactorily make up for what has been lost. Nevertheless, it can be a real substitution and make up, in great measure at least, for the loss of visual background and what it implies.

5. LIGHT SECURITY

The meaning of the loss of light security, as we saw earlier (page 34), consists in the acceptance of the false but widespread darkness concept of blindness, involving in some cases the factor of "lovelessness" unconsciously associated by many persons with "lightlessness."

The first step in restoration of light security is to open up to the blinded person the ideas put forth by Cutsforth and Chevigny (page 31). He may begin to consider the possibility that perhaps he has simply accepted a common notion without foundation in fact, and thus be brought to re-examine his situation and to realize that actually he is not "living in darkness." This is not a very deep approach; yet on its own level it can play an important part in the process of rehabilitation.

Beyond this, the work is not so simple nor so direct. Often enough, the balanced blinded person with a good degree of insight may be further helped simply by recognizing the general fact that for many persons the loss of light is connected with the loss of love or with feelings about the loss of love. Here true group psychotherapy may be of value, finding its own depth without too direct an interpretation to the individual who might be harmed, while at the same time giving him the supporting knowledge of the "commonality" of the feeling.

But only the professional person trained in depth psychology and psychotherapy can judge whether such group psychotherapy is sufficient for a given individual, whether it might be beneficial in helping him bring out some of his feelings about lightlessness and lovelessness and about blindness itself, and whether it is wise to bring these feelings to the conscious level or safer not to disturb them.

In any case, an acute feeling of loss of light security is not universal among blinded persons, although it is very common, nor is the interpretation of it as connected with feelings of lovelessness necessarily the true interpretation in every case. The worker who, happening on this idea, tried to interpret it to a blinded person as the answer to all his difficulties would be moving well beyond his depth and might do great harm. Adult feelings about blindness and infantile feelings concerned with light and the absence of love are not things to be tampered with. And when there are in fact deep and disturbing meanings in this loss, it is time for professional help.

But all agencies and workers with the blind need to undertake a job of public relations to do away with the false darkness concept of blindness which causes the loss in the first place and which raises a serious barrier to the understanding of blindness and to the acceptance of blind persons in sighted society. The sooner we destroy this

false concept, the sooner will the time come when the blin
of the future will not have to suffer from this loss at all.

One aspect of this task is to see to it that we do nothing
implement the darkness analogy. (It might be a good idea if the desk of every executive in work with the blind were equipped with a sign reading BLINDNESS IS NOT DARKNESS, BUT THE ABSENCE OF SIGHT.) This means going over all our literature to make sure that *nothing* of the light-darkness theme is included in it. It means giving up all the publicity and fund-raising "gimmicks" built around this theme. For some, it means re-examining the very name of their agency and the implications of that name. (The Industrial Home for the Blind in Brooklyn, one of the largest and best-known agencies in the United States, recently abandoned the use of its "light buoy" symbol and of the name "light buoy" applied to some of its activities, because of the realization that the light-darkness theme works against the best interests of the blind.)

This abandoning of the darkness theme will do even more to affect the public attitude if, while we are changing over, we explain to the public through every means at our disposal what we are doing and why. But in doing so, we shall need to be on our guard against sentimentalists; otherwise our attempts to educate will only result in more false sentimentality, expressed in headlines like BLIND LIVE IN LIGHTSOME WORLD, SAYS AGENCY.

The big job to be done is to initiate a positive program of public education. We have the means to begin *now*. Agencies for the blind reach millions of people each year with direct mailings and other direct publicity. Some of the larger agencies also have public relations staffs with ready access to the sources of public education by mass media. If both these means are used, a great deal could be done to educate the public in the real situation of the blind and to do away with the light-sight, darkness-blindness way of thinking. Efforts by individuals and individual agencies can do a great deal here, but a complete job can be done only when this subject has been discussed among workers for the blind, and common action agreed upon and undertaken.

12

Restoration of Basic Skills

6. MOBILITY

THE LOSS of mobility is perhaps the greatest of all the reality losses of blindness; it intensifies what might be considered the other greatest loss, that of social adequacy, both in its reality and its emotional aspects. Restoring mobility to the extent needed for normal life and work is necessarily one of the major objectives of a rehabilitation program, and modern developments have at last made it possible to achieve this objective.

The use of dog guides (introduced into this country in 1929 by The Seeing Eye, Incorporated) was a first step. A second was the Army program for the rehabilitation of blinded servicemen, later taken up by the Veterans Administration, which developed, under the leadership of Richard E. Hoover, the Hoover cane and the technique for its use. These have contributed a major share to the working out of the theory and practice of mobility therapy as bound up with the whole process of rehabilitation.

Here again the need for professional training must be emphasized, for the mobility therapist takes the life and safety of his trainees into his hands. The field has been developing so rapidly that it is not surprising to find many partially trained or even wholly untrained persons volunteering to show blind people how to get about. But to give a blind person confidence without proper and thorough training is worse than nothing. We can hope for the day when some form of license to give mobility training will be required. In the meantime, blinded persons and their families should be aware of the fact that not every mobility course offered by an agency for the blind is taught by a trained mobility therapist — on the contrary, too many are taught by completely untrained or partially trained amateurs. A beginning toward the professionalization so greatly needed in this field has been made by the establishment of a course in mobility therapy at the Graduate School of Education of Boston College, leading to the degree of Master in Education in Peripatology (training grants for students given by the U. S. Office of Vocational Rehabilitation).

To understand the complexity of the problem of restoring lost mobility, it may be helpful to review what a person needs to perceive in order to walk with ease. He must perceive his present position (and perceive this anew with each step he takes). He must perceive his destination — not necessarily the final destination, but at least something of the direction in which it lies, also *a* destination which lies within his reach, and the immediate goal to be reached by his next step.

He must also perceive the obstacles along the route: those underfoot which he might fall over or trip on; trees, houses, parked trucks, baby carriages which he must bypass; protruding corners or branches which might injure him; and things falling or threatening from overhead.

He must perceive the path itself and all the changes in its horizontal or vertical plane — steps down or up, drop-offs, open manholes, slight or major turns to the right or left, sudden or gradual changes in grade, and whether the footing ahead is secure, rough, slippery.

He must also be aware of the possible or imminent mobile obstacles which may be approaching some point ahead on his route. And he needs to perceive something of the general environment in which he is traveling.

The problem of restoring mobility is, therefore, primarily that of training the blinded person to use his remaining senses and the travel tools which extend the reach of his senses to perceive all these things. We have already discussed the training of the senses; the greater part of this chapter can therefore be devoted to the various travel tools. But it should be strongly emphasized that travel tools — even the rightly used human guide — are extensions of the blinded person's own senses, not substitutes for them. Whatever travel tool is to be used, sense training is absolutely indispensable if mobility is to be safely and adequately restored. But the blinded person's senses, however well trained, do not have the necessary reach for normal mobility; they need to be extended by the use of one or more of these tools. Complete training consequently requires both these aspects.

This training itself will remove a great part of the reality fears the blinded person suffers in moving about. But he may need additional help to take care of his neurotic fears. Many of these are part of the first panic of new blindness and can be handled simply by giving the necessary support. Many are the effect of the overwhelming total blow of blindness — the feeling that everything is hopelessly lost. These are relieved in part as the person is given realistic hopes of normal living and as he begins to discover for himself some of the possibilities of regaining his mobility. But he should not be left to himself to build up either unnecessary fears or false hopes. He should be assisted to make a realistic evaluation of what he has lost here and of the possibilities of mobility restoration.

Other neurotic fears, seemingly directly connected with fear of moving about, are forms of displaced anxiety, some connected with the over-all trauma of blindness, some with one or another specific loss. These fears may be lessened or dissipated by rehabilitation training, but such persons will more probably need some psychotherapeutic aid. The trained worker should recognize the existence of a need for expert help. In other cases the rehabilitation program, particularly mobility training, will take care of both reality and neurotic fears.

The four travel tools now in general use might be classified as those for dependent travel: the orthopedic cane and the human guide; and those for independent travel: the dog guide and the Hoover cane used with the appropriate technique. At the rehabilitation center and in professionally given mobility courses, training is given in the proper use of the human guide and in the use of the Hoover cane, while full information is given about dog guides.

The orthopedic cane—thick and strong, meant to support weight and just long enough to fit comfortably under the hand—is the type that comes to most people's minds when the word "cane" is mentioned. Almost every family has a member who used such a cane when he broke his leg or sprained his angle or became crippled with arthritis or weakened with old age. Strangely enough, this same kind of cane, which is actually a sort of crutch, has traditionally been associated with blindness and is still used by many blind persons. True, the blind man is always thought of as tapping or exploring with his cane as he fumbles his way along, not as leaning on it for support. Yet he is using a tool designed to substitute for strong legs, not one designed for his needs, to extend the reach of his touch senses.

It is no wonder, then, that the cane of the tapping blind man has become for many a symbol of groping, of helplessness, of extreme dependence, and that many blind persons, women in particular, strongly resist the use of any cane. The orthopedic cane, although better than no travel tool at all, certainly has no place in modern rehabilitation work.

The white cane, usually with a red tip, which has become familiar in recent years is somewhat longer than the orthopedic cane and so more useful. This is primarily a signaling device, a personally controlled traffic light; hence many blind persons are willing to use it who otherwise would not. But it has become a kind of badge of blindness, and using it is therefore strongly resisted by some.

The cane which does serve the blinded person's needs is actually not a cane at all in the traditional sense. It is a kind of antenna, a wand (like the water dowser's). This is the Hoover cane, which will be described later in this chapter (page 141).

The human guide. Training in the proper use of the human guide is basic to any course in mobility. Such a guide is needed while the blinded person is learning to use a means of independent travel, and later occasionally; in many situations, one will be forced upon him.

The human guide should be thought of and should think of himself as a travel tool, an extension of the blinded person's touch senses (including kinesthesis). The guide walks half a step in front (never behind), while the blind person very lightly but securely "grasps" the guide's forearm just below the elbow. Through this light grasp he can note every movement of the guide and often be aware that he is going to move or step, and in which direction, before he actually does so. An experienced and intelligent blind person can infer a great deal even from the tensed or relaxed attitude of his guide.

If, in addition to making himself a travel tool, the guide can describe some of the interesting sights along the way, so much the better in many situations. But he should remember that his primary job is not to be a kind of barker on a guided tour but a tool to extend the sense of touch, and thus the mobility and the independence, of the blinded person.

Agencies for the blind should certainly train their own volunteer and paid workers in the proper method and manner of guiding. But we cannot train all the sighted people who at one time or another will be acting as guides to the blind. It is consequently doubly necessary that we train each blinded person in the proper use of the guides he will be given. Such training should include the "Hines break," the method for quickly breaking the hold of the sighted person who attempts to assist him by pushing him ahead in traffic — a hazard frequently encountered by blinded persons who have regained mobility.

In this connection, it should be noted that wherever possible the human guide should be either a paid one or an impersonal volunteer furnished by an agency. It is natural for the blind person to be guided by one of his family on occasions when they would be accompanying him if he were still sighted, but to have his family — even his wife — constantly at his beck and call for guide service, or for them to feel that they ought to be, inevitably disrupts normal family relationships. The wife who constantly leads her husband wherever he wishes to go may be doing a very selfless service; but selfless or not, it may lead to a strain (and perhaps a very unnecessary one) on the marital relationship. Even though the wife or children may not feel any resentment over the virtual slavery involved, it is possible that the blind person himself may feel a strong resentment to it or guilt about it. His independence is best preserved if he is able to pay for a guide, and a volunteer is the next best solution.

The dog guide is a tool for independent travel available to some. To qualify, the blinded person needs to be in relatively good physical condition, to have a sense of balance, a sense of direction, and the personality factors to allow for the continued control of a dog. He also needs to have the kind of home and work environment which will be conducive to the use of such a guide. (The Seeing Eye, Incorporated estimates that less than 10 per cent of the blind in this country could actually qualify for a dog.)

Many blind persons who would be qualified do not want a dog guide. Some feel that a dog would interfere with their social or business life. Some do not like dogs, or a member of the family does not like them. Some complain about the dog's propensity to get involved in hostilities with other dogs. Some say it is too much of a nuisance to replace a dog when it dies. Some feel it is just as bad to be dependent on a dog as on a human being. Some have really strong reasons for not using a dog; others have strong prejudices against it.

But a blinded person who has the qualifications and who wants a dog guide will find one extremely useful. Like the human guide or the cane, the dog is a shelter and protection against things that might harm his master. But unlike the cane, he is an animate protection, an animal whose whole instinctual drive has been turned to protect his master as well as himself. He is thus able to afford protection not only from present but also from potential sources of danger, such as rapidly approaching cars, which his instinct tells him may harm his master.

Such a guide should be thought of as, again, an extension of the user's own touch senses, as a canine cane. Through the rigid handle of the harness which holds the dog, his master can feel and learn a great deal about the terrain, as the dog moves up and down, right and left, slows down and speeds up.

But it should be remembered that the dog does his work under his master's orders, the sense of direction being provided by the master. The command is not "Home, Fido," but "Right" or "Left" or "Forward." The popular conception that the blind man in the Bronx need only tell his dog guide to take him to the corner of Forty-second Street and Broadway and then hang on is, to say the least, slightly exaggerated.

Obviously then, training of the blinded person's senses should precede training in the use of a dog guide. It is not to be expected that dog guide centers should be centers for complete rehabilitation training, but it is noteworthy that the famous Seeing Eye school at Morristown manages to include some general sense training of the blind person in the brief period that he is there to get his dog. The majority of dog guide centers do not even do this much. They have fallen into the very natural mistake of building their institutions around dog trainers rather than "people trainers." In any case, the blinded person who is qualified and who wants to use a dog guide should first go through the regular course at the rehabilitation center. Then, with his senses trained and his total adjustment to his blindness under way, he will be in the best position to make the most of his training at the dog guide center and thereafter to use his dog to the best advantage.

There are many dog guide agencies in existence (their number is increasing) and they make frequent appeals to the public for funds. While the majority are reputable and well-intentioned, some few are not. California has had to pass legislation making a license necessary to operate such an agency. The blinded person and his family, therefore, need to be wary and to evaluate carefully the agency from which he intends to get his dog.

Even among well-intentioned agencies there are some which make it appear in their advertising that all blind persons are poverty-stricken and helpless; they may make a great point of the fact that they *give* the dogs to the blind (whether they could pay or not). Obviously such an attitude is not in the best interests of the blind in general or of the blind person who is getting a dog. This is the reason why The Seeing Eye, Incorporated makes it clear that blind persons are allowed the dignity of paying for their dogs. The charge is nominal (a needy person may pay over a long period of time), but the dignity of all who get dogs from Seeing Eye and that of the blind in general is preserved and fostered. Some few of the other agencies are adopting a similar system, but by no means all of them.

It is necessary to note here and to emphasize strongly the fact that *no person ever received a dog as a result of his or anyone else's saving the ripcords from cigarette packages,* although the rumor that by saving them you can help the blind to get dogs keeps springing up again and again in spite of all attempts to kill it. If the reader should hear of such a collection being made, he should send the information with the name of his local newspaper to The Seeing Eye, Incorporated, Morristown, New Jersey, which has a factual release ready to send to the paper.

The Hoover cane, used with the Hoover cane technique, is the modern tool for independent travel with which every properly rehabilitated blind person should be familiar. Even if he plans to use a dog guide, there will be situations in which he cannot use a dog, and times when he will have to be without one — when his dog is sick, or dies and must be replaced. Training in the use of the Hoover cane, which presupposes the training of the senses, is a "must" for every blinded person who wishes to regain and maintain his mobility.

This cane, as was said above, is not a cane at all in the usual sense, but a kind of antenna or wand, designed precisely to be an extension of the user's touch senses. Usually made of thin aluminum tubing not more than half an inch in diameter, it is tipped at the ground end with a wooden or plastic dowel and curved at the upper end like a shepherd's staff or bishop's crosier. The shaft is usually covered with a white material that will reflect automobile headlights at night, while the upper end may be wrapped with leather strapping like that used on golf clubs. Since the purpose of the cane is to extend the person's foot reach as well as arm reach, its length is determined by the length of the individual's normal stride. Canes are fitted to individual prescription and reach approximately to the breastbone.

The proper use of this cane must be taught by a therapist especially trained in the Hoover cane technique; the cane is almost worse than useless without proper instruction. But with it, the average blind person can learn to move with independence, ease and even grace. He can also learn to move along at a normal speed, and since there is reason to believe that the fast traveler can gather more information than the slow one, the trained user of such a cane will be safer as well as speedier than he could be otherwise.

Whether a rehabilitated blinded person should plan to use a Hoover cane or a dog guide (with a cane when the dog is for one reason or another unavailable) is a question that can only be decided by each individual for himself, in accordance with his own circumstances and preferences. The dog guide can do things that the cane cannot and vice versa; only the individual can decide which he is to use as his ordinary travel tool. But the rehabilitation center should certainly see to it that complete information is given to the trainees about dog guides (St. Paul's has a representative of Seeing Eye cover the subject fully and answer questions) and that nothing is done to prejudice him one way or another about his final choice of a tool. It is essential that the trainee come to realize that he needs both the rehabilitation training *and* a travel tool if he is to regain and maintain his mobility.

Various attempts are now being made to bring together research workers interested in the development of a guidance device for blind persons. The ideal device would have to be a "stepdown," an obstacle detection device and a recognition device all in one. Most observers agree that the perfected device is years away without far more research than is now being directed to the problem, although a breakthrough in one or other aspect is possible at any time.

It is essential that the blinded person realize that today every indication goes to show that such a device, if and when it comes, will still demand complete sensory training. This appears to be the consensus of all the researchers. And they also believe that no device would be satisfactory which in any way interfered with the intake of knowledge through one of the major senses.

7. TECHNIQUES OF DAILY LIVING

The loss of the techniques of daily living is, as was pointed out earlier (page 41), one of the most continually humiliating and frustrating of all the losses of blindness. Restoration of these techniques to the greatest possible degree is one of the important aspects of a rehabilitation program.

But even in the early weeks of blindness a beginning can be made: helping the blinded person back to normal eating by indicating the place of each kind of food on his plate, helping him to arrange his clothes so as to dress himself most easily, etc. A valuable aid here is the so-called braille watch — an ordinary wrist or pocket watch with strong hands, raised markings at some of the hours, and a cover that can be opened easily. Equipped with such a watch, practically any intelligent blind person can know what time it is. This device is an amazing morale-booster to newly blinded persons, removing dependence in an important area, reorienting them as to time, and providing a stimulus to hope that they can learn to do other things. It may even be an important factor in restoring reality contact.

In the rehabilitation program, the complex problem of restoring the techniques of daily living involves the training of the senses. It is worked on indirectly in the various courses in communication, in mobility, in shop and other skills, and by the therapeutic work of the psychosocial staff. Beyond this, four courses seem necessary: in housekeeping, home repair, personal hygiene and general techniques.

The housekeeping course includes the techniques everyone needs to keep his living quarters and personal belongings clean and tidy. It also aids in restoring confidence in the senses. It is not aimed at making efficient housekeepers out of people who never kept house when they were sighted, but at teaching blinded persons the special techniques they need to do what they were capable of doing before: run a house, wash and iron, sew and mend, tell what is in cans and bottles and packages by a system of marking, cook, clean house. Thousands of trained blind persons do run their own homes successfully, and a blinded person who previously had this ability and has not regained it cannot be considered rehabilitated.

Similarly, the course in home repair is not meant to make do-it-yourself experts out of persons who were not such previously, but to increase confidence in the senses and to enable the trainees to carry out the simple carpentry, plumbing, electrical and other repair jobs they were accustomed to do before blindness. (The purpose of the *shop* course, it might be pointed out here, is precisely the restoring of confidence. As one woman graduate wrote to St. Paul's: "After getting used to the horrible noise of that big power saw, I no longer get panicky when a big truck roars by me on Main Street.")

The course in personal hygiene teaches the special techniques blinded persons need to care for bowel and bladder functions, gives information on hygienic problems for men and women, and includes the techniques necessary for administering household first aid. This course may also include, for the large and increasing number of blind diabetics, instruction in the technique recently developed at St. Paul's in the self-administration of insulin by means of special syringes with ampules purchased already loaded from the druggist. The sense of security and independence gained by the trainee from this device is startling.

The course on general techniques gives training in perception and awareness of the elements involved in the ordinary activities of daily living, with the aim of enabling the trainee most effectively to substitute the use of his other senses for that of sight. It also gives information about helpful techniques and deals with the attitudes needed to cope with the problems raised by blindness in such daily activities. For example, to handle the problem of pouring liquids, the blinded person needs to be made aware of the different pouring rates of liquids of different consistencies and given a technique for measuring; he also needs to air and discuss any fears he might have about burning himself with hot liquids.

Above all, he needs to be shown the need for, and the attitude necessary to develop, an orderliness beyond that required by sighted people, to have a place for everything and everything in its place, if he is to find conveniently the things he has put down. Yet this must never be allowed to become a fetish, as in the homes of some blind persons whose blindness so rules the household that nobody dares rearrange the furniture.

This course includes drill in important techniques, training in the use of various devices not included in other courses, information about the wide range of devices available for special needs and where they may be obtained, and information about new devices that may be developed.*

It also provides the general background for the instruction in special techniques given in the various skill courses, such as keeping accounts in the braille course, writing a check in the handwriting course, solving shopping problems in the mobility and visualization courses. And it deals in particular with techniques for handling the problems a blinded person ordinarily faces in dining, so that while special difficulties may occasionally arise, they will be relatively minor ones, and the trainee will be able to eat normally at home or at a restaurant, with the table manners he had before blindness.

This course also gives the techniques necessary for presenting a clean, neat and attractive appearance — for recognizing spotted or wrinkled clothing, arranging and marking clothes so as to find the desired color combinations, for shaving or putting on make-up and caring for hairdo. Slovenly appearance, garish make-up or wild color combinations are not a mark of blindness; they indicate rather a lack of training or the existence of emotional problems in the individual.

And this course, finally, takes up other daily problems not handled in other courses: how to fold bills of different denominations so that they will be easily distinguishable in purse or billfold, how to use a dial telephone, how to look for systematically and find a dropped or

* The American Foundation for the Blind, 15 West Sixteenth Street, New York City, has a special department to collect and disseminate information about such devices and to work on new ones. The catalogue, including infomation about timers, thermometers, tools adapted to the use of blind carpenters, needle-threaders, etc., is available from that institute.

mislaid object, how to shake hands, how to become quickly at home in a strange guest room or hotel room.

At the end of such a training program, the blinded person should have the assurance that, while difficulties about the techniques of daily living will still come up, he has the balanced attitude, the general principles, and the chief techniques needed to handle these problems or to work out means of handling them as they arise.

13

Restoration of Ease of Communication

8. WRITTEN COMMUNICATION

As Chart A indicates, many tools are available to restore various aspects of written communication to the blinded person. The work of the rehabilitation center is to teach whatever skill is needed to use these tools, to acquaint the trainee with the existing resources both as to devices and reading material, and to give him a realistic appraisal of current progress in research.

There is good reason to believe that in the very near future machines will be available to produce braille books and magazines with a speed and in a quantity so far unknown. A far more adequate solution would be a machine that could actually "read" ordinary print and handwriting aloud. Such machines have already been invented, although none has been practical enough to be produced. Scientists who have studied the problem feel that there is a good possibility that such a machine will be invented, but no one expects it for some time at the present level of effort.

None of the available devices nor any combination of them — nor, so far as one can see, any possible future inventions — can *completely* restore to a blinded person his previous ease in reading and writing. Yet with intelligent effort on his part and on the part of those aiding him, and with the available tools, a great deal can be done to serve many ordinary reading and writing needs and some extraordinary ones. Chart A lists these tools, their advantages and disadvantages,

Chart A

Tools Available for Reading and Writing for the Blind (R & W)

Tool	*Skill Needed to Use*	*Advantages*	*Disadvantages*
1. Human substitute	See text.	See text.	See text.
2. Braille	Skill in reading and writing easily mastered by normal person (see text).	Privacy and independence.	As to *writing:* few sighted people can read it; as to *reading:* bulky, unwieldy, limited material.
For Reading			
Printed (press-transcribed)		Professional touch. Uses both sides of paper by "interpointing" process — less bulky.	Too expensive except when several hundred copies needed.
Written (hand-transcribed)		Good for specialized needs.	One one copy made at a time, mainly by volunteers.[1]
(*a*) by stylus and "slate," a metal frame fitting over the paper, with apertures guiding the stylus.			
(*b*) braille-writer, 6-key instrument like typewriter.		Faster than above.	As above.
New process of "mimeographing"		Production of many copies.	Disagreement about legibility; not yet widely used in U. S. A.

For Writing (*a*) stylus and "slate" (equivalent of pen or pencil).		Portable.	May be uneven.
(*b*) braille-writer (equivalent of typewriter).		More even and so more easily read.	Less portable.
3. Talking Book (R) Official (activity of Federal Government; professionally recorded 33 rpm records.)	Ability to run record player; knowledge of resources, especially *Talking Book Topics*, published by American Foundation for the Blind.	Greatest single contribution of our century in this area. Machines placed with (and serviced for) blind persons free; records made available through regionally designated (not subsidized) circulating libraries; free mailing privileges.	Few magazines (except *Newsweek* and *Reader's Digest*). No newspapers, except "News of the Week" section, New York *Times*. Machines [2] and records bulky. No great fidelity of reproduction. Mail circulation leads to deterioration. Service of machines often inadequate. Relatively few titles, though constantly increasing.
Talking Book (non-official; professionally recorded and nonprofessionally; all speeds, multicopied on wire, etc.)	As above.	For specialized areas, texts, professional books, etc.[3]	Sometimes extremely amateurish, with errors and lack of clarity.
4. Recording and other play-back devices for R & W (considered so important that dictating machine is	Simple skill required for operating.	Enables blind person to dictate and then listen back; of particular value to students for recording material read to	Machines often costly; quickly obsolete.

Tool	*Skill Needed to Use*	*Advantages*	*Disadvantages*
given free to every service-connected blind veteran.)		them for later reference; also useful in composition, making notes, and for corresponding with person owning similar machine.	
5. Radio (R)	Push-button type better for elder persons. Knowledge of programs *must* be made available.	A necessity of life for the blind, so important that American Foundation will furnish one free (through local agencies) to any blind person unable to afford it.	*Not total answer* — highlights of news not the same as Sunday *Times* or daily paper; few classics read, etc.
Short-wave or FM		Extends range of programs.	Seldom any announcements of future programs.
"Ham" radio (R & W)	Ordinary operating skill	Allows for broad range of active and passive communication.	
6. Typewriter (not a special instrument for blind). (W)	Touch typing; some teachers put markers on anchor keys, but *not* necessary.	*Very* helpful means of restoring written communication. If person does not possess skill already, should be taught at rehabilitation center, by home teacher or through recorded instructions.	Cannot read back what he has written, see mistakes, etc.
7. Handwriting aids (Script Guides) guide hand or writ-		Important that blinded person continue to use his hand-	

ing instrument so that it will write in straight lines, not run over letters, etc. (Marks Writing Guide seems to be the best.)	writing. Absolutely necessary he learn to write his signature: "X, his mark" reduces him to the status of illiterate. These devices enable him to write firm, clear hand.
8. Raised line drawing board (put out by American Foundation): drawing a line with pen or pencil makes a line discernible by touch.	Makes maps, direction charts, etc. available, opens up new means of description.
Mathematical devices, slide rules and music writers are also available for the use of the blind.	

[1] Perhaps the greatest need here is for closer co-ordination of the work of these volunteers, so that there will be no unnecessary duplication. Increasing efforts are now being made to get the titles transcribed in accordance with the real needs of the blind, rather than, as so often in the past, in accordance with what some well-meaning person thinks they *should* be.

[2] Some research effort is now going into very small transistorized machines which can be played on a battery, and which use very thin, small plastic disks. But obviously any change-over would be complicated and expensive. Even more expensive will be the change-over which now seems probable (already started in England) to transcribing all official Talking Books onto tape which would be enclosed in an easily handled cartridge.

[3] Even more than in the field of hand-transcribed braille books, there is at present a need for national co-ordination of this service to make more books available to students and professional readers, and to avoid wasted effort.

and the skill, if any, needed to use them, but some further remarks need to be made about some of them.

The human substitute, who reads and writes for a blind person, is the most ancient of the communication tools. This is the most versatile tool of all, but it may have serious drawbacks that the others do not. It gets tired; it is available for only limited periods (usually of its own choosing); it is often disinclined to work when needed. It often becomes selective while being used (deciding that the blind listener "wouldn't be interested" in this or that). It necessarily invades privacy. Where other devices lead to independence, this one can lead to great dependence. And it can often make the listener feel that if he doesn't listen to a certain thing or is not satisfied with a certain amount of reading, he is an ingrate (which perhaps he is). These remarks are not meant to derogate from the value of the many readers who do excellent and generous work; but it is important that readers and the agencies who furnish them see the work of reading in its proper focus.

The main point here is that the reader should think of himself and be thought of *as a tool.* His job is to read what the blinded person wants to have read, *not* what the reader thinks the blinded person needs or should have or ought to like to have read or not read.

For the members of the blinded person's family to serve as his readers might seem like the ideal solution. The use of *some* members at more or less *set times* for *brief* periods may work out under the right circumstances. But, as with using the services of members of the family as guides, if this is accepted as the basic solution, it too often sets up relationships of drudgery, dependence and slavery totally foreign to the love that proposed it.

There is often need of "interpretation" to the family in helping them come to this viewpoint—interpretation being the process carried out by a trained professional of assisting an individual, either directly or, more frequently, by eliciting the information from him, to understand some of the psychological forces involved in a situation. The blinded person also may need such interpretation (unless he has been forearmed during his rehabilitation training), since he may come to have serious guilt feelings over hi... family (whether or not they actually feel enslaved), ... faction with them for not reading more (especially w... his demands are unreasonable), for having voices that ... nervous, or for not reading well.

The use of neighbors may often (though not always) prov... satisfactory solution of some part of the reading problem. There a... many cases recorded of men who, on their way home from work, leave their lunch pail at the door of a blind neighbor while they go in for half an hour to scan with him the parts of the daily paper not covered in the newscasts. Many people would be glad to volunteer a little time each day to help out a blind person nearby, but often such possible readers need to be told that their services would be appreciated. And here again, interpretation may be required, both to the neighbor and to the family, so that neither he nor they will feel that he is taking over what is properly a family responsibility.

The best solution here, as with the guide, is that the blinded person be able to pay for the services of a reader — who is then clearly an employee working under the direction of his employer. Formerly, the services of children were the most available and the most frequently used; in our day, those of older people may be easier to come by — people who are retired on a small pension and are glad to earn a little, and who also would welcome the opportunity to do useful work.

The next best solution, generally speaking, is the volunteer reader provided by an agency — if he is trained, emotionally stable and properly motivated, clearly aware of his function as "substitute eyes" and nothing else.

More readers are greatly needed (and most of them must be volunteers) to read material otherwise not available to blind persons: specialists to read texts to students and professional material to professional persons, and an army of general readers ready and willing to read the essential and nonessential things that blind people would like to have read.

Some combination of family, neighbor, and paid or volunteer

must, finally, be worked out by the blinded person himself to [his] needs and circumstances. But clearly, there are many aspects of [th]is problem in which he needs instruction during his training period.

Braille, is, of course, the great tool available to blinded persons for independent reading and writing; no literate person can be considered rehabilitated unless he has come to accept the idea of using braille and has learned to read and write it in accordance with his needs and ability. Braille is a kind of code made up of raised "pinpricks" to be read by touch, the number and relative positions of the dots determining each symbol. In its simplest form (grade one), each symbol stands for a single letter of the alphabet. In grade two, the one in which most magazines and books are transcribed today, certain symbols stand for whole words, as in shorthand.

Learning braille simply means mastering a fairly simple skill. It does not require any special intelligence, and it is a rare person who does not have the low degree of tactual sensitivity demanded. Fingers calloused by years of hard labor read braille, as do fingers partly desensitized by the advance of disease. What is needed is not extreme sensitivity, but the actual acquiring of the *skill* needed to differentiate one dot and one position from another. It resembles many skills in that the process of learning may at times seem very slow, but the final result is sudden. It is sometimes very helpful to the blinded person, in the midst of the frustrations and failures of new blindness, to compare the process of learning braille with that of learning to swim. Day after day you do everything as you are told to, and yet you sink; then one fine day you do things "just as you did them the day before," but to your amazement you are afloat and swimming.

With braille, as with many other skills, the greatest blocks are not so much physical or intellectual but emotional: lack of self-confidence and the fact that braille is a symbol of blindness. The whole rehabilitation process helping the blinded person to accept his blindness should be of aid here. But the overcoming of these problems, which are usually hidden in the unconscious, requires more than ordinary teaching ability. The degree of success attained by the student is very often not so much in proportion to the student's aptitude as it is to

the degree of the teacher's belief in braille and in the poss
the blinded adult's learning and using it. The time needed t
braille varies with each individual, with his emotional attitu
motivation and aptitude, and with the skill of the teacher a the
frequency of the lessons. At St. Paul's, the trainees use grade one braille for marking purposes in shop and kitchen by the end of the second week, while at the end of the sixteen-week training period, the majority are sufficiently acquainted with grade two braille to develop its regular use. When an overburdened home teacher, however capable, can give a blinded adult lessons only once or twice a month, the process naturally takes much longer than at a rehabilitation center where five lessons are given a week.

Once learned, braille, like any other skill, is rarely lost. But speed in using it is the result of practice, and may lessen if the skill is not used regularly. The quickest braille readers attain approximately the speed of the average sighted reader, the possibilities of speed being limited by the fact that although some sort of scanning is practiced by all expert braille readers, the scanning cannot be as far ahead as is possible to sighted readers. It is an interesting sidelight that many persons who have lost their sight in adult life find that after reading braille (entirely by touch, of course) for a considerable period, their "eyes get tired" and they get "eye headaches," just as a sighted person might after a protracted period of reading.

Many standard works are available in braille and many devoted workers are busy transcribing more reading material into braille by the various methods noted on Chart A. But relatively few of the new fiction and nonfiction titles constantly pouring off the presses find their way into braille. There are only a few braille magazines, and these mainly of an "inspirational" nature, and no newspapers.

Again, braille material is necessarily bulky and unwieldy compared to print. So far as expense in mailing is concerned, a postal regulation enables braille books to be sent free between the library and the blind person; all that is needed is to mark the package "free reading matter for the blind." A similar regulation concerning subscription magazines would be helpful so that if there were, for example, a braille edition of *Newsweek*, it could be carried at the same charge as the much lighter ink-print edition. In this way the person could pay for the subscription to a magazine and not be forced, as at present, to accept it without cost.

Another disadvantage of braille is that so few sighted people know it, and not all blind persons (estimates say less than 25 per cent), especially among those who have lost their sight late in life. Therefore the blinded person cannot use it either for reading his mail or for writing letters.

Thus braille is by no means a total answer to the problem of restoring written communication. Nonetheless, it is *one* of the answers, and such a valuable one for many purposes that anyone capable of reading and writing who loses sight should master it. Even if he was never "much of a reader," he will need braille for business and household notations, memoranda, and many other uses.

Talking Books. Most braille readers are Talking Book readers as well, though few expert braille readers are so accustomed to touch reading that they do not enjoy hearing things read aloud. Others make use of the Talking Book for general reading, but have become conditioned to the use of touch for learning purposes, and so want in braille all the material that they really need to study. The question is, then, not whether a blinded person should use braille or Talking Books; he needs both. (The availability of Talking Books has not meant, as was and sometimes still is feared by some workers with the blind, that the motivation to learn braille will be lessened.)

Some blinded persons, especially those who were particularly rapid readers when they had their sight, are frustrated by the slowness of voice reading in comparison with sight reading. A few students, and others who are reading for information rather than pleasure, play their recordings on machines slightly geared up from the speed of 33 revolutions per minute, thus getting in a few more words a minute, though sacrificing pleasantness of tone. There is also the possibility of making some specialized Talking Books using the "condensed reading" method experimented with by telephone companies, especially in connection with international telephone communication. The reading is done on tape, and then the tape is excised so as to shorten pauses and the time taken to say vowels and consonants, while leaving the words intelligible.

Other recording and playback devices. Some students have made use of these to record the professor's voice during whole class periods. But this is generally frowned on, and there is no reason why a blind student should be given such an extraordinary privilege. A few students have used a special device enabling them to take notes by talking into these machines without disturbing people around them, but this method is not recommended. The greatest usefulness of such machines for students is in recording for future reference the material read to them by their readers (see Chart A).

The choice of a machine in this field of many choices must be governed not only by personal needs but also by personal taste. Some prefer fidelity of reproduction to other qualities; some prefer simplicity of operation; some want disks that can be played on the standard Talking Book machine. The task of the rehabilitation center is to indicate the possibilities of using various machines, to give the trainee the opportunity to learn about different types, and even to examine and test them if he has special reason to be interested.

It should be emphasized that in this problem of restoring ease of written communication, the question is not one of choosing between various major tools. *Every one of the major tools* should be mastered by the newly blinded person, and information given him about their different possibilities and their availability.

9. SPOKEN COMMUNICATION

This restoration is not, like the one we have just been discussing, a fairly clear-cut matter of skills and devices. The blinded person knows that something has happened to his ease in communicating with other people, but he does not know clearly just what has happened or how much. He may blame himself, feeling that something besides his blindness has happened to make him "peculiar" or that the whole problem must exist only in his own mind. Or he may blame those around him as being stupid and thoughtless. And the sighted people with whom he tries to speak do not realize clearly what has happened either, nor what the real difficulties are. They feel that he is now somehow "different"; they feel embarrassed by him and for him, and do not know what to do to make communication easier for him and for them.

Restoration involves, therefore, helping the blinded person to recognize this loss as one of the effects of blindness and to accept it as a fact so as to be willing to take the means to overcome it, indicating the means, and giving him practice in using them. Restoration also involves bringing the public in general, and the family of the blinded person in particular, to some awareness of and consideration for his special difficulties in spoken communication.

The work of helping the blinded person himself is carried out by the whole training program *and* by a special course in spoken communication; that of helping the family is most effectively done by family seminars at the rehabilitation center. The work of public education is the more general responsibility of agencies and workers with the blind.

The very existence of a special course in spoken communication as part of the training program indicates to the blinded person that this loss is an objective fact experienced by all blind persons, and the analysis of what it involves further helps to free him from blaming either himself or others and prepares him to take the necessary means of overcoming it. But the basic prerequisite to using these means effectively is the trainee's "acceptance" of his blindness — brought about by the whole therapeutic activity of the rehabilitation center in the psychosocial area. Sometimes the word "acceptance" is used as if the blinded person were expected to *like* his blindness. There is nothing healthy about this approach. What we mean by "acceptance" involves facing the fact of his blindness with all the difficulties it involves, accepting himself as a blind person, and acquiring an attitude which allows him to move forward to overcome the difficulties.

Once the blinded person has achieved this emotionally balanced attitude toward his blindness, he can solve many of the difficulties of spoken communication by frankness. But until he has adjusted to his blindness, any words of explanation, stern or jocose, even the prettiest of practiced speeches, will only arouse emotions, and the wrong emotions, in his hearers. *Unconscious speaks to unconscious louder than any words.* If blindness is an emotional disturbance ruling him, this disturbance will be communicated to others; if blindness is a part of him and a part which he has under emotional control, the simplest words will serve.

Thus, if he is not sure whether he or some other person is being addressed, he can simply ask, "Were you speaking to me?" or the equivalent. Otherwise he would have to remain silent unless addressed by name or answer every question unless someone else's name were mentioned — either way only embarrrassing himself and everyone else. The frank question may also give him the opportunity, without evoking any false pity or exaggerated admiration, to explain the need for addressing him by name.

Again, in the early days of new blindness, or occasionally later under certain circumstances, he may not know just where the person is who is addressing him, or he may be unsure whether he himself is facing the other person and "looking" at him as he talks. Or, in a group of people, he may have difficulty in knowing who is sitting where. Here again, if there is no other way of finding out what he needs to know, he can simply ask.

Many of these difficulties will be eliminated as he gains skill, particularly in the localization of sounds. But in general, the blinded person who has "accepted" his blindness should be able to accept help and ask for it frankly when necessary. Above all, he should be able to put others at their ease either by direct statement or by indirect communication of his own attitude. And he should use frankness in such a way that his blindness is considered as only the incidental factor it must be in any given social situation, not as the center around which the situation revolves. Not, of course, that he should act as if his blindness were less than the major handicap it is, but it should never be allowed to become the chief focus of conversation. Moreover, if he can allude to his blindness casually, without forced humor, it may do a good deal to remove the emotional tension created by his presence in a group of sighted people unaccustomed to blindness, and so help to restore communication all around. He will also be educating the members of this group to realize the need to address blind persons by name, to identify themselves, and — above all — to accept blind persons as ordinary normal people with a special handicap.

The course in spoken communication discusses the social methods that may be used to acquire information and relieve tension in one or another situation. It also shows the trainee how to use his developing sense powers — those of hearing in particular — to identify and localize other speakers and also to gather information about them: their height, position, approximate age. And further, he learns to infer from their vocal expressions, as he once did primarily from their facial expressions, what kind of people they are, how they are feeling, etc. (This, of course, is only the conscious development of the power we all exercise to some extent in telephone conversations — judging how a friend is feeling from the way he talks, making judgments about someone we never met on the basis of the way his voice sounds and how he expresses himself.)

Training in visualization is particularly important here, to give the trainee the habit of making up a mental picture of the surroundings in which a social situation is taking place and of each of the persons involved — an active picture showing the position and part of each person in the whole gathering, his expressions, gestures and so on.

The course also gives the trainee instruction in how to make further inferences from what he perceives: how to judge the meaning of gaps in the conversation in relation to the topic and its possible emotional content for the people present, the possible psychological significance of certain slips of the tongue, rustles, and fidgeting sounds, breathing symptoms of tension, certain types of coughs and sneezes, clearing the throat, the sounds of cigarettes being lighted or snuffed out, etc.

As the trainee gains skill in gathering and interpreting all these various kinds of information, he will become able to make fairly accurate estimates of his hearers' reactions to what he is saying, and — what is most difficult for blind persons — to tell just when to come in on a conversation. In a group of blind people, there always seems to be an extra amount of conversational noise — the chief reason being that it is difficult for any of the members of the group to know just when they can say a word without competition. In a mainly sighted group, it is usually enough if the blind person indicates that he would like to say something — by leaning forward, looking eager, or looking as if he were starting to speak.

Finally, in the whole training program but particularly in connection with spoken communication, the blinded person needs help to avoid (or to correct, if he has already acquired) "blindisms" — the habits, tics or mannerisms that are directly or indirectly the result of blindness. Such things (which include the absence of the sighted mannerisms people are accustomed to) cause a sighted person's attention to become focused on the handicap of the blind person he is trying to talk with and make normal give-and-take difficult or impossible.

Blindisms of posture include unnatural attitudes in standing or sitting — too great rigidity or looseness — combined with unusual awkwardness as to position and motion of head or hands. Blindisms of gait include a protective kind of shuffle and a hesitating way of walking with hands just held back from groping. Blindisms of voice include the "broadcast voice" mentioned earlier (page 49) and the tendency to verbalize common among insecure persons of all kinds: to use big words for their own sake, to seek out sesquipedalian verbiage when a ten-cent word would do. Blindisms of facial expression and behavior include the bland smile that never changes, and such habits as rubbing the lids of the eyes or probing the empty sockets.

What might be called negative blindisms — that is, the disturbing absence of sighted mannerisms — include the failure to change expression to meet the needs of the situation, to look people in the eyes, to look around a room or out a window when it would be normal to do so, to doodle with pen or pencil.

Not every blind person, of course, has acquired all these blindisms, and many have not acquired any of them. But it is important to understand and differentiate among their causes, so as to be able to help blinded people from acquiring them or to do what can be done to cure those already acquired.

Blindisms may be due to the fact that the blind person is never reminded visually of the gestures, mannerisms and attitudes of sighted people and cannot see his own, and so he is not aware that he is failing to do things he once did or acquiring new mannerisms or tics; or they may result from his being ill at ease in using gestures or moving normally for fear of knocking something over or appearing awkward. But unnatural ways of holding oneself and of moving, or the set, bland smile, may also be the effect of emotional disturbance.

If it is not clear whether the cause of some particular blindism is emotional or not, we should let the experts decide. To tell a blinded person about his blindisms might well simply make him more self-conscious and so add to his difficulties and disturbance. Generally speaking, the easing of tension that comes with the work of the rehabilitation program on both reality and emotional factors will do something to lessen blindisms from emotional causes. But direct work on them should be done under expert guidance.

The blindisms resulting from other causes are usually quite amenable to correction, but they are far more amenable when they are detected early. For example, the habit of letting the eyes wander up into the head so that only the whites show is in most cases quite easy to correct early, but almost impossible to eliminate when it has persisted for a long time.* (This is another reason for giving the blinded person the benefit of rehabilitation training as soon as possible after blindness.) Before blindisms have become set habits, simply alerting the person to the fact that he has begun to acquire one or

* When damage to the eye muscles is the cause, or when this habit has become too fixed to be eliminated by exercises in focusing, the person should be urged to wear opaque glasses.

another mannerism may be all that is needed. Beyond this, of gait and posture are directly worked on in mobility train warning against and correcting those of voice and manner i of the course in spoken communication.

A very important part of this course also consists in helping the blinded person *not to acquire blindisms,* by pointing out what the most common ones are and by directing his effort toward the retention and cultivation of sighted mannerisms.

In this connection, the trainee's ability to visualize the other persons with whom he is talking is cultivated, so that he not only hears what they are saying but also sees in his mind's eye their faces as they say it, and so "watches" every change of expression and mood. By doing this, he will begin almost automatically to mirror on his own face the expressions he visualizes on theirs, as he once did from actually seeing these expressions.

For the purpose of retaining normal facial expression, he should also be taught to practice consciously now and again what all of us do at a level below consciousness: to visualize his own expression, to see himself in a kind of mental mirror as he takes part in a conversation. St. Paul's has worked out a series of exercises carried out by the trainees as individual "homework," in which they stand alone in front of an actual mirror (serving as a prop to the imagination) and attempt to visualize their own faces as they express anger, anxiety, fondness, amusement, etc.

This does not mean, of course, that blinded persons should try to overact facial expression, but that they should work to keep normal facial reactions alive. It is perhaps especially important here that the traineee be shown the need of remaining aware of the expression in his own eyes (including the expression in the facial area surrounding the eyes) as he "looks at" things near and far away.

And finally, the course in spoken communication should alert the trainee to the importance of retaining and cultivating sighted mannerisms of behavior so that the absence of such things will not make people feel, without quite knowing why, that he is "different." A certain blind lawyer (who lost his sight in his teens, gained degrees in law and in social work, carried on a private law practice, and has been active on the boards of various social agencies and headed a state agency for the blind) has consciously cultivated such mannerisms so that nothing that he fails to do reminds anyone of his blindness. His office is equipped with the usual books and pictures; his desk with a pen and pencil set, a pad and blotter. When he is talking with someone, he picks up a paper clip occasionally and plays with it in an abstracted sort of way, or, when the discussion grows more concentrated, he may pick up a pencil and start doodling with it on the pad. In the course of the interview, he may get up and look out of the window in back of his desk. Or, if there is anything to be discussed in the papers on his desk, he will take them up and hold them, occasionally looking down at them or gesturing toward them with his other hand. The purpose behind all this is not, it should be emphasized, to try to pretend to anyone that he is not blind, but simply to prevent those who visit him from being distracted from the conversation by any vague feelings of disquiet that might be aroused by a lack of sighted behavior.

Thus the whole rehabilitation program, and in particular the course in spoken communication, can do a great deal toward restoring to the blind person what he has lost in this area. But those with whom he will be speaking also need to be shown what they can do. Communication is a two-way affair, and many difficulties result simply from the thoughtlessness of sighted people.

The need to educate the public in this regard is, of course, only one aspect of the need for a continued and constant program to give the public some real understanding of blindness. We cannot give all the public such an understanding, but through the direct and indirect means available, in particular our own publicity, we can at least reach many of those who are especially interested because of their contact with blind persons in employment or social situations — and these are precisely the people who most need to gain an intelligent approach to the problems of blinded persons.

Leaflets of "Do's and Don'ts in Dealing with the Blind" are already in existence. While some of them have a tone of "At your Ease among the Head-hunters," they do give useful information. They indicate, for example, the importance of using some term of address when speaking to a blind person or to someone else in his presence, so that he can know who is being addressed; giving him some hint before breaking off a conversation or leaving the room (preferably by some unobtrusive method such as continuing to talk while going to the door, so that he can tell by the sound of the speaker's voice what is happening); adding verbal description to gestures when this is needed for understanding (for example, with the gestures that accompany "over there," "so long," "so high").

And it should surely be possible for public education to do something about the puerile "who-am-I" guessing games in which some engage their blind acquaintances. People who expect their switchboard operator to recognize their voice over the phone will marvel if a blind person does the same thing when they meet: "Good old Joe; wonderful this sixth sense he has developed!"

And it might even be possible to get that portion of the public whom we can reach to realize that *any gestures or facial expressions referring to the blind person in his presence must be avoided like the plague.* Anything like this that we would not do if he could see is actually, however well intended, a way of taking advantage of his blindness; it can be a most cruel way of making him feel cut off and alone when he realizes that his friends are conducting unheard conversations right in front of his face.

Another point that might well be brought out concerns what is sometimes called "the bridge of touch." It is certainly true that ordinarily, aside from telephone conversations, the sight of the person with whom we are talking, and his sight of us, provides a kind of bridge across which verbal communication can travel. When the blindness of one party destroys this particular bridge, the sense of touch can, if need be, provide another. (This is one reason why the handclasp may be especially important to blind persons.)

But sighted people, in a well-meant effort to establish sympathetic communication with a blind person, occasionally tend to overemphasize the need for such a bridge — a need which exists only when verbal communication proves totally inadequate as the means of establishing the "presence" of one person to another. It is well to remember that this bridge is a possible one (the ophthalmologist who sits on the corner of the bed of a patient with senile cataracts may be violating hospital rules but be a better healer than if he obeyed them.) But generally speaking, there is no reason why the blind person should be subjected to handholding by affectionate or nonaffectionate adults any more than a sighted person should.

The family of the blinded person, obviously, needs, far more than the general public, to be given information about his needs with regard to spoken communication. For families who are willing to undergo it, periods of blindfolded experience may be helpful in gaining some realization of these problems as well as some of the other "factual" problems of blindness. But this experience should *never* be suggested to people who will think that as a result they will "know what blindness is."

Families also need a great deal in the way of interpretation as to the meaning of the loss of spoken communication, of their own part in it and in restoring what has been lost. This is one aspect of the overall problem of giving the family an intelligent approach to the blindness of one of its members, and in many cases some direct casework will be needed. But a great deal can and should be done by means of family seminars held in connection with the rehabilitation program (see page 241).

10. INFORMATIONAL PROGRESS

The means for regaining informational progress are given in the various courses of the rehabilitation program already mentioned, particularly by those in training the senses, in mobility, and in written and spoken communication. But the loss of informational progress is something over and above the losses directly dealt with in these courses; its effects are not immediately evident, but rather cumulative over months and years. Yet these effects can be serious to every blinded person and very serious to some. This loss, therefore, needs to be kept in mind and dealt with specifically during the rehabilitation training, especially during the final weeks when the trainee is making definite plans for the future.

A special effort is needed to alert the trainee to the fact of this loss and the reasons for it, to the possibility that he may stagnate in his present degree of knowledge of what is going on in the world around him unless he makes plans consciously to do something to prevent this, and to the various means available.

It should be pointed out to him that the increased use of his senses is sharpening his ability to make inferences and judgments from the information they give him. He must train himself not to overlook anything that comes to him in the way of sense information. He must develop a reasoning process, a kind of "detective instinct" telling him what this information means in a broader perspective. Thus will come increased knowledge and the possibility of true intellectual perception.

It should also be pointed out that by the development of this "detective instinct" and by the use of the various techniques of judgment and inference given him in the course in spoken communication, he may become more aware of people and their actions and reactions than he was before he lost his sight. Even though his reading of printed words is now somewhat restricted, there is nothing to prevent his becoming a more and more skillful reader of people; and by so doing he can learn a great deal he never knew before about human nature and about what is going on in his world.

Again, he should be shown the importance here of the mobility he is regaining. The platitude that "travel is broadening" applies very practically to the blinded person; he needs to travel — to the corner store or the neighbor's house and as far as his opportunities allow — to find something of exploration, newness, adventure, to keep and to broaden his circle of friends and acquaintances and the number and scope of his experiences.

He should be shown also the need for using the various means of written communication that have been restored to him and to make plans to be supplied with what he wants and needs: braille books, Talking Books, personal correspondence, human readers, radio (making provision to get information about programs, whether through a sighted friend or a braille program furnished by an agency), etc.

With his regained mobility and ease of spoken communication, he will have the means to increase his opportunities for communicating with other people and for getting to know new things. The possibilities of adult education courses, community lectures, travelogues, discussion clubs, and community betterment projects should be indicated so that even a person who never previously considered taking part in such events may see how they might benefit him now. Not that he should be urged to change his cultural level or to become a "joiner" if he never was one, but he should be shown the need and the possibility for going out to seek new opportunities of acquiring knowledge and acquaintances in accordance with his background, training and tastes.

Above all, he should be shown that he will need to take advantage of every opportunity, and to make opportunities, to increase greatly the number and the intensity of his interpersonal relationships and of new experiences. It should be emphasized that these new relationships should *not* be restricted to those with other blind persons; the whole effort must be directed toward a broadening of relationships within that general circle of sighted people in which he has found his whole life experience.

With regard to keeping up with special fields or special interests, in some cases his family and friends can assist him by sharing these interests, discussing and growing together with him in knowledge of them. This must not mean any disorientation of other people's interests; if it can happen naturally, well and good. But a lifelong martyrdom of trying to show interest in what they really find boring would not be good at all; it would inevitably be discovered and be very harmful to the blinded person. Nor should he allow his interests to become tyrants ruling the household. A far better solution, where it is at all possible, is for him to look for companionship and the means of growth among those who already share the same interests.

In other instances, especially for reading purposes, he may need to plan to "buy sight" if he can afford it.

In any case, he will certainly need to call on sighted observers at times. It is therefore important, particularly in connection with informational progress, that he be shown how to make the best use of the eyes of others. This means that he be taught how to elicit the kind of descriptions that will be most helpful to him, how to ask the systematized questions which a particular situation may call for — questions which will enable him most effectively to fill in the visualized picture he is trying to make. In general, this involves asking the questions which will give him first the *gestalt*, the whole "feel" of the thing, and the details later. (It is worth noting that often he will get more from the descriptions of children than from those of adults; his questioning will elicit the information he needs, while it will be given with the freshness of observation frequently found in the young. But there will be areas in which he will need the trained observation of an expert in the particular field.)

Restoration of informational progress, then, is mainly a matter of giving motivation and opening out possibilities of using the means already involved in rehabilitation training. But it is most important that this be adequately done.

14

Restoration of Appreciation

11. PERCEPTION OF THE PLEASURABLE

THE VARIOUS kinds of pleasure once afforded to the blinded person by looking at things that were "good to see," can be almost completely restored. Here, as we saw in discussing the loss, the pleasure came not from the visual qualities of these things, but from their presence.

As the blinded person learns to perceive the presence of such things by means of his own sense activities, including the power of visualization, and learns to make that perception an "embrace" of their lovableness, likableness, satisfyingness, he will regain pleasure — and essentially the *same* pleasure he once took in seeing them: he will find them "good to perceive."

Consequently, the work of the rehabilitation center here is to show the trainee what this loss consists in, to help him analyze the various reasons why he found things "good to see," and to indicate how he can best use the means being given him in his rehabilitation training to find things "good to perceive."

No analysis of these reasons can be exhaustive, nor can it clearly separate one from another; many different reasons often make one person or thing good to see or to perceive. Nevertheless, the following list may be useful in helping the blinded person to realize that almost all the various kinds of "pleasingness" he once perceived by sight can still be available to him by other means.

(1) Man gets pleasure from looking at the *ownership object* — from looking at the things which are his. The selfish extreme is the the miser who takes great pleasure in looking at his gold. It is not the "visualness" of it that pleases him; it is the "hisness." To a normal degree, this is true of us all.

It is sight that brings all these things to the "looker," that gives him the present knowledge of them. But the seeing is not the reason for the pleasure. The reason is the perception; it is the knowledge; it is the fact of ownership.

(2) Man gets pleasure from looking at the *affection object* — from looking at those people to whom he is bound by ties of affection — husband and wife looking at each other; children at their parents; good friends at one another: "It is good to see you."

And yet, here again, it is not the *sight* that gives us pleasure; it is all that the sight means; it is the immediate awareness of the presence of the affection objects. It is the fact of being present to them; it is the obliteration of distance.

(3) Man gets pleasure from looking at the *good object*, one which has qualities which attract us so that the sight of them gives pleasure. A child passing on the street may elicit this feeling. He may not be especially beautiful, but some quality about him arouses a response in us so that in seeing that quality we are immediately given pleasure. Again, as was mentioned in discussing this loss, there is the loss to the man or woman unable to see the person of the opposite sex. The quality of "goodness" might be a quality of manliness or a quality of womanliness which makes him or her good to look at.

All these and many other qualities of "goodness" make things "good to see." Yet, as we analyze, it seems evident that the pleasure is not found in the act of *seeing* but in what we *perceive*.

(4) Man gets pleasure from looking at the *comely object* (meaning "beauty" in the broader sense — loveliness, handsomeness, prettiness; fine to look at, appealing). It is pleasing to see anything that has a certain rightness to it, a certain consonance: the shiny new car, the freshly painted house. Here again, it is not the looking or the seeing, but the total *perceiving* that really gives pleasure.

(5) Man gets pleasure from looking at the *object dear by association.* To see the house one was brought up in, for example, may be a real source of pleasure because of the pleasant memories it evokes. Or the pleasure that men get from seeing field and stream is partly this kind of pleasure — the pleasure of association.

(6) Man gets pleasure from looking at the "*well-making*" of things. It is good to see the craftsman at work, to see order and purpose showing forth in the making of something. The pleasure that so many men get from watching work on an excavation is not, as it is so often characterized, just the pleasure of looking at a hole in the ground. It is the pleasure of watching accomplishment, creation of a kind — men working for a purpose with romantic and fantastic earth-movers at their command. This is good to see, but the pleasure is not just the sense pleasure of vision.

(7) Man gets pleasure from looking at the *designed object.* The thing well made is good to see. The more we are aware of the intelligence and skill involved in its making, the more it pleases us to see it. Well-kept books appear to the accountant as a "thing of beauty." Seeing them, he sees the design, the intelligence that went into them — and he is pleased, not so much because he *sees* as because he knows. Once again, the pleasure is not merely the end-organ pleasure in the eyes or optic nerves.

(8) Man gets pleasure from looking at the *familiar object.* Here is the security of the known, of that which does not threaten with great areas of the unknown. Thus he likes the sight of his home town, of his own neighborhood, and of the people that he knows. And here again, it is the knowledge that these things are present rather than the actual sight which provides the satisfaction.

(9) Man gets pleasure from seeing the *new object,* the unfamiliar object. Herein is the pleasure of obtaining new information, of gaining new knowledge, of learning, of satisfying curiosity. The countryman in the city, the city man in the country, the person on a foreign tour has this pleasure. He enjoys seeing new sights. And yet it is not seeing them but knowing them that is satisfying.

(10) Man gets pleasure from seeing the "God-reflecting" object —

clear star-filled sky at night; sea moon over wind-filled sails; towering crags and mountain vistas; rolling lands stretching into a distant sky; countless lights in a diamond; shoots on a tree; the awakening of a flower. The sight of any of these may arouse in a man feelings of the presence of eternity, a wonderment which brings him from the majesty of the created to the glory of the Creator. If he is separated from God and the knowledge of God, he may have a feeling only of awe and of the immediacy of mystery beyond him. He may think only of the greatness of nature. But even here, a pleasure is tasted which is more than that of the senses. And clearly enough, not the sight but the meaning is what pleases.

(11) Man gets pleasure from seeing the *sex object*. Here again, there may be an overlapping of many of the different aspects already mentioned, particularly the affection object. But entirely separate from love, there may be this pleasure, the properly used, or misused, pleasure of a God-given appetite. Here that which is "good to see" may indeed be morally good and pleasure-giving, or it may be morally bad but still give sex pleasure. Here we come to an aspect in which the pleasure of *seeing* may be different psychologically for the man and for the woman. For the woman, the pleasure that will be felt will be the reflected, reasoned pleasure of anticipation more than the immediate pleasure of seeing. But, for the man, there is in the act of *seeing* already a gratification, a beginning of actual sexual pleasure.

Thus, only in this one specific aspect of the visual perception of the pleasurable does a part of the pleasure, at least for the man, consist in the actual *seeing*. In addition, however, there are the various pleasures of the knowledge of the presence of the object already noted above.

It might be helpful to see how all these different aspects can be present in one act of seeing. Imagine, then, the couple who have been married for some years and whose love has deepened with the years. On a particular day, while the wife is busy about the house, the husband sits back meditatively enjoying the sight of her.

The words *ownership object* may seem harsh, but one of the reasons for his quiet pleasure is that she is his; there is a pride in this fact that builds his love and good feeling.

Affection object becomes perhaps a weak phrase. He feels a glow of pleasure in knowing that she is present to whom he gives himself, the object of his deep and deepening love.

She is the *good object* in that she is all that she was made and meant to be. She is woman, and fully woman; there glows in her a certain humanity which does his heart good and which is indeed good to see.

But also he feels pleasure because she is the *comely object*. There is a rightness, a consonance to her — the manner of her dress, her carriage, herself. He sees in her a "beauty" which the analytical aesthete might not see. She is right for him, and it is a pleasure to look at her.

It does him good to look at this *object dear by association* — "We clamb the hill thegither." Memories flood in of dear times — hard times and pleasant times — in which they grew together. And to see her now is good.

He watches her, busy with the "*well-making*" of things, and there is a pleased feeling in him as he watches — the order, the purposefulness, the method in the making. This is good to see, and he sees that it is good.

The *designed objects*, the things that she has made well, give him new pleasure as he looks about at them and returns to his thought of her who made them. Even their children have something of this about them — products of both of them, the children whom they have brought forth and raised. He sees them now, and they are good; and the work that she has done in the raising of them again brings him back to the pleasure that is his in seeing them and in seeing her.

Certainly by now she is the *familiar object* with whom he is at home, no hidden threat to his security but dear support to his strengths and weaknesses. She is a part of him and a pleasure to look at.

Yet still there is something about her of the *new object*. For there are new discoveries in her, the divining of new depths of personality which continue as time passes and new experiences, new outlooks come and make part of the whole life experience. Life is discovery, and each new discovery is good to see as it becomes a part of a clearer whole.

God-reflecting object she is, of awe and mystery. Starry vault or precious flower never reflected more clearly the glory of the Creator than does she, with all that her qualities, her subtleties, her mysteries, her goodness, her totality reflect of the greatness of the Infinite Wisdom and Love who created her. Good, indeed, to see her.

And this wife of his bosom is the *sex object*, pleasing to him in the expression of their love — moving with him to that God-given expression of their mutuality, the giving-accepting externalization of their inner oneness in the act of physical union. Herein, the leaving of self, no longer two but one. And in the pleasure-filled glow that is a part of him, visually he reaches out to her, with sight he embraces her.

Here, then, are some of the aspects under which we find people and things "good to see." And all of them, except the last mentioned, are aspects under which the blinded man can find people and things equally "good to perceive" without sight, *if* he learns to look for and recognize their presence by means of his other senses. Obviously, other sense activities besides sight are involved to some degree in the sighted person in conveying the knowledge of the "presence that pleases" under each of the aspects noted above. The task of the rehabilitation center here is to bring out how these sense activities may take over the role formerly played by sight. Here, then, with only one exception, a true restoration is possible if the rehabilitation program and the blinded person do their part.

There remains a further factor which we mentioned in discussing this loss — what might be called the pleasure of visual perception itself, the loss of pleasure in the sight receptor. We think of this pleasure much more readily in connection with the so-called lower senses. There are times when the very joy of being alive is one with the pure sensual pleasure of having and exercising our senses. Perhaps on a fine, full morning in the country, when all nature is awake, we may have a sudden and full awareness of being alive and of being creatures of sense. To breathe sharp clear air through nostrils open to receive and to savor; to smell; to taste the tang of air; to stretch and flatten every muscle and fiber and to sense deeply the stretching and flattening; to reach, to touch, to feel, even to know the non-masochistic pleasure of cold pain on warm skin — this is to be alive in a sense world, where one can have renewed gratitude for the senses and where there is pleasure from their very exercise.

Is there any such sensual pleasure in sight and hearing, in the so-called higher senses? We might well have added to the list for our clear country morning the alertness to every sound, or the clear far-seeing of all things around. We might, but there is a difference here. Now we are more interested in the object of the sense than in the sense activity itself. So directly, so immediately do these senses contact their object that we scarcely think of or savor the sensual pleasure of their use.

Yet there is a sense in which the actual *seeing* is important, and especially so to some people. Light is the medium for sight, but light, color and form are all "appropriate objects" for sight. And of all these, color has the most intimate emotional connotations.

The ability of color in itself to lift or depress a mood has been the object of many studies. But such studies are quite superfluous in considering the joy that a burst of color can bring to individuals. The explosion of color that excites emotion when one comes from a dim or artificially lighted building into a spring or autumn sunset needs no research to tell us of its existence. Nor is laboratory work necessary to tell us of the intense pleasure some people find in the vapored color harmony of a distant haze.

The loss of this special pleasure was implied in the section on the loss of visual background; it was alluded to above in the discussion of the "God-reflecting" object. But beyond this, it is a loss which demands to be recognized in itself.

What can be done about it? Is it completely and irreparably gone for the person who loses sight? I, personally, do not believe so. I strongly believe that on the one hand, the deep feelings which color evokes can be evoked by the other senses, particularly those of smell and hearing, and that on the other hand, the blinded person who retains strong color memories can often evoke by visualization (far more accurately than any precision of shape or form, measurement of space, movement of parallax or the judgment of perspective) the clear bright fullness of color.

To exaggerate the possibilities of restoration here — or for any other loss — would be more serious than to exaggerate the loss itself; so it is important to note that the substitution is not the original, that at times it will seem like a shoddy imitation. But there is a degree to which what was lost here may be restored, and it is essential that we who are working in rehabilitation recognize it and work for its accomplishment.

12. PERCEPTION OF THE BEAUTIFUL

In order to discuss what can be done to restore what is lost by blindness in the visual perception of the beautiful, we need first to have some notion of what "the beautiful" is and of what the perception of it consists, even though any discussion of aesthetics might seem foreign to the field of rehabilitation.

Popular language today uses the word "beautiful" so broadly that it has almost no meaning at all. We apply it to things having an appearance that fits in with the fashions of the day ("the beautiful new car"); to those that have a certain appeal to our senses ("the beautiful girl") or general appeal ("the beautiful baby"). Or again, we apply it to things which have a certain goodness that pleases us (a "beautiful character," or even "a beautiful steak"). But beauty in its strictest sense is something more than any of these qualities or even the sum of them.

In the previous section, we used the word "pleasurable" to cover all aspects of things that cause them to please us when we perceive them. Here we are discussing the loss, not of such pleasure, but of that special aesthetic *gaudium*, the least inadequate translation of which is "delight." And what causes this delight in us is the beautiful.

The philosophers speak of beauty as that which gives a "ray of intelligibility to the heart." Aristotle speaks of beauty as arousing no desire beyond itself, for the desire is allayed by the immediacy of the object, by the sensation and the knowledge of it which comes with the beauty experience. Aesthetic delight is found in an experience of true beauty which is "intuitive-intellectual," in which sense and intellect combine. The "embracing" of the object has an immediacy in which there is no need for reasoning. And in the presence of great beauty, there may be an "ecstasy" in which the beholder is "raised above himself." The poets speak of this as a "temporal glimpse of the eternal."

To the majority of classic theorists, the perception of beauty is possible only by means of the "higher senses" of sight and hearing* — the reason being that in the exercise of these senses, intellectual perception follows so directly and immediately on sense perception as to form but one single act. In the exercise of the other senses, the perception of the sensation itself intervenes and prevents the immediate sensory-intellectual contact needed for the perception of beauty. Thus the beauty of the dance would not come from the pleasure of kinesthetic abandon or control; it would not consist in free or rhythmic movement — but in this movement *seen*, seen actually by the onlooker, seen in imagination by the participant.† The beautiful in poetry would be in the auditory beauty of its lines and of the visual images it evokes, together with that of the meaning it conveys.

There are many other schools of thought among aestheticians, some of which would give other elaborations of the nature of beauty. Some, for example, stress the integrity of the object and the perception of its "well-making" — which would mean that the perception of beauty could come through almost any of the external senses. But these aspects would seem to be included, at least for our pur-

* Some would also include the sense of smell.

† Many persons who object to the theory that beauty comes only through the higher senses quickly adduce the ballet as an objection. Many of them certainly enjoy the ballet, but few dance it.

poses here, under those which are good to see rather than beautiful, the aspects already dealt with in the previous section.

One wonders how widespread in our civilization the perception of the beautiful in this strict sense really is. My experience goes to show that only one or two out of a group of fifteen or so blinded persons really feel this loss as a death that holds real and exquisite pain. To the others, this is no death at all, for they have never "lived" in this way.

But for those who have lived, this loss is a very real one. And we owe it to them to do whatever can be done to restore it.

With sight closed off as a means of perceiving beauty, the blinded person is left with the sense of hearing. And there are also great possibilities inherent in the power of visualization.

Hearing. Our task is to help the blinded person substitute auditory perception of the beautiful for the visual perception which has been lost. This means that the rehabilitation center must open up to its trainees the whole world of sounds, must give them a new awareness of sound, its meanings, its qualities. Our aim must be as broad as this. It cannot be restricted to any eclectic searching for "beautiful" sounds, but must include a recognition of assonance, of discord, even of cacophony. We must help our trainees to find the goodness in homely sounds, the fineness in ordinary sounds, the meaning in the whirring of a motor, the integrity in the measured ticking of a clock. Bird sound, wind sound, brook sound, animal sound, insect sound — few of them are beautiful in themselves, yet the appreciation of all of them is almost a necessity if we are to come to the true beauty of any of them or of a single combination of them. We must reveal the breadth of human sounds — voice sounds, word sounds, and speech sounds — and an appreciation of them which can be a basis for the search for beauty.

Beyond this is music. The stereotype of the blind musician is false and, like most stereotypes, it is harmful. The widespread popular conception that every blind person is a musician, a music lover or a critic of music is erroneous. It is only another way of making blind persons "different."

The fact is that some blind persons have "tin ears," and some blind persons who might enjoy music just have no desire to.* There is no reason to believe that the situation will be any different among newly blinded adults. Some of them will have no capacity for appreciating music, and some of them will have no interest in it. To make music too much a part of our rehabilitation effort would be to attempt to force them into the stereotype.

But for the person who keenly feels the loss of the visual perception of beauty, music is of great importance. Not everyone who had great love for visual beauty will immediately find a worthwhile substitute in the auditory beauty of music. Yet if the capacity to appreciate beauty through the visual sense was there, it is almost certain that the capacity to appreciate beauty through the auditory sense is also there. It may be blocked by lack of experience or by prejudices of one kind or another, and if so, it is the job of rehabilitation training to remove the blocks.

In these days of high-fidelity sound and of frequency modulation radio stations, the opportunity for the music lover to hear good music is immense. It may be, too, that some will be led to a greater appreciation of music by learning to play a musical instrument. Obviously the rehabilitation center is not a place for teaching the playing of musical instruments, but the blinded person who is interested should consider learning. There are also good music appreciation records available which can be a quick way to open out the joy and the beauty of good music, a step on the road to the day when the experience of aesthetic delight will come to the blinded person through the medium of his sense of hearing.

Visualization. If beauty in the true sense can be perceived only by sight and hearing, it might seem that in working with the sense of hearing we have done all that can be done to restore to the blinded person the possibilities of perceiving beauty. But there is still more

* On the average, the taste in music of the person who has always been blind will probably be above that of the sighted person, not only because some blind children, without other sense interests, may come early to an interest in music, but also and especially because the schools for the blind usually emphasize music.

that can be done — through the powers of visualization men
above. As Beethoven enjoyed the beauty of music even after he
totally deaf, the man who once had sight can enjoy the beauty of visual things after he is totally blind.

This brings us back to the whole theory of visualization and its value to the blinded person. I believe that beauty memories can be recalled, and that many individually remembered visual images can be combined to bring to the mind new pictures — pictures of things that the blinded person has never seen before, which are present in front of him here and now. Development of this power will involve training and practice, but *with* training and practice I believe that the newly blinded person can maintain his visual memories. On the other hand, unless he does make use of his powers of visualization, he may well lose his sense of visual form, shape and perspective, just as we know he can allow himself to lose his memory of color.

If a blinded person is to continue to appreciate objects visually, they must be brought to him through description or (this may seem paradoxical) through his other senses or through a combination of description and sense intake.* Thus he could, for example, come to appreciate a piece of sculpture visually. By handling it, feeling it, "brailling" it, he could bring to his mind a knowledge of it which would in his mind's eye form into a visual picture of this piece which he held in his hand. The beauty he found in it would not be in the touch image or in the kinesthetic image (neither of which need necessarily be pleasant); it would be in the visual image. If the object were truly beautiful to see, and if his reflected image of it were true, then he would have once more a visual perception of the beau-

* The possibility of making up a visual image by means of material furnished by the other senses is, I believe, the source of the common belief that beauty can be perceived through the sense of touch, and that therefore blind children, for example, can be educated to the perception of the beautiful by giving them visually beautiful things to feel. If these children have a store of visual images which can be developed and recombined, they could certainly profit aesthetically from "feeling directed toward visualization." But I believe it is unrealistic to try to foster the perception of the beautiful directly through the feeling senses. They are simply not capable of it by themselves.

tiful — implicit and intuitive, rapturous, a reflection of eternal truth and beauty.*

Or the blinded person might be in the presence of beauty too vast and majestic to reach, too delicate to touch, or laid in a dimension which no sense but sight could reach. Here it must be description that paints his visual image — words that communicate, that etch a picture in his mind. And in this picture is the beauty which he *would* see — and now *does* "see" — as the visual perception of the beautiful is in this way restored to him.†

But this will not always happen. Inept words, fumbled words, words of sighted people who cannot really "see" or cannot commu-

* Historically, most of the effort made so far to teach sculpture to the blind has directed their attention to that type of sculpture which appeals to the sense of sight. Attempts have been made to make reproductions of great sculpture available to blind children — not that they might gain a knowledge of the form of great sculpture, which might be laudable, but that, supposedly, they might get from these reproductions an aesthetic delight — something which I believe to be impossible through the sense of touch, or at best to come about by pure chance. For sculpture is made to be seen, not to be touched. True, it has no sculptural quality unless it has a "touched" quality. But this is a "seen-as-touched," rather than actually touched, quality.

Now it is possible to imagine a sculpture for the sense of touch, but it would be difficult for any but congenitally blind persons to devise it. It might, in fact, be ugly to the sight, just as many beautiful pieces of the sculpture we have are ugly to the touch.

For those of us who hold that true aesthetic experience can come only through the senses of sight and hearing, it would be necessary to postulate the possibility that for *congenitally* blind persons the sense of touch becomes one of the higher senses. This is not an impossible postulate, since recent experimentation has indicated that the visual cortex is energized in congenitally blind persons.

But, if this is so, the sculpture which would give true aesthetic *gaudium* to this group would almost certainly be unlike any sculpture which we know. What would be its modes and its material? What can we say? Would it have any appeal to those who have had sight? Again, we do not know. But we can speculate on the possibility that in the course of history, some blind Michaelangelo, some blind Rodin, produced works of art that should have been for the ages; but that the works were ridiculed and eventually destroyed by a sighted public which could not know that a sculpture could exist for the sense of touch, and so never bothered to touch them.

† What about the congenitally deaf-blind? It would seem as if their perception of beauty would have to be almost purely intellectual — the perception of the beauty of meaning without the normal sensory component which is an intrinsic part of this experience as we know it. But, as was said earlier, the whole organization of a congenitally blind person's sensorium is still a matter of conjecture — and still more, that of the congenitally deaf-blind.

nicate what they do see may, instead of restoring the perception of beauty, arouse all manner of frustration at its loss. And at best, a long period of adjustment and of learning will be necessary for the person who is going to use any of the means which substitute for sight, and in the process there may be many frustrating and pain-filled experiences.

In spite of these shortcomings, I believe that rehabilitation has many tools at its command with which to overcome much of the pain of the loss of the visual perception of the beautiful.

Smell. As was noted above, there is a school of aesthetics which includes the sense of smell among the "higher" senses, capable of bringing aesthetic delight. Although I do not personally believe this, nevertheless the school has sufficient authority to warrant the inclusion of some suggestions as to the development of this sense along these lines. Something of what was said about hearing applies here — that it is not just a question of choosing beautiful smells, but rather of opening up a whole world of smells.

Here, though, our task is far more difficult than with the sense of hearing. No sense faculty is so inhibited and limited by a confining snobbery as is this sense in our day. By a prudery as vulgar as the Victorians', smell and odor have become almost as indelicate as were arms and legs; "fragrance" and "scent" may be mentioned in conversation today as once "limbs" were proper but not "legs". One may recognize perfume and bouquet, but to smell smells is almost indecent.

The person who would appreciate beauty through the sense of smell must become familiar with strong smells and delicate, man-made and natural, good smells and bad — and all the ordinary smells, the "homely" smells, with their connotations, their involvements, their frame of reference. The newly blinded person must come to know and assay and evaluate smells, odors, fragrances, perfumes, scents, bouquets in their fullness as the basis for appreciating the smells which may bring beauty. Earth and new hay, the sweetness of a fine manure, woods, fields, animals and farms, open fires, new-killed meat, hickory smoke, the clean smell of salted fish. The smell of morning, of evening, of full day, of dry day and wet day, and the smell of the different winds. The smell of people, of locker rooms and of drawing rooms, the smell of good tobacco and of different soaps — all this and much more is the necessary basis for appreciating the beauty of smell which is beyond it all.

To help restore the perception of beauty through the sense of smell, the rehabilitation center, while working with the sense of smell for purposes of general information, will also work with perfumes, incense, and the recognition of fragrant flowers and herbs. These things are not for every blinded person any more than are music appreciation courses, but, for those who have suffered severely in the loss of the visual appreciation of beauty, they may be an important factor in total rehabilitation.

But, even if that school of aestheticians is correct which holds that beauty may be experienced through the sense of smell, the setting aside of areas of public parks or botanical gardens as "fragrance gardens for the blind" cannot be sufficiently condemned. The segregation of the blind involved is highly detrimental to those so segregated. And even more harmful is the effect on the sighted public, for such "gardens" build up a new stereotype, which involves ideas that these people should be segregated, that they have interests different from normal people, that they are helpless to take part in normal pursuits and that the public should pity them as they go their separate way, basking in other-worldly fragrance.

15

Restoration of Occupation and Financial Status

13. RECREATION

THE RESTORATION of recreation is a most important part of our work — so important that some have considered it almost the *only* work needed for the blind. This it definitely is not. Recent psychological studies indicate that there is an element of mass escape in the present widespread search for obvious forms of recreation, and that the truly adjusted person can find refreshment and relaxation without formal recreation programs.

Nevertheless, since blinded persons have been subjected to the multiple and repetitive trauma of blindness, they have a special need of the new life afforded by real recreation, and to restore this to them is one of the important aspects of our program.

We need to be clear as to what we mean by recreation: not a series of activities designed to fill every moment of leisure time — the modern feeling that people need to be "doing something" every moment is a frightening phenomenon — but activities that allow room for true leisure and contemplation and send the person back refreshed to his living and working.

The task of the rehabilitation program is, consequently, to help blinded persons gain the attitudes and skills that will make recreation possible; to open out to them a wide choice of potential forms of recreation; and to see to it that they actually return to recreation sighted companions, to help them understand and begin to overcome the serious difficulties involved.

Needed attitudes and skills are gained through the whole program — the course in spoken communication being particularly relevant. The attitude of some individuals toward recreation may need to be worked with — some persons suffer from a neurotic sense of guilt about taking any recreation or a particular form of it, and so tend to rationalize "giving their time to frivolous things," by making benefit to their health or to their intellectual life or to other people, or the gaining of useful skills their motives for recreation. Others tend to make recreation a form of escape. In either case, it ceases to be real recreation. Blinded persons, therefore, need to be shown, perhaps in group psychotherapy, the true place and meaning of recreation in life and its special place and meaning in their future lives.

In considering the forms of recreation now possible for him, the blinded person is faced with the fact that some forms — perhaps some of his favorite forms — have become absolutely out of the question or practically so. Special psychiatric aid may be needed to interpret the meaning of some special loss and to help the individual see what can be done to compensate for it. But the great need here is to open out the many and varied possibilities that remain. This should not be done in some vague, general way, but by concrete discussion, making the principles clear and awakening each person's own imagination to consider which of these possibilities might be most appealing and most feasible. Chart B is intended to furnish the core for such discussion, but by no means the complete material.

In opening out wide possibilities of recreation, several factors need to be kept in mind. The possibilities must be numerous and varied enough for each individual to be able to find forms of recreation suited to his personality, his tastes, his training, his background, his prejudices, his likes and dislikes. Some newcomers in work with the blind are made very happy by learning that there are special checkerboards and checkers for the blind, as if this and similar devices somehow solved the whole problem of recreation. We need to keep in mind that special checkerboards are very helpful — but

Chart B

Recreational Activities and Possibilities of Restoration

Activity	*Possible*	*Impossible*
	I. MAINLY INTELLECTUAL	
	(a) "Spectator"	
Reading	See section on restoration of written communication.	
Plays and movies	Enjoyment possible as soon as senses and abilities developed to follow what is going on.	Silent movies, pantomimes.
Lectures	Greater source of enjoyment — important to develop new sources of information.	
Symphony and jazz concerts	Developed use of senses can enable participation in real "event" or actual concert; the person should be urged to make effort and not be content only with recordings, TV and radio.	
Radio	Avoid satiation and too great dependence. Care needed to make schedules of all programs available.	
Television	See plays, above. Valuable source of recreation if rightly used, especially as part of social pattern, aid to enjoying conversation.	
Spectator sports	See plays, above. Begin with events that are broadcast, bringing pocket radio; great value in actually attending.	
Museum visiting, window-shopping	Possible source of great enjoyment through eyes of intelligent companion who can give competent descriptions.	

Activity	*Possible*	*Impossible*
	(b) "Participant"	
Chess	Excellent for blinded persons who enjoy chess.	
Checkers	As above.	
Scrabble, Chinese checkers, dominoes	Have been adapted for use of blind.	
Cards	Quite possible as soon as person knows enough braille to read marks and buys braille cards or marks a regular pack. Bridge quite possible if sighted person tells blind the contents of the dummy.	
Visiting	Continued source of recreation and important for continuing and expanding interpersonal relationships.	
Conversation and discussion	Should be developed as arts. See section on restoration of spoken communication.	
Parlor games	Verbal games, active part in pantomimes, etc.	Guessing aspect of pantomime.
Oratory and debating	Quite possible. Gaining of extra poise here may help total adjustment.	
Dramatic activities	When the person can take a part adequately, being sure the group expects as much of him as before blindness.	Most parts impossible.
Touring	Can still bring new experiences, acquaintances — very important for this. Possibility of using eyes of others to "see sights."	
Eating out	People, atmosphere, different food all still available as soon as he has trained himself to perceive all these.	

Activity	*Possible*	*Impossible*
	II. INTELLECTUAL AND PHYSICAL	
Arts and crafts	Quite possible to continue with many of these and to master new ones. See text.	
Hobby and collecting activities	Quite possible to continue with many of these. See text.	
Music making	Blinded musician should learn braille notation to continue active.	
Sculpture	Can be tremendous recreational experience for some, even artistic achievement.	
Finger painting	Perhaps useful for stimulating powers of visualization as training medium, otherwise frustrating for most people.	
Painting, drawing, etc.	See above.	
Do-it-yourself activities	Home repairs, laying concrete, fixing plumbing, tinkering with electric fixtures, etc., all quite possible. Course given in rehabilitation center.	
Cooking	Both men and women can get great pleasure from ability to cook extraordinary dishes extraordinarily well.	
	III. PHYSICAL	
	(a) MILD AND SOCIAL	
Dancing	Should be taken up in many cases, even by those who never danced much before — pleasure not interfered with for long, social importance greater.	

Activity	*Possible*	*Impossible*
Picknicking	Includes many activities still quite possible and opportunities for being socially one of group.	
Quoits and horse-shoes	Offer difficulties, but many blinded persons gain enjoyment from them; blindfolded matches indicate possibilities and limitations.	
Billiards		Not possible.
Ping-pong		Not possible.
Walking	May have great recreational value when mobility restored with dog guide or cane. Recreational value depends on degree of ease, lack of tension achieved.	
	(b) ACTIVE AND SOCIAL	
Tennis		Not possible.
Golf	Modified form of team play possible, companion acting as caddy-coach, setting up ball and describing lie. Real recreation both to former golfers and new players. Not a segregated sport, in spite of international blind golfers' tournament. Usually play with sighted.	
Bowling	A source of recreation as "people's sport." No feeling of pressure or need of great skill. Special portable bowling rail may help though most do not use it.	Spot bowling.
	(c) TYPICALLY ACTIVE	
Hunting	Duck hunting (shooting from duck blind with sighted companion). Being member of hunting party.	Any kind of shooting on horizontal plane.
Fishing	Big game fishing, most forms of casting, including surf casting, deep-sea fishing, etc. (Whistling cork useful gadget).	Probably wading in stream.

Activity	*Possible*	*Impossible*
Target shooting	Shooting at a sound emanating from target center. More useful for training hearing than truly recreational.	No kind yet found really feasible. Attempts at designing a whistling bird for skeet shooting so far unsuccessful.
Trapping	Restricted because of difficulty relocating traps. Trained woodsman can still find pleasure with companion — e.g., take boy along and teach him about the woods.	Usually impossible alone.
Tramping and hiking	Usually restricted to well-known terrain, even with braille compass, except with companion.	Not completely.
Camping	Can be contributing member of group — cook, dishwasher, help in tidying up, etc. Should be urged to continue if he enjoyed it before.	
Mountain climbing	In tourist sense — ascending of safe and well-marked trail, with companions.	In full sense of conquering peaks, etc.
Horseback riding	Quite possible if reasonably skillful, knows horse and can depend on him, avoids terrain with low hanging tree branches, etc.	
Sailing	With a group, if many changes of direction do not upset his sense of orientation and so disturb him.	Impossible alone because of difficulty of picking up silent obstacles.
Rowing alone	Under certain circumstances, e.g., when audible sound coming from pier.	Ordinarily.
Rowing — crew or tandem	No problem.	

Activity	*Possible*	*Impossible*
Canoeing	Like rowing, except advantage that canoeist faces forward where best sound localization lies.	
Speedboat racing	Some enjoy being one of the crew; can steer in nonracing situation with guidance.	
Swimming	Favorite sport with many. Needs proper conditions — well-developed sense of sound localization, reasonable precautions.	In isolated unprotected situations. (Blind persons have drowned when unable to locate shore and their cries for directional help went unheeded.
Diving	Enjoyed by some athletic blind persons. Proper precautions necessary (water in pool, no one in the way).	
Skin diving	Quite possible.	
Water skiing	Already a hobby with many.	
Boxing	Shadowboxing, punching bag have value as exercise, improving coordination. Some may find them recreational.	In true sense.
Track and field competitive sport	Shot-putting, discus hurling, hammer and javelin throwing.	Other forms.
Running	Offers feeling of freedom; recreational if no competition involved. Needs willing running guide.	Racing in real competition.
Baseball, basketball football, hockey, etc.[1]	Can be expert coaches.	Completely out so far as playing goes.

[1] Handball and squash and all sports involving fast-moving ball or similar object are completely impossible.

Activity	*Possible*	*Impossible*
Skiing	Cross-country seems most possible. But expert blinded skiers are continuing downhill, with companions as "skiing eyes" going ahead and giving audible signals.	
Skating	Figure skating no problem if enough free space. Other types usually need sighted guide.	
Iceboating	See sailing.	
Bobsledding	As one of team.	
Snowshoeing	With a group, but hampered by fact that snow is the "blind man's fog," laying heavy blanket over possibility of sense knowledge — whether on the ground or in the air. Demands reorientation of interpretation of information and adds to difficulty of mobility.	
Fencing	Excellent form of recreation; no modification of classic form needed.	
Driving a car		Completely out; see text.

only for checker-playing-blind-people-when-they-want-to-play-checkers. Free choice is of the essence of recreation, and to have one's choice limited to checkers and the like does not solve the problem.

Here, as in every other area, we must be careful not to try to impose our own higher or lower cultural level on a blinded person. Yet we must also be alert to help him develop any new interests he may have gained in the changed circumstances of his blindness and rehabilitation. We might well indicate to the blinded person how much snobbery exists with regard to different forms of recreation, snobbery both of the lowbrow and highbrow variety — the baseball fan looking with anti-egghead superiority at the lecture-goer, the lecture-goer being grateful that he is not like the rest of men who waste their time at ball games; the symphony fan disdaining the track-follower, and the track-follower thinking slightingly of those who listen to music instead of feeling the pleasures of life. If the blinded person begins to recognize such snobbery, it may help to remove some of his own prejudices and thus open out a wider choice.

And finally, it is essential that the once sighted person be shown how once more to *find his recreation among sighted people.* To force him or encourage him into a specialized and segregated blind group, even for recreation, is to move him further away from the sighted society in which he belongs, to which we are trying to return him. He may find a temporary strength in the "out-group," but it is strength that fails very quickly when he returns to the "in-group," and one which mobilizes and reinforces all his feelings of "difference." Such segregation can speedily break down any motivation to reorganize for life — which includes recreation as well as work — as a participating member of a sighted community, or any progress he may have made toward that reorganization.

In using Chart B, it should be kept in mind that in all the forms of recreation classified as *intellectual-spectator* (the word "intellectual" is used in the broadest possible sense) and in every other "spectator sport," the spectator, if he is really to be recreated, needs to be an emotional participant, identifying himself with the protagonists on the playing field, in the book or on the stage. This is one reason why blinded persons should be encouraged to go to plays, games and concerts rather than staying at home and listening to them over the radio — the emotional participation is much more direct and intense when one is actually part of the situation. For this reason also, blinded persons should be encouraged to look beyond the limits of the soap opera and other similar purely passive forms of recreation which exercise *only* the emotions and these in an exhausting and satiating way.

In discussing *arts and crafts* as means of recreation, the stereotype of the blind beltmaker, wallet-lacer, etc., needs to be taken into consideration. A certain use of the arts and crafts is still taken in some quarters as being typical of blind persons. It is advisable to point out that in cases where this is true, the blind person may well not be doing it for recreation. Practicing some craft may be, for the needy, a means of earning a little pin money; for the bored, a way of passing long hours; for those learning braille and other techniques, a means of training the touch senses. Leatherwork and metalwork of various kinds are produced by persons who are blind, some of it of a rather high quality. But crafts should never be urged upon blinded persons — as they often have been in the past, although the tide now seems to be turning against it — precisely because of the stereotype.

Various *hobby and collecting* activities that were favorites with persons before they lost their sight may well be retained after blindness. There are blind philatelists who are no mean experts. A surprising number of blind persons collect snapshots of their trips. One trainee at St. Paul's took great pleasure in taking candid camera shots of fellow trainees and staff. One blind person at least was a collector and repairer of clocks.

To the young active male, there is a special importance in *physical sports* — that large group of sports which (while increasingly performed by women in our day) are psychologically masculine in character. These involve physical competition, competition of man with man, competition of man with elemental forces — the sea, the forest, storms, winter, animals. They afford an opportunity for men, particularly young men, to relieve themselves of aggression, of the hostility for which civilized mores allow no other outlet.

It is here, more than anywhere else in this field of recreation, that the young active male is hurt when he loses his sight. Here, in the sports where manhood is tested, he is wanting. He loses much of the male companionship and male competition he needs (and perhaps too the female admiration of his proficiency). At the same time, he loses a normal outlet for the energy and drive within him that cry for release. It is especially important that we restore everything that can be restored to this group of young men, and salvage everything that can be salvaged.

The special meaning, to young men in particular, of *driving a car* needs to be dealt with. It means status, a sense of power, technical ability, adulthood, even manhood (witness the derogatory masculine attitude toward women drivers). The absolute and irreparable loss of the ability to drive can be very serious, with deep-seated effects. Here it is helpful, and in some cases, necessary, to help the individual by interpretation to gain some insight into the meaning of this loss.

In helping blinded persons actually return to one or another form of recreation, it is essential that the worker keep in mind the "frustration factor" involved — the feelings that may overwhelm a blinded person when he begins to take up once more a form of recreation which was formerly one of his favorites. Few other situations have as great a power to bring home to him emotionally the full impact of his disability. It may involve a new awareness of things he can no longer do, with a feeling of hopelessness about ever being able to do any of them again. It may include supreme embarrassment. He may feel that he is being constantly watched to see how he will make out (which may well be true). In a crowd he may experience a real phobia. Many a blinded person has quit, wet with anxiety, after his first return to what was supposed to be a recreational situation.

To prepare him for this return, the blinded person needs expert help that will include competent interpretation *before* the traumatic situation occurs and aid in "working through" the situation afterward. He should be equipped also with the full realization that he will find nothing "recreative" in many forms of recreation the first or second or perhaps even the tenth time he attempts them. If he is ever again to participate in them with enjoyment, he may need doggedly to try and try again until the frustration factor is overcome.

Here we must work to arouse the necessary motivation for this doggedness and perseverance in the blinded person himself. We cannot treat as children adults who have lost their sight — and this is certainly to be especially avoided in the field of recreation. Yet there may be times during the rehabilitation process when the trainee must be forced to "recreation" for his own good, by scheduling periods in which he is expected to go back into society to take part in one or another form of recreation, even though as yet it holds no recreational value for him.

For recreation is itself a factor in rehabilitation. It may be used during training in such a way that the blinded person will occasionally "feel like a new man" — and this will be its function in his future life when he has overcome the frustrations and found the kinds of recreation most appropriate to his needs and circumstances. But during training and the period of further adjustment after training, recreation has a potential value in really making him a new man. Experts in education today point out the value of recreation for the development of personality and character; experts in rehabilitation need to be alert to its value for re-education in cases where personality and even character development have been interfered with. And for all blinded persons, beyond the temporary stimulation it may (or may not at first) afford, the very fact of returning to recreation among sighted people can give a lasting stimulus by bringing home the fact that normal living among normal people is again possible.

But unless by inner motivation and by actual scheduling blinded persons are assisted "over the hump" of return to participation in the social life of the sighted community, there is grave danger that they will slide into the social life and specialized games of the segregated blind community, with all the surrender of hope and of ego-strength involved therein.

The restoration of recreation is, then, not the comparatively simple matter of providing blinded persons with games to play or "things to do"; it is a complex question requiring intelligent and persevering effort on the part of the blinded person and of those who would help him.*

* Many recreational activities involve companionship, and it is important that this companionship be normal, the kind that the blinded person would have enjoyed if he still had his sight. This would normally include the companionship of

14. CAREER, VOCATIONAL GOAL, JOB OPPORTUNITY

For almost all men and for a great number of women blinded in the "productive years," final placement in suitable and dignified employment is the keystone of the rehabilitation process.

This does not mean simply getting a blinded person *some* job. He has lost not only his means of earning a living and his occupation, but also the status that went with it and in many cases his vocational goal and prospects for advancement in a special career, involving his whole way of life and outlook for the future. If he is placed in an unsuitable job or one which offers no possibility of advancement, we are not solving the problem. Historically, "vocational rehabilitation" began as simply "job rehabilitation," but now the concept is expanding to include "vocation" in the wider sense.

Suitable employment — if it really is suitable — restores job opportunity and financial security; it may do much for the blinded person's feelings about himself, relieving him of his fear of dependence and restoring him to his proper role in his family and neighborhood.

But the very importance of returning to work produces a tendency to get the blinded person into a job without prior rehabilitation. This is a subtle working out of the denial mechanism which says that blindness is a minor handicap ("After all, the big trouble is that a man loses his work; restore this to him, and he will be all right"). As a consequence, often enough, persons with the best potential for complete rehabilitation are sent back into the community psychologically unprepared and lacking in knowledge of skills and resources. While they are fully capable of earning a livelihood, they are not given the knowledge and training which would make them fully capable in other areas of their lives. And when a disorganized,

---

both men and women. When the companion is not of the person's own choice, but a guide furnished by an agency, we should avoid letting the convenience of the agency (the greater availability of male or of female guides) exclude this normal fulfillment, leaving the blinded person with only masculine or only feminine companionship in recreational activities and depriving him of the normal co-operation and competition with both sexes.

unskilled blinded person (however skillful he may be at his work) returns to a community position, he may do great harm to himself and others.

Placement in suitable employment is, therefore, not the *whole* of rehabilitation nor the foundation stone. But it is certainly the keystone for the vast majority of young and middle-aged adults. Without it, rehabilitation does not become a solid reality.

This means that the person whose blindness has cost him his position after years of employment or in his own business or profession needs to be returned to that same job or profession, with the same possibilities ahead as before. When this is impossible, he must be assisted to find an equivalent position with equivalent possibilities. And — far more difficult — the person blinded too early to have been employed or to be launched in a career needs to be helped so that he will have a future equivalent to that he would have had with his sight.

Before we consider the role here of the rehabilitation center, of the job counselor and placement expert working with the center, and of agencies for the blind generally, we need some concrete ideas about the kind of work that blind persons can and cannot do. Chart C gives an outline of various possibilities.

Those occupations in which sight is absolutely essential for doing the work are completely closed. If a person's work was of this kind, and if no transfer is possible to a similar type of work or to an allied field in which sight is not required, then he must face a complete reorientation and a complete change in his vocational objective. Unfortunately, such a tragic situation, in which years of skill, effort, and seniority go down the drain, leaving a man or woman thirty, forty or fifty years old with the necessity of starting all over again, is quite possible. We can help to make it less tragic by aiding a person like this to make the necessary reorganization, and also by helping him to start in a line of work suitable to his qualities and capabilities (if not to his training and experience), rather than forcing him into some stereotyped form of work.

As the chart indicates, the possibilities of a person's returning to the same or similar kind of work expand in relation to two factors,

Chart C

Types of Work That Blinded Persons Can and Cannot Do

Type of Work	*Examples*	*Solution*
(A) *Work that blinded persons can do or be enabled to do.*		
(1) Work in which sight has little or no connection with the essence of the job.		
(*a*) No change in job needed.	Certain types of law practice, of teaching; psychiatry; secretarial work; certain types of work with machines.	Rehabilitation training and return to work.
(*b*) Some new tool makes job possible or easier.	Telephone switchboard and dispatching work (special type of board available for blind operators).	Rehabilitation training, training in new device, return to work.
(*c*) Slight modification of job.	Secretary-bookkeeper takes over more secretarial work; bookkeeping given to someone else.	Rehabilitation training, reassignment of tasks, return to work.
(2) Work not requiring sight similar to former work which did require sight.	Supervisory work in same field: police patrolman becomes desk man at headquarters or telephone man; fire fighter becomes a member of safety inspection team. *Or* work in allied field: general practitioner moves into field of psychiatry; lawyer in some	Rehabilitation training, period of preparation for new work.

	field requiring sight moves into one in which sight is not needed.[1]	
(3) Work in which sight is not necessary for job itself but is indispensable condition. See text.	Salesman who must drive to customers; many types of executive work.	Rehabilitation training; use of eyes of others purchased by self or provided by employers.
(B) *Work that blinded persons cannot do.*[2]		
(1) Those in which sight is essential to the job.	Driving any kind of vehicle; piloting; surgery, optometry; filing and cataloguing; mail sorting; bridge worker, riveter.	Rehabilitation training and either A2 above or complete reorientation of career and vocational goal.
(2) In which sight is essential for		
(a) safety,	Commercial fisherman; certain operations on steel-mill floor.	As above.
(b) efficiency, or	Clerk in supermarket or hardware store; cashier at movie.	As above.
(c) both.	Wheeling supplies or products from one part to another of busy machine shop.	As above.
(3) In which sight is not essential to job itself but for some task inseparably connected with it. See text.	Secretary-filing clerk in business too small to rearrange work; salesman not far enough up ladder to hire driver; not too promising junior executive.	Rehabilitation training, look for new job, *or* complete reorientation may be necessary.

Type of Work	*Examples*	*Solution*
(C) *Work out of the reach of the congenitally blind and those blinded before receiving training, but available to those already trained.*		
(1) In which sight is needed.	All kinds of medicine and allied fields in which personally made and observed experiments are demanded as part of the training.	In present state of things, person must be directed to other vocational goals. In future, more secure professions may be more flexible.
(2) In which sight is needed in apprentice and early years.	Most kinds of law practice, in which early stages involve much filling out of forms, etc.	Not easy, but some lawyers have worked through it.

[1] It might be noted here that at least one specialist in internal medicine returned to the same field after blindness, keeping up his practice and teaching in hospitals.

[2] It is hazardous to list such jobs, because often when the list is made one hears of a blind person who has proved that one or another on the list can be done by at least some blind persons.

the first being how much experience in the given field the blinded person already possesses and how far "up the ladder" he has already climbed. For if he is sufficiently experienced and established, he will be able to purchase sight, or have it provided for him by his employers.

An outstanding example of what can be done along this line is that of a blinded man who was in the building supplies business, his special line being to look over jobs under construction, to figure and bid on them. After rehabilitation training, he solved his problem by hiring young apprentices to act as his eyes, to drive him to jobs, guide him around them, answer his well-put questions, and do any writing required. Thus he supplies himself with the needed sight and also gives invaluable training and experience to one young man after another.

In the same way, a business or industry which does not wish to lose the services of a valued employee with a responsible job may make it possible for him to carry on as before by assigning him special secretarial help, either full time or for set periods during the day. In the latter case, the secretary might, for example, read the morning mail to him while he makes braille notes; she might dictate onto a recording machine the telephone numbers he is to call during the day or other necessary memos. Whatever the exact work that needs to be done, there are cases in which a company can save itself from the loss of a trained and experienced employee by purchasing and furnishing for him the sight that is a *sine qua non* to his effective functioning.

While the crack salesman at the height of his career can hire the services of a sighted person to drive his car and so manage to continue as before, the novice or only semisuccessful salesman may be completely unable to do this, and must face the reorientation of his career and vocational goal. And so also, with many other types of work.

Yet when the blinded person has ability and energy he might do well to take a chance on purchasing sight if he can in any way arrange to do so, even if this means spending a good proportion of his income for the length of time it will take him to get established. In general, if the career a blind person has already embarked on (or has in mind) is one in which qualities other than sight are what essentially make for success, and if there is reason to believe that he has these qualities, he should give serious consideration to every possibility of purchasing sight to carry out any aspects for which sight is necessary.

But here the problems of those born blind, and of those blinded in early youth or at any time before they have gained training and experience, are vastly greater than those of many persons blinded in adult life. Some careers which would be quite possible in themselves are closed off because sight is needed to get the prerequisite training. For example, a general practitioner of medicine might move into the field of psychiatry, but a person who becomes blind before going through medical school could not become a psychiatrist because he could not take many of the required courses (at least no way has yet been found).

The problems of congenitally blind and youthfully blinded persons are not our primary concern here, but we need to be aware of them as part of the general picture; also, their special difficulties serve to indicate the very real advantages afforded by previously acquired knowledge, skills, and experience if the blinded person realizes or is shown how to make the best use of them.

The second factor in expanding (or contracting) the possibilities of returning to the same employment is the ability and willingness of the employer or superiors to adapt the previous job to the blinded person's new qualifications, or to let him try out in a job in which sight is not essential and his experience could be useful. The secretary-filing-clerk-bookkeeper in a small business, for example, can go back to the same job if her employer can and will arrange to have her do only secretarial work, while someone else takes over her other duties. Otherwise she cannot — though she can still look for a secretarial job somewhere else. Or the police patrolman might be given the job of desk man at headquarters; the fireman might be given a desk job or become a member of the safety inspection team. But if his superiors cannot or will not give him such a job or if he does not have the necessary qualifications, he will have to look elsewhere and perhaps completely reorient his vocational goal.

This factor is in many cases (but not necessarily) bound up with the first — most employers will do a great deal more for a valued and experienced worker than for a tyro or marginal one. Possibilities of restoration here depend on a great many factors, some within the blinded person himself, some without. Each person presents an individual problem and needs individual help both in relation to his potential job and in fitting him to return to work.

The first task of the rehabilitation center in this area is to equip the blinded person with the skills and attitudinal reorganization required for "total adjustment" to blindness. It should be emphasized that this is as necessary for the person who can return directly to the same job or profession as for the one who must completely reorient his whole work life. The second task (unless the individual can return directly to work) is to stimulate, while giving the skills and reorganization, the imagination of the blinded person by opening out to him the total range of available possibilities. The third task is to furnish or arrange for the best specialized professional job counseling available and to furnish the job counselor and later the placement worker* with the most complete scientific and human picture possible of the person to be employed — his strengths and weaknesses, his training and experience.

The task of the job counselor is to relate this picture to what can

* Combining the positions of job counselor and placement worker, as is too often necessary today, puts a great burden on one person, since the strengths demanded by the two types of work are quite different. Both need to be realistic and have a broad grasp of jobs and job opportunities for blinded persons. But the job counselor needs natural empathy and trained understanding — traits usually found in the calm and quiet person — while the placement worker needs to be the more aggressive man of action and trained salesman. It would be almost impossible to be outstanding in both jobs. Until every agency can set up separate positions, consequently, it is necessary to screen counseling-placement personnel with extra care.

be ascertained about the community where the individual is to work, and on this basis to develop with him the plans which have the most realistic prospect of success.

Some persons will then need specific job training. The task of the rehabilitation center here is, when necessary, to help the individual graduating from the center find where to get this training. But it is *not* the task of the center (nor of the whole field of work for the blind) to *provide* such training. A blinded doctor who intends to become a psychiatrist needs to take the usual courses and hospital residency required for this specialization. A blinded woman who intends to do stenographic work needs to take the courses in a regular secretarial school. Persons who need to be retrained for one or another industrial job or trade can find such training in the special night courses available in many community high schools or, as is advocated by the Health and Welfare Fund of the United Mine Workers Association,* in a community trade school in his own community or elsewhere.

Not only would it be impossible for rehabilitation centers or agencies for the blind to provide specialized training, but also undesirable — for it would simply mean setting up another form of segregation and one that is completely unnecessary and unrealistic if rehabilitation training has been successful.

The final step is the actual procuring of a job. It is quite possible that the blinded person can seek and find his work himself. Or he might call on the services of a placement expert to survey the job he has in mind in order to ascertain whether he could handle it competently or to get any information about it that might be helpful. In other cases, the placement specialist, with his survey of a business or factory, may be indispensable in convincing an employer of the feasibility of hiring a blind person.

Everyone concerned in this process should remember throughout that it is the blind person himself who must make all the final decisions. He may be aided by the rehabilitation personnel in gaining

* History will note the tremendous impact of this group on the field of rehabilitation. The effect of the fund has been higher standards and better rehabilitation throughout the field.

needed motivation and exploring possibilities, by the job counselor in deciding on a particular type of work, and by the placement worker in finding it. But nowhere along the line should he be pushed in one direction or another. As an emotionally mature adult, it is he who must make the final choice. If he is not an emotionally reorganized adult, we have no business assisting in his placement.

We should also remember that working with blinded people is like working with sighted people: blindness is no guarantee of employability any more than it should be a bar to it. The person who never held a steady job when he was sighted is unlikely to do so when blinded. The marginal worker or job jumper who becomes blind will probably continue to be one when he is blinded (and may well become a very vocal critic of the placement workers who cannot find him the suitable employment he does not really want at all). There may also be persons who only worked well and steadily because of social pressure to do so. When this pressure is relaxed by blindness, some may prefer to sit at home and complain of lack of job opportunities rather than work hard at those offered to them.

But, sad to say, even when rehabilitation personnel, job counselor and placement worker, and the blinded person himself have done their best, dignified and suitable employment may still be impossible to find because of the lack of knowledge and consequent prejudice about blind people on the part of employers.

The pioneer placement workers who in the recent past first opened up jobs for blind persons in regular industry made an enormous contribution. Their work is being carried on and developed today by the trained job counselors and placement workers who work to educate individual employers and companies as to the employability of blind persons and to find the right jobs for the right blind persons. Here is a constantly expanding field for specialists, not only in industrial but also in white-collar placement, with perspectives opening out in agricultural placement as well. The activities of these "keystone" workers need more and more to be broadened and reinforced by the backing of everyone else in the field of work with the blind in particular and the handicapped in general, with a frank recognition of the major difficulties facing them.

From the fact that blind persons can expertly fill many jobs, some people infer the false notion that placement of blind workers is not difficult, and consequently are critical of placement personnel. Rehabilitated blinded persons do not, it is true, have the employment handicaps of some other disabled persons: standing or sitting in one place, for instance, does not cause the injury or pain that it would to those with back injuries; repetitive manual functions have not the same potential for harm as they would to those injured in the upper extremities, and are not as tiring as to the muscularly paralyzed. Work tolerance is not the danger factor it is for the cardiac patient or a person with arrested tuberculosis, nor the fatigue factor that it is for the paralyzed. There are not the bowel and bladder difficulties that cause stress to many paraplegics. Blindness does not of its nature bring the accident-proneness found even among those not considered handicapped, nor the repetitive physical illnesses inherent in many disabling diseases.

If the public, and particularly the employing section of the public, were aware of these facts, placement of rehabilitated blind persons would indeed be relatively easy. But as things are, most employers have very strong emotional feelings which interfere with the hiring of blind persons. Moreover, most placement workers are expected to find employment not only for properly rehabilitated blinded persons but for many others whose rehabilitation has hardly begun. Their job is an extremely difficult and often thankless one.

But if the backing we give to placement personnel is to be effective, it should be only a part of the effort of general agencies, agencies for the blind, specialized schools, relatives and friends of blinded persons, and blinded persons themselves to work together for the day when there will be the same opportunities within the community for blind and sighted persons alike to get jobs suited to their talents and abilities, to follow a worthwhile career, to achieve a vocational goal both realistic and worthy of the individual. This end toward which we should all be striving includes equal pay for blind and sighted persons alike. It includes equal choice as to staying with a job or leaving it to seek another, equal opportunities to go ahead through stages of promotion — and equal possibility of being discharged because of poor work or being laid off in hard times.

Since perhaps only one in every five thousand Americans in the employable years is blind, there is certainly sufficient opportunity among the wide range of jobs that blind persons can carry out as well as their sighted counterparts to make our goal a realistic one. Yet a tremendous amount will have to be done in order to attain it. Research is needed in the rehabilitation field itself to give new insights into the problems of blindess and new methods of dealing with them, in the field of sociology to uncover more fully the sources of prejudices about blindness so that we may know better how to combat them, and in the field of job specifications to learn more exactly where sight is absolutely necessary and where it is not, and to assist in developing methods and devices.

A massive, continuing campaign of public education is needed to do away with all the current false notions about blind persons, above all that they are by definition poverty-stricken and helpless. Such a campaign will have to point out that there are far fewer jobs that blind persons cannot do than those they can do, giving many varied and precise examples of the kind of work that blind persons are doing and could do if they were allowed to. In this way, the notion of stereotyped "blind jobs" and "blind skills" — a notion that makes perfectly good crafts such as broommaking, and occupations such as operating stands, seem distasteful to those blind (or sighted) persons who might otherwise find them acceptable — could also be disposed of.

Above all, this campaign would drive home the fact that judgment, reasoning power, general intelligence, personality, empathy, sales ability, imagination, experience, inventiveness, leadership, loyalty, mathematical ability, the capacity for repetitive manual operation — qualities which business, industry and the professions are all seeking

— are to be found among blinded persons just as frequently as among sighted. In fact, the country's greatest untapped potential for such qualities lies among its handicapped population.

But now and in the future, the most effective factor in achieving our purpose of expanding job possibilities will be the blinded persons who have benefited fully from their rehabilitation training. As more and more emotionally mature and well-organized blinded persons move into the professions, into business and into industry, they will open the way for more and more to follow them, and by their general effect on their community will make easier the acceptance of blinded persons in an increasing number of occupations, until the whole potential field is opened out.

15. FINANCIAL SECURITY

Of all the losses resulting from blindness, this is one which society could completely eliminate if it so wished.

Obviously, the more types of work and jobs that are opened up to blind persons, the greater will be the number of those able to achieve the resulting financial security. But the earnings of those who do regain employment are seldom adequate to pay off the indebtedness incurred by the sickness expenses of blindness — in some cases including not only the expenses of oncoming and early blindness, but also those of long and recurring periods of hospitalization, costly medicines to be taken over a long period of time, special and expensive diets. In the majority of cases, there is the expense of a considerable period of readjustment, retraining and finding a job. Moreover, no matter how complete the rehabilitation of an individual, his expenses will inevitably be somewhat higher than those of a sighted person living at the same level, and expenses will rise as he needs to purchase sight.

And of course there are some blinded persons among the group we are considering, and very many among the increasing old-age group and those with additional disabilities, for whom the financial security of a well-paying job is out of the question.

As things are, although medical costs are rising, the charity of doctors and the special rates offered by some hospitals to the needy do something to ease the burden; so does the increasing amount of hospital and medical insurance carried by more and more people. Here we can only urge, as one aspect of our educational campaign, that everyone take out some form of regular "catastrophe" medical insurance.

All of us who work with the blind, as well as doctors, hospital workers and laymen, can certainly help blinded persons avoid the unnecessary sickness expenses incurred by not accepting the finality of the doctor's verdict, once it has been given as final. We should of course not discourage blinded persons from seeking reasonable consultation, but we should do everything possible to urge them not to continue unreasonably seeking new doctors and new "cures."

Beyond this, we can inform blinded persons about the nature of the relief grants now given by the joint action of state and federal governments under Title X of the Federal Security Act, the so-called Aid to the Needy Blind. This is not, nor was it intended to be, "security," but *relief*, and relief on the basis of need. Like Old Age Assistance, Aid to Dependent Children and Aid to the Permanently and Totally Disabled, it is a substitute for (and a vast improvement on) the poorhouse of another day. It has probably kept many people from starving and is an excellent "floor" below which a person cannot fall. But it is not restoration of financial security, any more than the poorhouse was.

We can also, where necessary, put the blinded person in touch with one of the numerous private agencies for the blind throughout the country. Some are set up to give emergency aid or supplement the income of a client over a brief period, but even those which have a heavy budget can give at most a pittance, not an adequate income. In any case, this is not financial security but emergency aid, and too often it becomes "charity" in the pejorative sense — "charity" without love, establishing a relationship of dependence and indebtedness and even of total insecurity.

There is also the possibility of dependence on family and friends.

And there are the "benefits" run by the community and gifts established through radio and newspaper appeals. All these may and do help in a crisis, but they too operate in the realm of pity, and they do not add up to security, since such efforts usually culminate in one grand gift and then vanish.

All these attempts to help blinded persons financially involve a great deal of time and effort as well as expense, and they do not succeed in restoring financial security. If society could find an effective way to restore financial security to its blinded members, a great deal of the effort now fruitlessly devoted to this purpose might be directed elsewhere. And this would be to the greater benefit of blind and sighted alike, not only because our efforts could be more fruitful in other areas, but because blinded persons, relieved of the anxiety of this loss, would be in a position to overcome the other losses more successfully and so to become fully participating members of society.

The record of the blinded veterans of World War II gives outstanding witness to the value of some real restoration of financial security. The disability compensation which they receive monthly from the Veterans Administration is a good sum (even though, unfortunately, since it was not tied to an escalator clause, it is lower in value because of inflation than it was intended to be). When its size first became known among civilians in work with the blind, some said that with the motivation of financial need now removed, people receiving such a sum would never adjust to blindness and would certainly not seek employment.

The record of these blinded veterans* has proved these objections unfounded and should stand as a norm for the treatment of blinded civilians. No group of blinded persons in our time has a better record for adjustment and employment. There are many reasons for this, including the excellent rehabilitation training given these men and the extra willingness of employers to take on a veteran with service-connected blindness. Yet it shows conclusively that restoration of

* *See World War Veterans in a Postwar Setting,* published in July, 1958, by the U. S. Veterans Administration, a massive statistical study and sociological analysis and a major contribution to work with the blind.

financial security does not decrease motivation for rehabilitation or employment. Instead, it decreases areas of anxiety so that the person may function more easily. It decreases dependence on family, friends and agencies for the blind and allows the person, with new dignity and security, to move forward toward rehabilitation.

What, then, could society do to restore true financial security to its blinded members? Private insurance cannot provide the answer. Most insurance companies today make little effort with regard to coverage for loss of sight, beyond contract clauses allowing the discontinuance of premium payments in the event of blindness or allowing for a small lump sum payment for the loss of one or both eyes. And it would be difficult to work out a low-priced premium contract. It would be those persons most liable to blindness (from hazardous working conditions or heredity) who would be the ones most inclined to take out blindness insurance, and so the insurance company would either have to charge exorbitant rates or refuse contracts to its most likely customers. And, as with any completely voluntary plan, there would remain many people uncovered.

The one answer, then, is *public insurance: cradle-to-grave coverage against blindness* made part of the *social security insurance* carried through the United States Government. Some political scientists object that our social security system is not properly called "insurance," that technically it is not insurance. But I strongly believe that the analogue to private insurance is sufficiently strong to allow social security properly to be called "insurance" under logical semantic development. In our culture, it is of the greatest importance to the dignity of the individual that this analogue be maintained and that the payee see the payment as a *quid pro quo* in return for payments made.

Such public insurance against blindness* would in no sense be

* This idea of insurance payment to blinded persons, rather than relief or "pension" payments, was first presented to the author by Captain Alan Blackburn, who was in great measure responsible for developing the Army's program for the rehabilitation center at Old Farms Convalescent Hospital, Avon, Connecticut, which was of such great importance to the blind in this country. It was Captain Blackburn also who first discussed with the author the idea that blind-

relief. It would not be a pension payment, nor a payment from society out of the goodness of its heart. It would carry no means test, since it would be insurance and not a payment on the basis of need. Payments would be made to all those carrying the insurance — rich and poor alike, those working and those not working — on the basis of fulfilling the established condition: the existence of legal blindness (see Chapter 23).

Naturally, there would be difficulties in working out such a plan, particularly for those born blind or blinded before they had taken out social security, since they would have made no payments, and for those already blind prior to the inaugurative date of the insurance system. But these and other problems could be solved, as the social security system has already worked out various complexities and is continuing to do so.

At the present value of the dollar, payments should be around $85 a week, tied to some escalator clause according to fluctuations in dollar value. Receiving a sum like this as an insurance payment due in justice according to an established contract of the individual with the Federal social security system, blinded persons would be able to live with the self-respect brought by financial independence. And they would be able to purchase sight so as to restore more completely the losses in other areas and to achieve more quickly and surely a normally independent and participating position in their society.

---

ness is actually made up of a number of different losses, each of which must be considered by itself in working out a program of restoration.

16

Restoration of the Whole Personality

16. PERSONAL INDEPENDENCE

ONE AIM of rehabilitation training is to restore to the blinded person as much *reality independence* as possible, so that his objective need to depend on others beyond the normal give-and-take of life will be reduced to a minimum. The training of the senses and the various skill courses — particularly, perhaps, those in mobility and in the techniques of daily living — are of primary importance here.

But however greatly the blinded person benefits from this training, he will still need *more* help than most people — not a great deal more if he is properly rehabilitated, but *some:* in reading, in keeping up with things, in certain mobility and social situations, and so on. Moreover, certain forces outside himself will be at work attempting to impose upon him a greater degree of dependence than is necessary or healthy. Special work is needed, consequently, to help the blinded person establish the firmness of *inner* independence required to handle this situation successfully.

This work is especially needed by the person who has always had a dependent personality: without adequate assistance it will be very difficult for him not to give in completely to the unusual dependency factors of blindness. It is needed also by the person who could cope with the normal dependency situations of life but is now overwhelmed by the massive dependency of new blindness. Diminishing this dependency objectively does not of itself necessarily restore the alance to personality; the normal personality cannot accept an abnormal degree of dependency without some inner struggle, particularly in a culture such as ours which stresses personal independence.

The whole milieu of the rehabilitation center, therefore, must be oriented toward the restoring of independence of personality to each trainee; and it must be imbued with an atmosphere communicating to each the strength to work toward independence. The process of rehabilitation must be one of inner growth, assisting the trainees to move from finding their strength in the rehabilitation staff toward finding it in themselves. This involves on the part of the staff, as was said earlier, the capacity to give warm human support in the beginning and to withdraw support gradually, while continuing to give human understanding. The essence of this important phase of the rehabilitation process might be described as a weaning without the withdrawal of love; without it, nothing is accomplished except to transfer dependence from family or friends to the staff members.

Interpersonal relationships, whether within the rehabilitation center or outside it, can be very helpful in communicating the needed strength, but *only* if they are relationships leading to independence. A multidisciplinary center has, of course, the great advantage of many different personalities working toward this common end, not only giving a general atmosphere of strength leading to independence, but also affording a variety of opportunities for individuals of different personalities to form such relationships.

This process of assisting blinded persons toward inner independence is an extremely important but also a dangerous field. This is why, as was brought out in Chapter 9, a psychiatrically oriented staff, making up a total therapeutic environment, is essential.

Therefore in work with the blind generally those of us who are not experts can best help a blinded person toward independence simply through his relationship with us and our agency (relationship understood as *temporary*) as we try to serve his needs in one or another "reality" area. But we can only give this help if in our contacts with him we are at once sufficiently human and sufficiently detached; if we are really interested (without self-deception) in helping him to achieve independence from ourselves and our agency; if we are not too involved in his feelings; and if we ourselves do not inwardly need to have him dependent on us. If we are thus sufficiently mature and independent in ourselves, and particularly in our attitude toward handicapped persons, then we can give to dependent blind persons the same kind of aid which a maturely independent parent gives to his children, a teacher to his students, a friend to his friend. Beyond this, we should leave the work of restoring inner independence to the experts.

In addition to regaining *inner* independence, the blinded person needs to be made aware of the psychological mechanism which causes people to try to make him unduly dependent. He will almost certainly have to face this phenomenon in the public generally, in his acquaintances, in his own family, and it may be even in workers for the blind. He needs to be forearmed, not by any open interpretation about his particular situation, but by a general knowledge of this phenomenon, so that he will be able to understand what is happening and resist it without resenting it.

Work with the public with regard to the dependency aspect of blindness — what kind of extra assistance blind persons really do need and how best to give it and what they do *not* need, since they are not helplessly dependent, submature individuals but normal, active persons — is part of the general work of education we should be carrying out in all our literature and publicity (see Chapter 18).

But some special work with the families of blinded persons is usually needed here above all — and it may be very difficult and delicate work indeed. Overprotective parents, children, husbands, wives, relatives or friends will usually resist strongly anything that we may try to do to change an existing relationship, even though it is one of unhealthy dependence into which a person has been forced by blindness.

Of course, such people are not consciously trying to block what is good for the blinded person. (It is unfortunate, perhaps, that they are not; if they were, one could fight them openly, without inflicting so much pain and feeling so much guilt.) They are well-meaning, sympathetic, kind; but they are seeking to protect or enforce a dependent relationship, not for the good of the blinded person, but because it satisfies some need of their own.

The wife who unconsciously is pleased that her husband's blindness is keeping him at home and dependent on her strongly resists seeing that this is true. She is in no way anxious to learn this truth about herself; this is not the kind of truth that anyone likes to face. She will rather be anxious (again unconsciously) to protect herself *from* learning it. And so with the overprotective husband, parent, etc.

Occasionally at least, such a situation is incapable of solution except by helping the blinded person to build up his inner independence and by forearming him against the forces that will be working to make him or keep him dependent. But usually there are various ways in which families can be assisted to foster rather than stand in the way of the rightful independence of the blinded member (these will be discussed in Chapter 17). One important factor here is for families and friends to realize the degree of reality independence achieved by the blinded person in the course of his rehabilitation training.

17. SOCIAL ADEQUACY

Loss of social adequacy is for the great majority probably the most severe trauma which blindness brings, as was already said in discussing this loss. And, as was also said before, this loss has two phases — in the individual and in society.

The loss of social adequacy — in the blind or in any other minority group* — may originate in the individual or in society. In either case, both become involved, since forces operate on both sides to keep up the barrier which refuses to let the person be "adequate." When an individual ceases to be personally adequate, society fails to

* In this and the following chapter, the situation of blinded persons in society is treated as analogous to that of a minority racial group. This does not mean identity between the two situations. Blindness is an anomaly in a sighted world; membership in a minority racial group is anomalous only when the majority group gives prime consideration to racial origin.

accept him. When, on the other hand, society fails to accept an individual, he may well cease to be personally adequate.

Loss of social adequacy may, and in the case of blindness does, involve a minority group prejudice on the part of society. The loss of adequacy by many members of a group may cause society to fail to accept the group as such. The failure of society to accept the group may lead, in turn, to the loss of individual adequacy on the part of more of the group's members.

Whether the loss be a group or an individual affair, there is a continued interaction: less adequacy making for less acceptance; decreased acceptance, being felt, making for still further inadequacy and so for still less acceptance. A vicious circle is set in motion, and one that is very difficult to break up.

True enough, the minority prejudice which the blind suffer from does not result generally in their being hated by society, as often happens to other groups when fanatics and demagogues fan the flames. The blind are not hated; they are rejected and pitied (another form of rejection). People do not ordinarily advert to "the blind" as a group, far less as a group potentially threatening the security of society, as happens in the case of race prejudice. They are only aware of the one blind person or the few blind people whom they meet or hear about. This is why rejection and pity, rather than hatred, are aroused. Yet the group factor is present, though latent, even here, since this one blind person stands as the present embodiment of all similarly "different" persons — whose existence is felt somehow to threaten "normal" life and society.

There is another difference which is distinctly and often bitterly to the disadvantage of the blind person. The Negro or the Jew rejected by society can identify with those whom he most dearly loves, his own family. But when the blind person is rejected, most often his own family is sighted, and thus is part of the society which rejects or pities him (or upon whom he projects such feelings). In these circumstances, the only group with which the blind person can identify himself may be the group with which he has nothing in common except his blindness — the group which will lead him farther and farther away from reidentifying with his own.

Society does not force this loss of social adequacy on the blinded person only from without; it forces it on him from within his own personality. For he comes from sighted society; he shares its misconceptions and its feelings about blindness, about himself as a blind person, about "the blind." And so he is not only made to feel himself inadequate; he may feel so anyway, very deeply, within himself. And thus, feeling inadequate, he will prove to be so, and decrease the possibility of his being accepted.

He may then react to society's rejection of him (and to his unconscious rejection of himself) by one or another type of compensatory behavior. In *The Nature of Prejudice,** Gordon Allport lists various types of such behavior resulting from the sensitization and concern induced by discrimination and disparagement. For the person who is basically extropunitive, these may be obsessive concern and suspicion, slyness and cunning, strengthening of in-group ties, prejudice against other groups, forms of aggression and revolt, enhanced striving; for the basically intropunitive person, denial of membership in his own group, withdrawal and passivity, clowning, self-hate, in-group aggression, sympathy with all victims, symbolic status-striving, neuroticism. This list gives some idea of the kinds of behavior which might be expected from rejection due to blindness. Any of these further increase social inadequacy and decrease the possibility of acceptance.

Thus one phase of the loss of social adequacy comes from within the blind person himself — and both he and those who wish to help him should clearly recognize this fact. If it is easy for us who work with the blind to begin to feel that this problem is all the fault of outside society, it is fatally easy for blind people themselves to do so. And the tragedy is that so many blind persons do allow themselves to believe this problem to be entirely external to themselves; they blame all failures in social adequacy on the public which will not accept them. When a blind person has this attitude, he will make

* Addison-Wesley Company, Reading, Massachusetts, 1954.

no adjustment to his blindness other than the paranoid one which causes him to blame all his failures on other people, to seek to be a parasite on society, and constantly to rail at society for not giving him enough to live on.

This attitude carried to its extremes causes a person to describe the problems of blindness almost entirely in terms of the errors, the stupidity, and the rejection of the sighted public. It leads to the unreasoning development of all kinds of segregated activities for blind persons, and spends itself in mobilizing the feelings of hostility and resentment from which it begins.

The ignorance and the consequent social rejection on the part of sighted people *is* a major factor in the problem of blindness. It would be entirely unrealistic for the blind person to ignore the fact. But to say that the problem is *entirely* the fault of the public is a dangerous and false defense on the part of the blind person, for it is one which will keep him from ever facing the problems which are within himself.

Another way of escaping from these problems is for the blind person simply to deny that they exist — to fail to admit to himself that there is any problem of acceptance. This escape also has many ramifications, and like the other it fails to meet and conquer the problem.

But the very fact that one phase of social inadequacy does originate in the blinded person himself makes it possible for us to break into the vicious circle and make it work for good. The blinded persons whom we help to regain social adequacy and to understand the forces involved in the whole problem will themselves influence their society to accept them and all blind persons — and so decrease the forces working for nonacceptance in the future.

Loss of social adequacy cannot be less than an extremely serious matter. Its restoration deserves our best efforts, and the magnitude of the job demands them. How most effectively to attack this loss as it originates in the attitude of sighted society is the very heart of the problem of educating the public about blindness — a vast and complex question to be dealt with separately (Chapter 18). Our concern here is the individual blinded person.

Rehabilitation training in all areas works toward the regaining of "objective" social adequacy. Professional help in re-establishing inner independence (discussed in the previous section) is of prime importance; the manner in which the blinded person can handle real problems of social adequacy and his own feeling toward sighted society depends in great measure on the degree to which in the course of his rehabilitation he has succeeded in building up anew a mature and balanced personality structure.

Beyond this, he will need some special help in clarifying and reorganizing his attitude to sighted society — which means clarifying his feelings about blindness and about himself as a blinded person. If he does not do so, he will still be ruled by these feelings, blaming society for holding them and concealing from himself the fact that he shares them; this will make him inadequate, no matter how willing to accept him his society may be. He may also need help in clearing his feelings of resentment that other people are sighted while he is not — feelings which he may have rationalized as resentment over the attitude of his society to him. This is particularly needed with regard to the immediate sighted society of his own family; otherwise his feelings about their sightedness and his blindness may do terrible things to his "family adequacy."

His feelings about other blind persons may also need to be clarified. Total rejection, open or disguised jealousy of successful ones, resentment against failures, complete identification with a blind group — any of these attitudes indicates deep feelings about his own blindness and about the sighted public from which he feels either excluded or accepted on sufferance.

The blinded person also needs help in distinguishing the social inadequacy resulting from his blindness from the inadequacy he would suffer from whether he were blind or not. Some blind persons habitually blame all their social failures entirely on their blindness. This attitude may be open or hidden (and thus more dangerous), and it is a very easy one for the blind person to adopt.

For example, a boy who loses his sight at thirteen or fourteen years of age, and months later takes a girl out for a dinner date for the first time in his life, goes with many kinds of feelings of insecurity. He is insecure about meeting the girl, about running into some of his "gang" while he is with her, about ordering a taxi, about tipping the driver or the doorman, about ordering the meal, about dancing, and about all of his action from the time he meets the girl until he leaves her.

The natural tendency of such a teen-ager is to blame all his insecurity on his blindness, not recognizing that every other adolescent has the same feelings on his first date. Unless he is helped to separate properly the blindness factors from the adolescent factors, he is going to be extremely inadequate in the teen-age society he is entering.

In the same way, the blinded adult needs to be shown the need to be as objective as possible in separating the blindness factors which keep him from functioning adequately from other factors which affect sighted people as well and have the same effect. Social difficulties are not concerned only with dinner dates; they occur in all our relations with other people. Even the opening of the door to an itinerant salesman is to meet a social situation which one must conquer. Ordinarily we do not use such words as "conquer" in discussing situations to which we are accustomed, since in normal emotional health we do not find any great challenge in them. Yet we should realize that life is a continuing round of new social situations (in the sense in which we are using the words), and blindness adds factors which may make meeting them successfully a real "conquest."

The will-he-like-me? will-I-like-him? will-I-impress-him? will-he-be-impressed? will-I-handle-the-situation-all-right? of adolescence is fortunately not a major conscious factor with most adults in meeting ordinary social situations. It is often just barely buried, however, so that new blindness may bring it to the surface in a disturbing way. With this factor in the picture, the opportunities for social errors added by blindness may cause real trouble.

In brief, the blinded person must be aided clearly to recognize the fact that his loss of social adequacy is not entirely the fault of sighted society but is due in part to himself and to realize that to this extent he can do a great deal about it.

Helping him to these realizations is a part of the work of total adjustment to blindness or total personality reorganization, still to be discussed. Group discussion of the dangers inherent in segregation of blinded persons for recreational or other purposes can be helpful here, bringing out from the group itself a great deal of recognition of the forces drawing insecure people to band together and of the ways in which the socially inadequate feelings of such a group implement their already existing fear and hostility. Group psychotherapy is even more important, and special work with individuals may be needed as well.

But whether by group psychotherapy or other means, it is vital that the blinded person be assisted not only to build up his own inner strength but also to gain an understanding of the difficulties experienced by the sighted public in meeting blind persons. The adjusted blind person will develop understanding and tolerance for difficulties which sighted persons have in this regard, and will learn to be able to help the sighted person toward a fuller understanding of the problems involved so that he can "be at home with blindness." With such balanced tolerance, the blind person will recognize the fact that there will be times when the ignorance of sighted persons will hurt and times when unusual examples of stupidity will anger him. But he will not go through life with an underlying resentment of sighted persons, or be driven into living in a world of the blind.

18. OBSCURITY

Blindness has a high "social visibility factor," not only because it is clear to people who see the blind person that he is blind, but also because his blindness — a mark of physical difference — is also the badge, the symbol, of the presumed social difference we have just been discussing.

In societies in which racial differences have a high degree of social importance, color and racial characteristics have a high degree of social visibility. But when racial differences assume their proper subordinate role, color and racial characteristics (although still easily recognized by anyone looking for them) have not the same degree of "social visibility." The person with very dark skin and Negroid facial characteristics living among a group of Caucasians is just as Negroid whether the society is race-conscious or not; but where race consciousness exists, he has a much higher degree of social visibility than when it does not.

The blinded person may himself add to the social visibility factor by his own deep neurotic feeling of difference or insecurity, of hopelessness that he can ever really overcome his blindness and live a normal life. It is no mere chance that our language has come to use the same word — attitude — for a person's emotions, feelings, and point of view, as for his physical position. Time and again, a person's inner attitude shows in his outer attitude: the psychic attitude has somatic reflections. This is often true of a person's attitude toward his blindness. As a result, the person with feelings of strangeness and helplessness usually manifests these in his external appearance and so communicates them to others, thus giving to his blindness a social visibility factor higher than it would otherwise have.

And finally, the blinded person may project his own feelings onto those around him and think that he is being observed even when he is not. This is a common phenomenon in self-conscious people, and blindness easily leads to an increased "consciousness of self."

In rehabilitation training there is little that can be done to make the *fact of physical blindness* less visible. Instead, the blinded person is helped to see how futile and even self-harming it may be to try to hide what cannot help being obvious — that the groping gestures of the person trying to protect himself and still hide his blindness merely implement all the feelings in the sighted public about the helplessness of the blind and of this particular blind person.

The use of a dog or cane is shown to be not a flaunting of one's blindness but the logical use of a necessary device by the person who recognizes that since his blindness cannot be hidden, he must use the tools which will lead to his independence. And in our day, to the public at large the dog and the special cane are more and more becoming symbols of a type of blind person quite different from the long familiar stereotypes. (The attempt to "pass" as sighted should probably be thus only indirectly attacked in a rehabilitation program, and understood as the symptom of an underlying difficulty which needs to be, and can be, treated.)

In connection with the *deep social difference* which the public presumes is behind the visible handicap, the blinded person can be shown that while the long-term problem will not be solved in our day, there is a great deal that he can do in his own immediate environment. The more he succeeds in changing the attitude of his environment toward blindness, and toward him as a blind person, the more does his blindness fade into the background as a "social visibility factor." * What is needed is a greater number of secure blind persons working in and around the community, educating the public by their very presence and thus more and more pushing the factor of social visibility into the background.

The blinded person's own feelings of strangeness, difference and helplessness which may add to the social visibility factor are dealt with by the whole psychosocial aspect of rehabilitation. As to the factor of projection, any form of insecurity makes a person fear observation, although at time he may challenge observation by a perverse exhibitionism, and often enough makes him feel observed even when no one is looking at him. The insecurity caused by new blindness is no exception. In fact it is even greater, since the blinded person cannot look back at those who might be observing him.

What is involved here is both the normal need of the balanced individual for privacy, and the greater need of the person who is

* This is analogous to the situation mentioned above of the Negro in a society which is not especially race-conscious. It is still apparent that he is a Negro, but the fact ceases to be uppermost in people's consciousness; it ceases to be a primary characteristic in their thoughts about him. It is possible for blind persons to bring this same situation about, not only in their own family circle, in their neighborhood, in their employment group, but also in their larger community.

insecure in himself. The rehabilitation process will not cut down on the amount of time that a person is seen. It will, in fact, if it is successful, encourage him to take part in social activities to such an extent that he will be seen more often than the blind person who is not rehabilitated. What rehabilitation can do here is to help change the self-concept of the blind person so that he will not think of himself as a helpless blind person, but will be in fact (and will be seen as) a strong person able to overcome the problems of blindness. A person with such an idea of himself goes out with an entirely different feeling about being seen, and the problems of being in the spotlight are greatly lessened. For example, it might be generally said that the truly independent blind traveler with dog or special cane does not receive offers of helps except at the times when he shows that he needs it, whereas (neurosis again foiling its end) the dependent blind person is apt to get offers of help when he is least ready to accept it, and also to find help lacking when he is really in need.

The danger always exists that a sensitive person will tend to project into this problem far more than is present in reality. The answer is not to be found so much in giving him intellectual insight into this tendency (although at times this may help), but rather in assisting him through to the problems which are underneath.

But all of us in work for the blind should guard against our own tendency to add to this particular burden of the blinded person by suggesting in one way or another that people will be watching him, that they will see his behavior as the reflection of our training, and that therefore he owes it to us to behave as we think he should. *Noblesse oblige* is a heavy burden for anyone; there is every reason why we should never inflict it on those who have come to us for help. The motivation of the rehabilitated blind man should certainly not be that of an obligation we place upon him. It should rather be found in his own inner principles — principles which he has been able to bring out with greater clarity in the course of the rehabilitation process — and in the security in himself which he has achieved.

19. SELF-ESTEEM

As was said earlier (page 73), self-esteem, the total opinion a person has of himself, has two distinct phases, the first being his objective self-estimate. It is almost impossible for anyone to have a self-estimate that truly is objective, but however realistic it may or may not be, the multiple losses of blindness are bound to deal it a serious blow. In one after another area, the person has been crippled by his new blindness.

It is not bad that self-reappraisal should begin in the time of extreme self-devaluation in the postshock and early mourning stage of new blindness. It is important, however, that the process of rehabilitation begin soon after, not so soon as to inhibit the grief, yet not so late as to allow the self-devaluation to become a set pattern or the building of various defense mechanisms to set in.

The task of helping the blinded person to overcome what he has lost in objective self-estimate should begin with helping him to form, early in his new blindness, as realistic an estimate of his situation as possible: what his prospects are, what chances he has of doing something and what difficulties lie in the way. This includes his facing the fact of his condition and understanding the meaning of rehabilitation in realistic terms.

This is a job for the hospital bedside and for the early weeks after blindness has struck. It does not necessarily require a psychologist to carry it out, but well-meaning people with the pollyanna approach are certainly "contra-indicated". It needs someone who is capable of giving a realistic evaluation of blindness and of the possibilities that this individual blinded person can overcome the problems created by it. It demands someone who will neither overplay nor underplay either the handicap itself or the possibilities of overcoming it.

With rehabilitation training, one after another area will be restored to some degree. The blinded person now finds himself competent in one thing after another that he thought he could never do again. He is not able to do *all* the things that he was capable of prior to blindness, but to a degree that he would not have believed possible he has developed abilities and learned of potentialities for further development.

He will, of course, perceive to some extent that this is happening. But he needs to be helped to realize the contrast between what he could do a month ago and what he can do today. This help is most effectively provided in a series of regularly scheduled personal interviews, in conjunction perhaps with a score sheet that lists all the losses of blindness with detailed progress marks to be checked toward a rehabilitation goal suited to the individual. This sheet might be along the lines of VA pamphlet 10-10, *What's My Score?* and VA Form 10-2555: *My Own Score,* designed for men with spinal cord injuries. These publications would also prove helpful in working out a progress chart for blinded persons who do not take rehabilitation training. In any case, the evaluation at each stage should be realistic and concrete, indicating the extent to which the person's self-estimate is entitled to rise as its objective bases are gradually rebuilt.

The family of the blinded person also needs help in making a realistic estimate early in his blindness and at various stages during the process of rehabilitation, since a family which refuses to face the finality of blindness, or one which considers it an irremediable tragedy, may make it practically impossible for an individual to make the self-reappraisal and do the planning necessary for his rehabilitation.

However realistically a person may evaluate the *objective* elements in his self-estimate, he makes this estimate finally in accordance with some yardstick of values. If the yardstick a blinded person has used hitherto has not been realistic and mature, it may be that in the course of the rehabilitation process he will come to substitute one that is.

If the person's measure of success and happiness has been the acquisition of money, he may discover, while he is being helped to regain the possibility of acquiring enough money for security, that although some elements in our culture equate status with money, true security is to be looked for elsewhere.

If the blinded person's complete measure of what the normal human being should be has consisted in the "body beautiful" ideal, he may discover that a number of people manage to be relatively satisfied human beings without being physically perfect, whereas the majority of the "body beautiful" group manifest some very interesting psychological phenomena.

If the blinded person's whole philosophy of life is erroneous, he may gain immeasurably if he comes to substitute a truer one. But he will gain only if he adopts the new one not because it will "make him happy" (as if it were an escape), but because it is the truth. It would seem as if, logically speaking, the pain of blindness would be mitigated by a belief in Divine Providence and belief in a future life with no blindness or distress, but the fact that a person holds such beliefs does not actually mean that he feels the pain of blindness any the less. But even if it did, he will be no better off if he adopts them as a kind of cosmic aspirin. For anyone who adopts any religious belief in order to "feel better" is using religion as an escape from reality. And it is quite possible that in embracing a new set of principles, some persons are in reality only attaching themselves to a new form of neurotic escape.

The gaining of a new yardstick — whether in the realm of religious or of ethical, moral, philosophical or cultural principles — may be favored in some cases by the fact that the multiple trauma of blindness has destroyed a previously held false set of values. In others, it may be impeded by the strong emotions aroused by the trauma, which stand in the way of any clarity of thought. But in any case, the objective of rehabilitation is to enable the individual to become a whole person once more — a person in a position to make his own choice of right and wrong, to make his own choice of the values according to which he will henceforth make his objective self-estimate.

As to the other phase of self-esteem, *self-image*, there has been little measurement of the effects of blindness on it, and still less of the effects of rehabilitation after blindness. But experience seems to indicate that the process of total rehabilitation can in most cases help a person to build a self-image much stronger and more satisfactory than the one he had after blindness struck him and before rehabilitation, and that he can gain greater equilibrium with this self-image than could otherwise have been expected. In a few cases, this re-formed self-image may be stronger even than the one the person had *before* he became blind.

This upbuilding of self-image would seem to be due in part to the induced insight of the rehabilitation process, in part to the generally therapeutic nature of good rehabilitation. Certainly a major factor here is also the blinded person's dawning recognition that he possesses and has given evidence of strength to face and overcome a major crisis in his life — a strength which he did not previously believe himself to possess.

The regaining of skills and the consequent rise in objective self-estimate are also involved here, but the whole question of rebuilding self-image, like that of inner independence, is bound up with the total personality reorganization, to be discussed in the following section.

20. TOTAL PERSONALITY ORGANIZATION

The restoration of total personality organization is, in a sense, the whole goal of rehabilitation, and how to bring it about is the whole problem. Personality loss is the effect of all the other losses, but restoration does not come about simply as the effect of rehabilitation in other areas. By the regaining of abilities and skills, much of the strain on the personality is removed, but help is also needed to repair the damage done to the emotional structure itself. Many of the factors involved have already been discussed in connection with one or another psychological restoration. Total personality reorganization is the dynamic synthesis of all these factors — making the blinded man once more a whole person.

As we saw earlier, this need for reorganization does not mean that there is anything wrong mentally with someone who has become blind. It simply means that he is a normal person under abnormal circumstances, who has suffered such a severe multiple trauma that only a completely abnormal person with an advanced case of schizophrenia would remain unaffected by it. The blinded person, therefore, precisely because he *is* normal needs special professional help to recover completely and to achieve "total adjustment" to his new condition.

This total adjustment might be defined as the attitude which enables the blinded person, in accordance with his own individual nature and capabilities, to face the fact of his blindness, admitting its severity without minimizing or exaggerating it; to do everything possible to acquire the substitute skills and knowledge needed; to have and to show the same emotions as before blindness; to mobilize his inner strengths around himself rather than around his blindness; to return as a whole personality to the society from which he came, integrally a part of that society, not making use of his physical defect as an escape or defense for himself or as either treacle or a club for those around him.

True adjustment is thus distinguished from maladjustment — a set and false attitude to blindness (easily distinguishable in theory, but not necessarily so in practice — a person who is quite normally angry or aggressively eager to do something to overcome his blindness is too often considered maladjusted).

It is also distinguished from partial adjustment, which may be either a normal stage along the road to full adjustment or a stage at which a particular person has stopped progressing.

And finally, it is distinguished from apparent adjustment — the kind that most easily deceives untrained workers and occasionally deceives all of us. Apparent adjustment is often found among those blind people who tell themselves that blindness is a "minor handicap," and in that euphoric group whom the uninitiated call "happy." These people pose a special problem, since in them are the seeds of an explosion — yet one which might never happen, and since it is especially difficult to help people to overcome a handicap which they believe they have already overcome.

Also to be included in the "apparent adjustment" group are those persons so often called adjusted simply because they never complain, because they have no capacity to become aggressive except in the most limited circumstances. They are capable of real hostility but incapable of expressing it; it is a hostility not suspected since it is buried under a constant air of friendliness. They can be more hostile than the average person without even being aware of it, but they do not have the capacity for normal aggressiveness.

True adjustment is not resignation to blindness; it is not compliance with everything that may be suggested; it is not contentment with things as they are; it is not even the ability to remain successfully employed. It is the complex entity described above.

The work of restoring total personality organization, of helping the blinded person achieve true adjustment, might be said essentially to consist in uncovering and strengthening the ego, while removing the defenses which stand in the way of its facing and overcoming the major handicap of blindness. This is a delicate and difficult task, calling for united efforts in a rehabilitation center which is essentially a psychotherapeutic community.

How this task may be carried out is, perhaps, best indicated in terms of an actual training program. We shall therefore describe what is done along these lines at St. Paul's Rehabilitation Center, including a chart (Chart D) showing the weekly schedule, to indicate how skill and psychological training are interwoven to make up a program for "total rehabilitation."

During a prolonged period of staff training before the Center took in its first group of trainees, the original psychiatric orientation was firmly established. This is communicated to new staff members by the general atmosphere, by a weekly training period (in addition to regular staff meetings), and by constant communication between the other members of the staff and the psychosocial department, which consists of two psychiatrists, a psychologist and a psychiatric social worker. Above all, the weekly group psychotherapy sessions for the core staff members ensure the continuance and inner growth of the Center as a psychotherapeutic community.

The Center is closed for a week every year to give the staff an

Chart D

St. Paul's Weekly Schedule

(Arabic numerals indicate the number of trainees as of January 1, 1961; the program has since been expanded to include sixteen trainees.)

Period	*Time*	*Monday*	*Tuesday*	*Wednesday*	*Thursday*	*Friday*	*Saturday*
I	8:15 to 8:55	Braille — 6 Shop Group — 4	Braille — 6 Housekeeping — 2 Shop — 2	Braille — 6 Fencing — 4	Braille — 6 Housekeeping — 2 Shop — 2	Braille — 6 Housekeeping — 2 Shop — 2	Group Fencing — 10
II	9:00 to 9:40	Braille — 4 Mobility — 2 Shop — 2 Counseling — 1 Housekeeping — 1	Braille — 4 Housekeeping — 2 Shop — 2 Counseling — 1 Free — 1	Braille — 4 Fencing — 6	Braille — 4 Mobility — 2 Housekeeping — 2 Shop — 2	Braille — 4 Kinesthetics — 2 Visualizing — 2 Shop — 2	Fencing — 4 Typing — 6
	9:40 to 9:55	COFFEE BREAK					
III	9:55 to 10:35	TDL Drill — 2 Mobility — 2 Counseling — 1 Housekeeping — 1 Spoken Communication — 4	TDL Drill — 2 Mobility — 2 Housekeeping — 2 Shop — 2 Counseling — 1 Free — 1	TDL Drill — 2 Imagery Stimulation — 4 Mobility — 2 Shop — 2	TDL Drill — 2 Mobility — 2 Shop — 2 Housekeeping — 2 Free — 2	TDL Drill — 2 Kinesthetics — 2 Shop — 2 Housekeeping — 2 Visualizing — 2	Fencing — 6 Typing — 4
IV	10:40 to 11:20	Mobility — 2 Visualizing — 2 Shop — 2 Free — 1 Spoken Communication — 3	Legislation Citizenship — 10 *Staff Meeting*	TDL Principles — 10	Mobility — 2 Shop — 2 Housekeeping — 2 Free — 4	Kinesthetics — 2 Visualizing — 2 Shop — 2 Housekeeping — 2 Free — 2 Counseling — E	Handwriting — 10

V	11:25 to 12:05	Mobility — 2 Visualizing — 2 Shop — 2 Counseling — 1 Free — 3	Mobility — 2 Shop — 2 Housekeeping — 2 Counseling — 1 Spoken Communication — 3	Imagery Stimulation — 6 Mobility — 2 Shop — 2	Gripe Session — 10	Spoken Communication — 10	Free — 10
	12:10 to 1:00	LUNCH					
VI	1:00 to 1:40	Personal Hygiene — 10	Typing — 6 Sensory Training — 2 Mobility — 2	Typing — 6 Sensory Training — 2 Housekeeping — 2	Typing — 6 Sensory Training — 2 Housekeeping — 2	Typing — 6 Sensory Training — 2 Visualizing — 2	
VII	1:45 to 2:25	Counseling — 1 Sensory Training — 2 Housekeeping — 1 Visualizing — 2 Mobility — 2 Shop — 2	Typing — 4 Sensory Training — 2 Mobility — 2 Housekeeping — 2	Typing — 4 Sensory Training — 2 Mobility — 2 Housekeeping — 2	Shop — 2 Typing — 4 Sensory Training — 2 Mobility — 2	Typing — 4 Sensory Training — 2 Kinesthetics — 2 Housekeeping — 2 *Psychosocial Meeting*	
VIII	2:30 to 3:10	Sensory Training — 2 Visualizing — 2 Shop — 2 Counseling — 1 Free — 3	Mobility — 2 Housekeeping — 2 Shop — 2 Counseling — 1 Free — 3	Housekeeping — 2 Mobility — 2 Shop — 2 Free — 4	Attitudes & Analysis — 10	Group Vocational Counseling — 10 *Staff Training*	
	3:10 to 3:25	COFFEE BREAK					

Period	*Time*	*Monday*	*Tuesday*	*Wednesday*	*Thursday*	*Friday*	*Saturday*
IX	3:25 to 4:05	Shop Group — 6 Visualizing — 2 Free — 1 Housekeeping — 1	Attitudes & Analysis — 10	Housekeeping — 2 Mobility — 2 Shop — 2 Free — 4	Mobility — 2 Housekeeping — 2 Shop — 2 Free — 4	Kinesthetics — 2 Visualizing — 2 Shop — 2 Housekeeping — 2 Free — 2	
X	4:10 to 4:50	Group Visualization — 10	Attitudes & Analysis — 10	Group Psychotherapy — 10	Self Appraisal — 10	Group Psychotherapy — 10 *Staff Group Psychotherapy*	
	5:35	DINNER					
XI	6:30 to 7:15	Spatial Orientation — 10					

opportunity to review the program, usually with the help of an expert in group dynamics. Thus self-evaluation and program evaluation are continuous. Every member of the staff is able to speak openly and freely about blindness, with no attempt to gloss over any difficulties. And as the individual staff members become aware of their own problems, they are encouraged to bring them to the staff psychiatrist.

Sixteen blinded persons come for training at a time, entering together in order to benefit from the use of group dynamics; the program, which is residential, lasts for sixteen weeks. The staff of some thirty people is alerted to give the utmost help and support during the early days and gradually to withdraw it in such a way that by the end of the sixteen weeks, the trainee is expected to be operating on his own strength.

A class in attitudes toward blindness is held three times a week during the sixteen-week training period. The attempt here is to bring the group face to face with all the implications of blindness and to give them some intellectual insight into its effects. This course is a rather direct attack on some of the psychological defenses, and its cumulative effect is strong. (Such a course should never, consequently, be attempted with blinded persons unless professional help is available to care for the reactions that may be aroused.)

The psychiatrist also conducts a weekly class in self-appraisal, directed toward a therapeutic approach to the trainees' problems. In its permissive atmosphere, this class has some of the quality of group psychotherapy, but it also contains a core of intellectual content, giving principles for the solution of the problems discussed.

A weekly "gripe session," in which the trainees can air complaints to the administrator, skims off "reality" problems, making the two weekly group psychotherapy sessions more effective. These sessions, led by the staff psychologist, allow the developing group to get deeply into an understanding and a working out of some of the problems which they have been considering intellectually in other classes.

Meanwhile, the trainees have the benefit of individual casework by the psychiatric social worker and individual counseling sessions with the psychologist and the psychiatrist.

These various approaches to the emotional problems involved in blindness make up one unified effort to assist each trainee in achieving true adjustment. With a strong professional teaching staff working at the same time on the development of the various skills, the sixteen-week course becomes a great push to restore total personality organization and to enable each person to return to his society as an integral and contributing member.

Sixteen weeks would seem to be a very short period for this complex work of "total adjustment" or "total reorganization." But, in addition to the total therapeutic environment, the very fact of blindness assists the process by removing some of the usual blocks to the uncovering of the ego. The trainee can admit to "nervousness" without self-devaluation, since everyone agrees with him that blindness is sufficient reason for feeling that way. Hence he is readier than he might otherwise be to accept the idea that he needs help in understanding his own reactions and in handling them.

The very fact of the low state of capability to which new blindness has reduced the trainee makes every bit of progress seem very evidently to be upward. Since he is advancing in his skill courses (and learning to do things that he probably never thought he could do), he is continually encouraged all during the period of self-evaluation.

It is certainly true that some blinded persons have been very successful in restoring their total personality organization without ever going near a rehabilitation center. But the problems involved in trying to carry out such a difficult and important task outside of a complete rehabilitation program are obvious. When circumstances make this necessary, the blinded person himself and those who are helping him need to keep in mind the essential elements of any real rehabilitation: retraining of the senses; regaining of skills and needed techniques (with the help of a home teacher capable of giving instruction in braille, a professional mobility therapist to teach travel, etc.); building up of inner strength through the proper support afforded by those around the blinded person — a support toward independence, given by someone capable of loving maturely; and, if it is available, social casework or psychotherapeutic help in facing the fact of blindness and reorganizing to overcome it.

It is worth repeating, in summary, that without an attack on the external problems of blindness, any work on the inner problems has little likelihood of success; and equally, without work on the inner problems — on total personality organization, work on restoring skills and capabilities is of little value. When both are carried out together, we are doing everything possible to help the blinded person achieve true adjustment to blindness, to give the person who has "died" to a sighted life the opportunity to live fully again in a sighted world.

17

Helping the Family

THROUGHOUT this book we have been considering the losses which blindness brings to the blinded person himself. But we need to remember that the members of the person's family also suffer a severe blow and that they too have lost a great deal — the losses varying with the relationship of each to the blinded person and his role in the family. These also are losses both in "reality" and psychological areas. Even if the blinded person was not the breadwinner of the family, financial problems will almost certainly arise, with many real difficulties affecting daily life. But these, disturbing as they may be, are in a sense unimportant compared to the emotional damage that may be done to those closest to the blinded person and to the whole family structure.

Anyone with a little imagination needs only to go through the list of losses to see what the effect of each might be: here is one of my family, someone close to me, who is no longer physically whole, who "lives in darkness," who has become strangely "different" and pitiable, etc. For, as the blinded person himself shares the general opinion of the public about blindness and blind persons — and it is the fact that he does so that causes a great deal, if by no means the whole, of the psychological damage involved in blindness — so too with his family. As the public generally unconsciously fears and rejects blindness by pitying and rejecting the blinded person, so too his family. And as sighted persons generally unconsciously feel ashamed of these reactions and so try to conceal them from themselves, so, but to a far greater degree, do the members of a blinded person's family, often setting up many and very disturbing tensions.

The members of the family, then, need any help that we can give them: help in understanding blindness, understanding what rehabilitation can actually accomplish for their relative and how they can be of real assistance, understanding and working through their own reactions to his blindness. This help cannot be as direct or by any means as complete as that which we can give the blinded person by rehabilitation training. Nevertheless, something at least can be done, and when the family is co-operative, a great deal can be.

It would be ideal if in the first days of a person's blindness his family could be given a realistic estimate of the situation and assisted to accept his blindness. This would help keep them on the one hand from giving him false hopes and encouraging him to seek useless "cures," and on the other from discouraging his undergoing rehabilitation training on the grounds of unnecessary expense, uselessness or needlessness. It would also be very useful if they could be shown at this time how best to help their relative regain confidence in his other senses and help him begin to train them and to regain simple skills.

Whether such early help can be given or not, a *family seminar* is a most valuable adjunct to rehabilitation training. Held at some convenient time during the last weeks of the training period, it can do a great deal to help the family understand what is necessary and thus facilitate the return of the blinded person to family life.

The family seminar at St. Paul's, for example, runs for two days. Talks by various members of the staff give a realistic picture of what the trainees are learning and of the progress of each course. Two of these talks present a condensed version of the course on attitudes toward blindness, and are followed by discussion periods having something of the character of group psychotherapy. The participants are thus given an opportunity to uncover their problems, and to see the way to solutions, in an atmosphere of "commonalty" with persons who have the same problems. Opportunity is also afforded for individual conferences, and a report is given to each family on the progress made by their relative.

Even in such a brief time, it is possible to give the persons who attend these seminars a great deal of information about the practical problems they and their blinded relative will have to face when he returns home, such as those concerning guides and readers, the need for keeping him in touch with programs and events, the factors to be kept in mind in spoken communication, and the possibilities of employment. Thus the family is in a position to make realistic plans for the future in relation to what the trainee will actually be able to do and what his own plans are. And besides, they will have gained at least the beginnings of insight into their own emotional reactions to blindness and those of their blinded relative.

In many cases this is all that is needed. In some, however, as was mentioned in connection with the restoration of independence, a great deal more work will be required if the family or some one member of it are to allow the blinded person to resume his independent status and role in the family. If it is possible, such a family might be put in touch with a trained caseworker from a general family agency — preferably one with some knowledge of the special problems of blinded persons. Caseworkers also may be able to do a great deal for families who cannot attend family seminars or whose blinded relatives have not taken rehabilitation training.

In some communities, it might also be possible for an agency for the blind to run a once-a-week evening course for the families of blinded people, which would serve somewhat the same purpose.

But since the question is mainly one of changing an attitude, an ingrained attitude toward blindness, some continuing work for families of blinded people is called for — to keep reminding them of what blindness really is and is not. Experience shows that a special newspaper, sent monthly or bimonthly into the homes of blinded persons, to be read by the members of the family to the blinded person (and to themselves), is of the greatest value here, both to them and to the blinded person himself.*

Such a paper should give news about blindness and blind people, and be so written as constantly (but between the lines) to drive home true ideas about blindness, a true "philosophy of blindness." It should not be a house organ for an agency, nor one devoted to news about group activities for blind persons. It should not limit itself to stories about blind persons who are sucesses, or culturally active, or models of citizenship. Its aim should be rather to inform the families of blinded persons about the wide range of activities engaged in by blind persons, showing the failures and mediocrities as well as the sucesses. Above all, it should show that blind persons are of all kinds and types, just as sighted people are — and so help to eliminate the various stereotypes and to communicate the idea that blind people are not "different." Here the education of the family broadens out into the education of the general public, to be discussed in the following chapter.

* The bimonthly tabloid-size eight-page newspaper *Listen,* published by the Catholic Guild for the Blind, 65 Franklin Street, Boston, and sent free to every blind person in Massachusetts as well as to others who request it, attempts to fulfill this function.

18

Educating the Public

The great need to do away with the false notions about blindness generally current and to replace these with true ones is obvious from what has been said already. As we have seen, this involves doing away with the "living in darkness" idea of blindness; it means doing away with the whole idea of "the blind" as helpless, dependent, pitiable people who are somehow "different" from the rest of us who make up "normal" society. It means replacing all these misconceptions and the stereotypes which result from them with accurate and concrete ideas about what blind people actually are doing — not only unusually talented blind persons, but average and below average ones as well. It means getting across the truth that blind people are individuals of all kinds and types, individuals who have a severe handicap certainly, but a handicap that can be overcome so as to make normal active living not the exception among blind persons but the general rule.

The first step in any program of public education along these lines must be the elimination of miseducation and misinformation. Our first job here is one of self-examination — not that we who work for the blind are insincere or responsible for false statements, but by giving wrong emphases in our publicity and making statements that are only partly true, we may be inadvertently confirming or adding to the misapprehensions of the general public. (In minority group tensions of the ordinary kind, the greatest danger comes from the demagogues who stir up feelings on both sides and bring tension to the point of explosion. It is interesting that in work for the blind one can find many people who believe that they can name the demagogues working on the out-group, stirring up bitterness among the blind. Yet there are few who advert to the existence of those unwitting "demagogues," the continuance of whose work depends on money raised by stirring up the "pitying prejudices" of the sighted public toward its blind members.)

We need, therefore, to ask ourselves such questions as these: Are there those among us, blind or sighted, who believe that blind people are "different" — different in their depth psychology, their personality needs, or abnormal in any way? Who believe that blindness is a handicap too great to be overcome? Who speak readily about the "normalcy" of blind persons but do not believe it? What drive in each of us attracted us personally to work with blind people? Do we ever speak of "our blind" or in any way act as if we owned them? Do we truly want blind persons to become independent of our agency? Of ourselves?

Unless we deeply believe what we teach, we will fail, whatever we say or have printed. Unconscious will speak to unconscious under our loudest words and between the lines of our writing, and will witness to what we really believe.

When we have examined ourselves, we can go on to examine our appeals and publicity, and to resolve henceforth to avoid giving false impressions of the pitiable plight of the blind. True, many blind persons are in financial need. But to make it appear true of all blind people as a necessary characteristic of blindness is not only to spread untruth, but also to render a disservice to all blind persons, rich and poor alike. True, some blind persons are helpless, and many of them are without anyone to help them. But we give an extremely misleading picture if we make this appear to be true of all. In this connection, we will avoid sounding the "darkness and light" theme entirely.

We will equally avoid the opposite extreme of building up notions about the wonderful abilities of blind persons, which gives an air of magic to blindness, or of seeming to suggest that "nature" provides any automatic compensation, either by way of some "sixth sense" or some unearthly "happiness."

Above all, we will avoid anything which would lead to generalizations about blind persons, enforcing already existing stereotypes or creating new ones, good or bad. The American Association of Workers for the Blind has already taken the lead in this campaign to clean up the publicity of organizations for the blind by drawing up a set of standards for fund-raising activities. The reader is urged to obtain a copy of these standards, either for the use of his own agency or for judging the publicity of the agencies in his community.

When we have thus eliminated false impressions and miseducation from our own publicity, we can understake the job of eliminating them from all public media. With regard to newspapers in particular, one very important aspect of this task is the avoidance of bad legislation seemingly in favor of the blind: the "gimme" or "handout" type of bill providing such things as free fishing licenses to blind fishermen or licenses to blind hawkers and peddlers. Such laws serve no useful purpose for the blind, conferring a dubious benefit on a very few while having a most unfortunate effect on the public attitude to the blind. They are products of a feeling about the blind which needs to be done away with, and they stimulate and reinforce this feeling. For when all the newspapers of a state, in small print or large, report the action on a bill in committee, its passage or rejection by the legislature or the governor, this provides the constant, repeated "hammer blow" type of publicity promoting the idea behind the bill — publicity that any advertising agency would envy because of the number of people it reaches and the subtlety with which it reaches them. When bills such as the above are introduced, hundreds of thousands of readers, even though they give these items only a passing glance, are reinforced in their feeling that blind people are helpless incompetents who vary their time between fishing and hawking wares (in beggar fashion) on street corners, and that none of them have the money to pay for licenses.

We should therefore do everything in our power to keep such bills from being introduced; if they are introduced nonetheless, we can fight them, giving our reasons for doing so (if we have the necessary moral courage).

Another means toward eliminating false publicity, but one that must be handled with care, is the letter of protest sent to newspapers, magazines, and radio and TV stations. Generally speaking, those responsible for the mass media never intend harm to blind persons, yet these media are continually giving harmful and misleading publicity to the blind, usually of a sob-sister nature. They use both fiction and news stories with trick endings — stories which seem completely pointless until the final sentence: "But, you see, Joseph is blind." They portray blindness wrapped in emotions of horror; they give a false halo to blind persons; they make heroes out of those who do ordinary things; they add an air of the occult to blindness; they picture the stereotype of the blind genius, the blind beggar or some other form. A favorite with comic strips, and with too many novels also, is to drag the hero or heroine through the bathos of loss of sight with final restoration.

And again, there is the "chummy" approach that uses first names or diminutives in referring to persons who are blind. Editors who take the greatest pains always to refer to Mrs. Eleanor Roosevelt as "Mrs. Roosevelt," will, after the lead paragraph, refer to Miss Helen Keller as "Helen" — a tip-off to an underlying, quite unconscious attitude of superiority and complacency. (This is not by any means confined to news writers; it is found among workers for the blind as well. Thus John Smith, the dignified and successful blind banker, becomes "Johnny" within five minutes after an introduction.)

Writers, editors and producers cannot be expected to know that all this sort of thing is harmful to the blind nor how harmful it is, unless they are told. A campaign to inform them would be most successful if organized on the basis of a monitoring and a clip service. The letters written should have no tone of bitter protest, none of the touchiness associated with minority group psychology; they should clearly be communications handing on needed information to responsible people who will presumably welcome it. And generally such information *will* be welcomed, if it comes in the form of a clear objective explanation of how and why their treatment of some subject was not in the best interests of blinded persons. Although writing such letters may seem to be closing the barn door after the horse has gone, it will alert editors and producers to be on guard against producing more material of the same nature.

The positive re-education of the public will be far more difficult to carry out. A total program would demand first of all extensive research, using all the existing material on group prejudice in other areas (such as that put out by the B'nai B'rith and the National Association for the Advancement of Colored People) in developing sociological knowledge about various types of prejudice, their origin and growth, and on the basis of this knowledge, examining the prejudices which exist against blind people. Then we could consider what would be the most effective means to do away with these prejudices, and work out a plan for concerted action by all agencies for the blind.

The very depth of the present prejudices, together with the massive problem of bringing about any change in a public concept, demands such an all-out program. Until it can be inaugurated, we certainly can and should do everything possible within our own spheres of influence to eliminate misinformation, to provide true and practical information about blindness and the "reality" problems of blinded persons, to educate the families and friends of blind persons, and to carry out, as occasion offers, publicity campaigns directed toward particular goals. But we cannot expect to achieve anything like the full effect desired until we can interest research centers in a complete study of the problem, and until workers for the blind are in a position to accept and co-ordinate their activities and to base a major campaign upon the findings.

Once more, our most effective means of public re-education is now, and always will be, the adjusted, mature blind person who in the course of his rehabilitation has been given insight into the problems which sighted people face in their approach to blindness and who is prepared to help them to a truer and fuller understanding.

Our work for the rehabilitation of blinded persons is itself, therefore, our most effective means of educating the society to which they return — of educating it to receive and accept blind people as the *persons* they are.

PART THREE

Special Problems of Various Groups

19

Special Problems of Different Age Groups

The study of blindness and rehabilitation that we have made so far — mainly in reference to the otherwise healthy person blinded in adult life — is typical in that the absence of complicating factors enables us to gain some insight into the problems of all blind persons and the general lines of all attempts toward their rehabilitation and integration into sighted society.

But not all blind persons become so in adult life. Some are born blind. Others lose their sight in infancy, early childhood or adolescence, and an increasing number become blind along with the process of growing old. Among the blind, as among the sighted population, a certain proportion suffer from other handicaps. And there is the large group whose handicap is not blindness but partial sightedness. We need now to consider the effects of these factors and the different approaches, skills and programs they may necessitate, beginning with the special problems of various age groups.

In analyzing the total situation of any individual blind person in any age group, we should take into account the fact that both the meaning and the effects of blindness vary in accordance with the age at which he lost his sight and whether he lost it quite suddenly or very gradually. For example, a person may have been on the border line of legal blindness* since early childhood, becoming legally blind

* "Legal blindness" is the term used to describe visual loss within a definition similar to that quoted in the footnote on page 29.

at thirty and totally blind at sixty; his situation will be quite different from that of the person who suddenly becomes totally blind at twenty or any other age. Even within the geriatric group, the person who becomes blind at ninety does not face the same situation as the one who loses his sight at sixty-five, and neither of them have the same problems as those of the aging person who has been blind since his middle twenties. A great distinction should be made, moreover, between those who became blind while their personalities were still in the process of formation and those who became blind in mature life. And the greatest distinction of all, as we shall see in Chapter 20, should be made between persons whose blindness is adventitious and those whose blindness is congenital.

1. THE PRESCHOOL GROUP

If any group among the blind needs a special approach and special skills, it is certainly this one. In our own day, fortunately, the professional treatment and care of these children has made remarkable advance.* One agency after another has established special services, and in many instances, agencies which had given little recognition to the need for professional training among workers with the adult blind were willing to recognize it here.

The American Foundation for the Blind offers constant professional consultative service to agencies, and in its preschool department has established a service making pamphlets and bibliographies available to parents as well as to workers in the field. Therefore it is unnecessary to go into detail here about the special needs of this group. Also the parents of a young blind child may, I hope, be guided to an understanding of blindness by this book. Some points, however, need to be stressed.

The first is the menace of the movable crib and playpen. No items in a household can do more to interfere with the sensory develop-

* Probably due in great measure to the scourge of retrolental fibroplasia in the United States from the 1940's to the mid '50's, which has also given great impetus to the move to integrate blind children in public schools.

ment, informational progress and normal growth of the blind child than these. When his crib or playpen is moved about from one place to another in a room, and one room to another and outside, the child is given no means of learning to orient himself. This little world of his which he feels under and around him is seldom twice in the same relationship to the sounds which he might gradually learn to recognize and identify, or to the smells, the feel of the sun coming through a window, the breeze from the door, or the heat from the radiator. The playpen particularly is not only nonoriented; it is also a solitary confinement cell, depriving the blind child of all the opportunities for exploration necessary if he is ever to learn about the world outside himself.

The child's crib, then, should be in a fixed place, nailed to the floor if necessary to keep the child himself from moving it about. And so with playpen (or high chair or any such convenience). But in general if would be far better if a blind child were *never* confined to any such thing except when asleep.

Opportunities for exploration must not cease with the playpen age, but must be continually developed and expanded. The constant attempt of the child to receive feedback must be encouraged, not only through his own exploration, but by satisfying his needs as they are expressed in the endless and baffling questions typical of children of this age. Growing blind children must be allowed to crawl at the crawling age, to wander at the wandering age, and to climb at the climbing age, and their curiosity must never be deadened but rather stimulated by every means.

What needs to be said beyond this can best be put in the form of a letter to the parents of a blind child. For it is not so much the child's problems as the parents' which must be dealt with if the child is to have a normal life.

TO THE FATHER AND MOTHER:

There are a great many things that you need to know in order that your child may have the normal life you want for him. There are things that you must know which other parents never have to worry about. In fact, you have to know them so that you won't have to worry about them.

You will get a great deal of help when you turn to the professional agencies for counsel — but make sure that they *are* professional. The majority of people in this work have no intention other than to do the best for the blind, including your child. Get counsel from us, but don't ever get dependent on us — and don't ever let your child get dependent on us.

Remember, he can make his way without undue dependence if, except for his blindness, he is normal. You may doubt that possibility at times — that he can really be normal and independent. But it might help you to remember that the author of this book is completely convinced of the possibility. Your youngster can grow with this handicap, adjust to it, live normally in a sighted society, and achieve the purpose for which God put him here. But a tremendous amount will depend on you, and on your willingness to let him do it.

You will certainly wish to learn as much as you can about blindness and its total meaning, and about all the possibilities of overcoming it — those already in existence and those that may be developed in the future. But more important are the things you need to know about one particular blind person, your child, and his reactions and feelings. You have to learn to distinguish his real thoughts and feelings from the ones which he may express, and also from those you may interpret as being his which really come from your own mind and heart.

This means that you, even more than do the rest of us, need to come to a mature understanding of yourself — because your adjustment to life and to the blindness of your child is so important to *his* adjustment. More than any other persons, you are involved in the total growth and the future of that child; if you fail to become sufficiently involved, he will lose the support he needs in growing; if you become too involved, you will choke his growth and stunt it.

You will need to know what your real attitude is toward your child. (Don't jump to that too quickly; certainly you love him, but there are other factors too.) And what is most important after this, and directly connected with it, you will have to know your own attitude toward blindness — not just the surface one, but the attitude that lies underneath.

These things may be hard for you to learn all by yourself. You can find some of them out, perhaps, by watching your own reactions when people talk about blindness, when they say the wrong thing, when they pity your child too much or reject him. But it may be that no matter how you try to discover your real feelings, you cannot do it alone. If so, there should be agencies in your neighborhood with trained personnel to help you.

Remember this: You love your child — but your love (if you are like the rest of us) is mixed, and other reactions are confused with it. It would be surprising if some of the emotions mixed with your love of your child did not have to do with his blindness.

Perhaps you can't admit this as a fact, but probably you can at least admit it as a possibility. Certainly you agree that (at least for a passing moment, and probably much longer) the news of his blindness was a terrible shock to you. Wasn't there perhaps a time of real revulsion at the thought of blindness in your child? And didn't you react when you first heard it with something of the reaction that bothers you so much now when you see it in other people? If you had those feelings, then perhaps you have some very guilty moments about it now, when you see *others* having the same feelings about your child. And just possibly you still have something of those feelings underneath. The thought that you might have needn't upset you; it is only human.

Possibly, too, there are still other feelings mixed up in your love for him. You might very well react from those instinctive feelings of shock and pity with feelings of possessiveness, a possessiveness which interferes with the fullest development of love. And just possibly, something in that little baby whom you felt everybody rejected reminded you of another baby whom you felt everybody rejected — yourself. If so, you may well have identified pretty completely with him; and no matter how much you may think you want to give him independence, you will spend a lot of time protecting him in one way or another from the cold world which has never given either of you very much love.

Do you see the possibility of your having certain mixed feelings in your love? You might do well to ask yourself just how you used to feel about handicapped persons (before your child was born or even conceived.) You might ask yourself how you felt about the handicapped children of others, and how you felt about the parents of handicapped children. And you might also ask yourself what kind of ambitions and expectations you had for the child you hoped would some day come along. All these are parts of the picture now, because they are parts of the whole situation into which you received the traumatic news that your child was blind.

Part of the situation, too, is the kind of feelings that you had in the past about heredity and hereditary "afflictions." This is true even if heredity has nothing whatsoever to do with your child's blindness (and the chances are very great nowadays that it has not.) If you once had vague ideas about "bad blood" coming down in a family, if you had all kinds of ideas about "afflictions," if you had vague feelings yourself about not being good (when you were three, or five, or ten years old), then all these things may still be disturbing factors which are somehow mixed up in your love for your child.

You may not like facing such possibilities, but if they exist, it is very important for you to recognize and overcome them.

For your whole effort must be toward a perfect adjustment to the blindness of your child, so that he and all your children may also have a perfect adjustment. With your adjustment must go a full and mature love for him and for all your children, a love which will tend toward their growth and independence — an independence even of you.

It is most important for you to keep in mind the difference between mature love and possessive love. The former frees, the latter strives always to hold, and thus never to let anything grow up and grow away. Possessive love is not truly love, but a neurotic substitute for love found in persons who have never really grown up. A part of it, with some people, is the false martyrdom by which they appear to suffer greatly for their children, but in reality they are using whatever they go through or do as another method of keeping their children dependent on them.

Now you may know without any doubt that you are free of this kind of loving, at least in its strongest forms. There are various degrees of it, however, and, if you are in any way unsure of your inner feelings, don't hesitate to find out about them. If they are interfering with your growth with your child, then the sooner they are corrected, the better.

If psychiatric problems are involved, probably you will need psychiatric help with them, whether directly from a psychiatrist or from a psychiatric social worker in one of the agencies for the blind. Just be wise enough to seek the psychiatric help that understands your spiritual needs as well. And when you are seeking spiritual help with any of these same problems, be sure that it is spiritual help that understands also your psychiatric needs. A combination of good spiritual and good psychiatric help may be needed to eliminate any lingering false feelings that your child's blindness is a form of divine retribution for something you may have done.

Don't be discouraged. Your child can grow to live a life of total adjustment to his total environment, loving God and his fellow men (both blind and sighted). His chances for doing this will be greatly enhanced if you, his parents, are both able to give to him a deep, mature, nonpossessive love — a love for him *as he is,* while making every attempt to aid him to grow to something stronger and completely independent, save for his dependence on God.

2. THE SCHOOL-AGE GROUP: EDUCATION, WHERE AND HOW?

Before discussing formal education, let me point out that some of the most successful congenitally blind men I have known were those whose parents gave them every opportunity to be real boys. One loving set of parents did not know that their totally blind son was borrowing a bicycle which he rode along highways with his sighted friends; they little realized that he spent some of his summer days diving off forbidden docks with his young peers; and they were greatly upset when the neighborhood policeman brought him home one day after catching up with him as he ran away from a boys' ball game on a "no trespassing" park lawn. Another boy, now a successful blind judge, tells of the horror of the grownups when they caught him and his sighted brother crawling along the third-story steel girders of a building in the process of construction. I myself, in answer to a request for information as to some special present for a twelve-year-old boy on a Western ranch who had lost his sight, once recommended a .22 rifle.

For, despite the qualms of parents, blind boys and blind girls must be given the opportunity for wholeness in their growing years if they are to be whole adults.

Education presents to us the special problems "Where should it be?" and "How should it be done?" Whatever may be said about segregation of the blind, it is well to remember that segregation for purposes of education presents a special case. Without segregation in the past, education of the blind would never have reached its present high position. The great and necessarily segregated residential schools for the blind have had a tremendous influence in developing the education of blind persons, not only in this country but throughout the world.

There remains the question, however, of the position of these schools today and in the immediate future. Are they the place for the education of all blind children all the time, of some blind children all the time, of all blind children some of the time? What is the place of the blind child in regard to them? Should they be completely done away with? To work toward an answer, we must examine some of the possible ways of educating blind children.

The *residential segregated school* is the classic center for the education of the blind child. It is a school for blind children and only blind children. There the children live and are schooled throughout the school year, returning home for vacation periods and (according to the policy of the school and the proximity of the home) for a greater or lesser number of week ends.

One variation is to have some non-resident children in such a school — children who live near enough so that arrangements may be made for them to attend the school by day and return to their homes when the classroom day is done.

Still another variation chiefly for high school is to have the residential school serve merely as a *residence,* with the students going to a public (or parochial) school during the day and returning to the school for the blind when their classes are over.

There are also *segregated public (and parochial) school classes.* The children live at home, and during school hours they attend a so-called "braille class" of the segregated variety throughout the school day.

Still another possibility is for the child to attend regular public or parochial school classes along with sighted children of his age and grade, but to go at regular intervals during the day to a "resource room" or "special aids center" in the school, where an expert teacher furnishes him with the special learning devices he needs (including braille). (This is the so-called "*integrated braille class*" system.)

Then there is the still more recent development of attendance at *regular public (or parochial) school classes with a special aids consultant* (the "itinerant teacher") who visits the school as needed to give her aid directly to the child or to his regular teachers.

Occasionally also the experiment is tried of sending blind children to regular public (or parochial) school classes, even though nobody in the school has any training to help them with special aids.

Again, an individual child may be educated through some combination of these methods (in his kindergarten years, for example, going to a regular public school, transferring to an integrated braille class for a few years, then being enrolled at a residential segregated school for classes, and perhaps going out by day to a public high school). In addition, there are such possibilities as educating the blind child at a residential nonsegregated school — sending him to an ordinary boarding school for sighted children, etc.

Another factor that enters into the complete picture is the availability of a summer camp for blind children. Such a camp has the qualities of "residence" and "segregation" which the classic schools

have. It seems generally agreed by educators of the blind that such
camps are bad for children from the residential segregated schools
(although some say they are necessary at some stages of develop-
tain blind children educated *outside* the residential segregated schools
ment). Some educators see them as ideal, however, for giving to cer-
some of the advantages of these schools.

Discussion of the benefits of the various methods of educating blind children has led to some heated arguments over the years. At present, it seems to be agreed at least that no one can call any method necessarily the best for *all* blind children. Like so many discussions, this one issues in great part from the feeling of those concerned, or at best from their personal experiences. It would be extremely helpful if some broad and objective study could be made to show the results of the different forms of education.

From an *a priori* standpoint, the residential segregated school has strong arguments in its favor and strong arguments against it.

In favor of such a school it is said that blind children are "deviates" with a deviation so strong that they (1) cannot be understood and aided in education by their own parents or their own families; (2) cannot be accepted as normal by classroom teachers, who will either pamper or neglect them; (3) cannot be accepted as normal by their fellow students if those students have sight; (4) cannot receive outside the residential segregated school all the added instruction, cultural aids, etc., necessary for them to offset the deprivations resulting from blindness; (5) cannot be educated without close, almost individual attention during and outside class hours; and (6) cannot, without lasting damage to personality structure, be exposed at an early age to the hopelessness of attempting to meet sighted competition.

Arguments against the residential segregated school are based both on the fact that it is "residential" and on the fact that it is "segregated." That it is residential means that the children must be "transplanted," that they must be taken out of their homes. That it is segregated means that they must be grouped as blind children, that they must be in a situation removed from normal contacts with sighted children.

Educating a blind child in a residential segregated school may consequently have serious and lasting ill effects, by (1) robbing the child of the natural love, or at least of the recognition of that love, of his parents; (2) taking from the parents the opportunity to understand their child during his growing years; (3) separating the child from his brothers and sisters, thus decreasing opportunities for mutual understanding and love; (4) creating a gap between the blind child and his sighted parents or sighted brothers and sisters which may never be entirely closed; (5) separating the child from a sighted world and thus making it impossible emotionally to educate him for that sighted world; (6) damaging the child's ability to compete and co-operate with the sighted, as he will have to do in future years, by taking him away from that competition and co-operation during his formative years; (7) building up in the child the strong minority feelings which segregation can develop; (8) making him (and other blind children) appear different in the eyes of sighted children, thus robbing him of future opportunities to be accepted among them; and (9) in general decreasing the number and quality of his experiences.

Each side in this argument is inclined to think that the opposing arguments are overdrawn (and certainly they are, with the emphasis and universality with which they are often stated). But each side is bound to recognize the value in some of the arguments advanced by the other group. Because of this, in each group of educators there are some persons who try to take all the arguments into account. The result is beneficial; the residential segregated schools try to keep up a strong liaison with the home, to send the children home as often as possible, and to arrange as many opportunities as they can for normal situations with sighted children; and the opponents try to work into their systems as many of the advantages of the residential segregated schools as they can.

No specific and certain answer is possible to the question "Where should blind children be educated?" It can be said that *some* children cannot get all the education requirements they need outside the residential segregated school, and also that not every child need be exposed to the disadvantages of that type of schooling. The difficulty arises when one tries to determine the best type of schooling for a particular blind child.

The solution can best be worked out by having a group of persons who know the whole situation assist the parents in making the decision. Such a group must have at its disposal a thorough analysis of the available resources for schooling, with the strong and weak points of each clearly set forth; a study of the family situation and of the relationship of the blind child to the other members of the family; a knowledge of the particular child, with his emotional and intellectual strengths and weaknesses, as well as any other factors which might alter the picture, and some sort of estimate as to his future vocational goals and opportunities (when he is of an age for these to influence the choice of schooling); and also a knowledge of the general community from which the child comes and to which he will be returning.

Higher Education

What we have been saying about education applies without distinction (although with different force of emphasis) to all schooling from nursery or kindergarten days on through high school. But with higher education there is no choice of methods, since no segregated education is available *or desirable* on this level. The question here is not "where" or "how," but rather "whether or not" in each particular case.

For some blind persons, higher education can be of great value. The selection of which persons should go on for degrees must, however, be based not only on intellectual and personality factors, but very much on the basis of realism — on the reality goals which the blind person has chosen, the possibility of his accomplishing them, and the frustration which will result if these goals are not achieved.

Higher education is a real necessity in many cases. Without it, obviously, some could not reach their vocational goals. (The blind young man who is out to be an attorney is a good example.) A graduate-level education can also be of advantage in reaching vocational goals for which it is not actually a necessity. Thus the blind college graduate is in a better position to compete with a sighted college graduate for a particular job if he has a master's or doctor's degree, while the sighted person has neither, than he would be if both of them were equal in educational background.

The possibility of blind persons achieving success in higher studies has been well demonstrated by blind students.

But it should be pointed out that for some blind persons college education is harmful, even though they are able to assimilate their college learning and achieve the highest marks. It is true that college opens up some new vocational opportunities; but equally true (and not so widely recognized) is the fact that it effectively narrows the field of vocational possibilities. It is almost impossible for the blind man who has completed college to go, without severe loss of self-confidence and feelings of frustration and inferiority, to a factory job, to a refreshment stand opportunity, to a transcribing job, or to any one of the hundred jobs which do not call on his college education. This statement may be countered by many who will say that this should not be so, that to say it shows a misunderstanding of the purpose of college, that there is snobbery in any such notion. Whether or not it *should* be so is another question, but I am firmly convinced that in fact it *is* so, and that as a result of a failure on the part of many of us to recognize it, certain blind college graduates are living rather unhappy lives today.

Whether on the nursery level or on the university level, therefore, the education of the blind person, like that of the sighted person, should be that best calculated to allow him to lead a normal and contributing life, with an emotional and intellectual balance which will make him at home in the world as we know it, while he prepares, along with the rest of us, for his home in the world to come.

3. THE YOUNG ADULT GROUP

The situation of the adult blinded after reaching maturity has already been discussed at length. But the person blinded in childhood or adolescence, and in particular the young adult blind from his earliest years, who has just finished his education and is facing life in the world, has special problems. Whatever his education, he is bound to have special difficulties in facing the problems of all young people — in finding and adjusting to a job and in adjusting to all the problems of adult life. These difficulties are especially severe, however, for the young person who has been given a segregated education, who has been among blind people for all his life so far, who has learned to cooperate and compete only with blind children, and who for the first time is out in a sighted world.

Some of the special difficulties of this group with regard to work and "vocation" generally have already been mentioned. The necessary adjustment covers much more than finding and holding a job. But even here, there was a time not so long ago when the schools for the blind condemned the placement agencies for not finding jobs for the graduates, and the placement agencies blamed the schools for not properly preparing the students.

In any case, this period of young adulthood is one of great and difficult adjustment to greatly changed circumstances. It has even been suggested that some kind of special rehabilitation center should be set up for graduates from classes for the blind, to prepare them directly for employment and adult life. This suggestion does not give due consideration to the work that the schools have already done in handling this difficult problem, nor would the establishment of such centers seem feasible. Instead, agencies for the adult blind should begin to train special caseworkers equipped to help with the many and grave problems which face young people during this adjustment period.

Without some such help at this time, segregated recreation programs and segregated work programs may begin to hold a special fascination. Young graduates of schools for the blind who during their school years made all kinds of resolutions that theirs would be a life in the world of sighted people find themselves turned back by the frustrations that they meet, or drawn back to a segregated existence, simply because there seems no other place for them. It is easy in such circumstances for the first pains of bitterness to take their toll; during this time many adjusted or potentially adjusted young people become turned in on themselves, steeped in the hopelessness of ever becoming a real part of the sighted world. And once such young people are drawn into segregated programs, it is usually too late to do very much about salvaging them.

Marriage of Blind Persons

One of the major problems for the young adult, blind or sighted, is obviously the question of marriage. And anyone experienced in the field of work with the blind knows that one does not need to be a marriage counselor in order to be asked questions about the advisability of marriage by blind persons.

Some people are so overcome by the thought of blind persons entering into marriage that they actually seem to believe that such a marriage would be immoral (and perhaps sexually perverse.) Others seem to feel that it is nice for blind persons to "marry each other" (although an old saw among blind persons says that it is "better to have windows on at least one side of the house," and for years segregated schools for the blind carried on an inner segregation of boy from girl lest marriages be encouraged).

Often enough, those who attempt to discuss the principles involved confine themselves to externals. They take up, for example, the question of the wife's ability to keep house or the husband's ability to earn an income for the family; or, if the question of children arises, they discuss it in terms of the ability of the blind parent to recognize childhood diseases or to change diapers. But other and more basic factors are frequently overlooked.

Hundreds of successful marriages prove that blindness of itself is no reason for not getting married. Yet generally speaking, reality factors like those just mentioned seem to reinforce the idea that at least one of the parties to the marriage should have sight. Family unity, family privacy, and family independence all suffer severe tests if both husband and wife are blind. The family unit may have to look for too much help outside itself; neighbors or relatives are brought into family matters — if only for the reading of mail or bills. This is particularly true if there are children to be brought up. Here sight is sometimes essential, and it is ordinarily to be expected that this be the sight of at least one of the parents. Yet we must recognize the fact that rare couples, both blind, have married and successfully brought up fine families.

More important than the so-called reality factors, however, are the emotional factors in the marriage, particularly the factor of emotional maturity — which blindness in itself neither gives nor takes away. The emotional implications of blindness to the person himself and to his sighted public cannot be overlooked in discussing this question of marriage. From what has been said on the subject in the first two parts of this book, we can conclude that marriage by a blind person and marriage *to* a blind person both call for *at least* the same degree of emotional *maturity* (we are not discussing *age*, and the two are not synonymous) as that of a sighted person to a sighted person. Yet persons too frequently enter into marriage without having adjusted to their blindness, and some are driven into marriage by their failure to make a good adjustment. Again, sighted persons too frequently enter into marriages with blind persons out of motives of pity, of protectiveness, or of overidentification — disguised though these motives may have been from one or both partners.

The emotional factors concerned in the upbringing of children should be given thorough consideration by the blind person about to marry and by the person about to become engaged to someone who is blind. The question is that of the ability of the blind parent to keep his role as a parent, to retain the respect that is due him, when the children to come will be old enough to recognize that their parent is "different." Included here is the ability to bring up the children in such a way that they will have a complete part in their peer group and a pride in their parents *as parents,* with their own lives being in no way warped or distorted. This is not at all an impossible problem for the blind parent who is truly balanced and mature (although it may still involve some of the difficulties inherent in minority group psychology).

Leaving aside questions of hereditary blindness, then, there is no reason whatsoever why a mature blind person, trained in the techniques which make him a part of the community, should not marry. Men and women of this kind have made highly successful husbands and wives and equally successful parents. But emotional maturity is of the essence.

Hereditary factors. The question of the marriage of blind persons brings with it the question of hereditary factors in blindness.* The medical aspects of this problem are thoroughly dealt with in medical literature. For the person with a general interest in the field of blindness, two points need to be made.

First, it should be clearly recognized that some forms of blindness are no more capable of being passed on to the next generation than is a broken leg. A great amount of blindness caused by accidents and by other causes, including certain diseases, is definitely *not* hereditary.

Second, other causes of blindness *are* familial, and more or less likely to recur in succeeding generations. Even if the disease itself is not clearly hereditary, it may be that there is an inherited tendency toward it. Ophthalmology in the last generation has learned a great deal about the hereditary character of certain eye conditions. Some few eye anomalies formerly suspected of being inherited have now been shown not to be,† while the hereditary nature of others is now more clearly known.

Before deciding on marriage, every couple who suspect that one or the other of them might be a carrier of blindness genes should, therefore, consult with a competent ophthalmologist for as complete a picture of the situation as possible. There is great variation in the method of inheritance from one blinding eye disease to another, and the ophthalmologist must make his findings not alone on the nature of the individual disease, but on the family history as well.

* The moral implications of the marriage of persons likely to pass on blindness to their offspring should be taken up by the individual with his spiritual director.

† Thus, a few short years ago, a great many cases of "congenital cataract—cause unknown" led the doctors to a study of the family tree and left them with the suspicion that there was a hereditary factor. The recent discovery that rubella in the pregnant mother sometimes causes congenital cataracts gave the answer to many of these cases.

4. THE OLD-AGE GROUP

An extremely important category for special consideration in our times is the geriatric or old-age group. Present statistics show that at least five and perhaps six out of every ten blind persons in this country are over sixty-five years old, and there is strong reason to expect an increasing proportion in the years ahead. For even if the proportion of elderly persons in the general population reaches a constant around 1970, as is predicted, their actual numbers will continue to increase. With the conquest of many factors causing blindness in children and young people, it is even possible that unless spectacular gains are made in overcoming the factors causing blindness in old age, the field of work with the blind may in great part become a subdivision of geriatrics.

The age of sixty-five is taken as the basis for statistics, since one can presume that most of the geriatric group will be above this age and relatively few under it. But old age cannot be measured simply by years of life or physiological change. Psychological and sociological factors enter in as well: the concept of "old age" is changing very rapidly in our day, and in two quite different ways. On the one hand, industry is setting its retirement age earlier and setting lower limits for those accepted for new employment. On the other hand, the life expectancy of the average American has been greatly lengthened, and people are now applying for entrance into old-age homes at least ten years later than they used to. In New York City, for example, the average age of first admissions to old-age homes moved from sixty-five to seventy-five years in slightly over a decade.

Old age, then, is in many ways a relative term. For our purpose here, we can best think of old age not so much in terms of years as of "wearing out" (and/or "rusting out"). Even before a person moves into the period when he could be considered a member of the geriatric group, he begins to feel a multiple loss, to suffer in some sense a multiple handicap. Physically, there has been a gradual loss of tonus, a change in metabolic functioning (some experts in geriatrics are attempting to define the "geriatric group" as those who have reached the advanced catabolic stage). Muscle strength and muscle tone are not what they were. At some stage, there comes a skeletal loss — actual loss of height and of teeth (those interested in geriatrics are putting increased emphasis on this dental loss). There is an increasing loss in the whole sensorium, a "sensory deficit," and with all this comes a loss in equilibrium, contributing to a great loss of mobility.

Along with these physical losses come others even more important to some people. The loss of contemporaries, the loss of one's accustomed world due to the rapidly changing conditions of our times — all may lead to a loss of interest in events and even in people. And, making it more difficult to "keep up," the years may bring a loss of learning speed and of abstractive power.

In our civilization, since wisdom and age are no longer equated, there is a serious status loss. With industry giving more and more of its work to the young, there may be the loss of a career. Independence may go by degrees or suddenly, and financial security be taken away. Millions of elderly persons in the United States are now attempting to live out their lives on an income which is less in terms of the adjusted dollar than was that of the WPA worker in the depths of the Great Depression.

Worst of all, perhaps, age usually brings a twofold loss of love: of persons to love and of those who will return one's love. With all this, it is not astonishing that in many cases the aged lose motivation and even time sense. All these losses mean a gradual stripping of all that one has known and been. Some elderly persons are "detached" in the sense that they seem to have been flung off by our accelerating world. Others may accept the enforced detachment as a preparation for the future, a peaceful dying to earthly goals. For them, old age may become a peak, with the world lying below it. The finite may gradually lose its importance and the infinite ahead take on something of the interest of a new venture. All the partings already endured may make the possibility of reunion all the more eagerly anticipated, and during the time of waiting, they may enjoy the absence of pressure and the sense of satisfaction in work accomplished.

Obviously, blindness has a different meaning for a person who has already undergone many or all the losses of old age than it does for the child, the young or middle-aged adult. The old person brings a very different attitude to his blindness: if not resigned to physical difficulties and deprivations, at least he is accustomed to them. Society does not expect so much from him; his age group is not expected and does not expect itself to compete; there is no "disgrace" involved in being blind. In fact, some persons in the geriatric group not only take their blindness for granted, but even seem to take a certain pride in it, almost as if it were a badge of distinction.

Thus to the extent that a person has really entered into the geriatric era, blindness may be less of a handicap than it is for younger people. But to the extent that a person has become advanced in years but has not accepted the losses involved in old age, or is so young in heart as to be leading an active life in spite of them, blindness may come as more of a handicap than to the physically younger person. Chart E attempts to outline these two possibilities in reference to each of the losses of blindness.

This does not mean, of course, that there are two completely separate groups in the geriatric category: each loss will affect each individual in accordance with his own personality and circumstances. But generally there will be the more or less negatively resigned and there will be those who try to fight against both old age and blindness. And it will only be the strong personality in the strong (though perhaps frail) body who can accept all these "dyings" and live out his years in peaceful and positive happiness.

One very practical question in each individual case will be whether blindness or old age is the blinded person's primary handicap and, consequently, whether he should be aided primarily by a worker for the blind or by a worker in geriatrics. Either way, it becomes increasingly important that workers in the field of geriatrics should understand the meaning of blindness and have some recognition of what

Chart E

The Effect of the Losses of Blindness on the Geriatric Group

Loss	*Mitigated*	*Enhanced*
(1) Physical integrity	When physical losses already expected and accepted. Feelings about sex differentiation of *relatively* minor importance, their meaning different.	When it increases feelings of disturbed integrity caused by resentment at other physical losses and makes situation seem more hopeless.
(2) Confidence in remaining senses	When sensory deficit has already been experienced and accepted over the years.	When it adds to the feeling that outside world is slipping away — new learning becomes impossible.
(3) Reality contact	When inclination already exists to float gently away into a pleasant past.	When it finally upsets precariously clung to contact with reality.
(4) Visual background	When mainly living in memories.	When it adds to the monotony of old-age situation.
(5) Light security	When it merely adds to accepted sensory deficit.	When it adds connotations of "lightlessness" to real loneliness.
(6) Mobility	When it merely adds to already accepted loss of mobility from other causes.	When such mobility and activity as were still possible were important for mental and physical health.
(7) Techniques of daily living	When dependence on others already accepted.	When independence still clung to, and daily pattern is upset; difficulty of learning new

Loss	Mitigated	Enhanced
		skills makes continued independence seem almost impossible.
(8) Ease of written communication	When so detached as not even to be interested in the daily paper.	When correspondence with scattered friends and family or reading is an important factor.
(9) Ease of spoken communication	If conversation mainly with small group aware of visual difficulties.	When conversation and communication with other people is an important part of life.
(10) Informational progress	Very much so for those living mainly in memories.	More than any other may separate individual from his world, bringing loss of prestige, of motivation, of taking any interest in affairs.
(11) Visual perception of the pleasurable	When living mainly in memories; when vivid experiences and sight of things has been gradually dimming; when process of detachment advanced.	When still taking pleasure in persons and things in the present, and so many other sources of pleasure are already cut off.
(12) Visual perception of the beautiful	As for younger group: severe for those who possess strong love of the beautiful, otherwise almost nonexistent.	
(13) Recreation	As not having same importance as for younger people — especially for working off physical energy.	When need has grown to fill time — much more difficult to find adequate forms.
(14) Career, vocational goal, job opportunity	For the vast majority who have already given up their career, no longer have voca-	For the few for whom blindness puts a final end to continued usefulness and career.

	tional goal and would not have a job in any case.	
(15) Financial security	Expenses incident to blindness may be less: some already incident to old age; less necessity to spend in order to keep up. May be less need of income, greater opportunity to plan for lesser income; has not the same social meaning.	When any additional expense adds intolerable burden to an income already too small for decent living; many older persons in this category.
(16) Personal independence	When dependence of old age already accepted.	When dependence of old age already resented and fought against.
(17) Social adequacy	When blindness accepted by the person and his society as something to be expected.	When still fighting to keep active role in society, and blindness finally "puts him on the shelf."
(18) Obscurity	Generally, for the whole geriatric group. "Visibility" the same, though not obvious for the homebound. Social aspect does not have same meaning — blindness may seem acceptable and even a kind of merit badge.	
(19) Self-esteem	When self-estimate made by a yardstick suited to their age; self-image also has been changing to adjust to advancing years.	When self-estimate still made on young and active basis, another loss is added to already severe losses — and when self-image has not adjusted.
(20) Total personality organization	If blindness does not mean the series of traumatic blows that it brings to younger people.	If old age itself has already affected personality organization. May hasten flight to unreality and world of memories.

to do about it, and that workers for the blind have sufficient knowledge of geriatrics to make the proper referrals when geriatric difficulties are noticed.

In the United States, elderly blind persons are now tending to seek out homes for the *aged* rather than homes for the *blind*, while homes for the elderly blind are finding themselves with empty beds. At least in the geriatric group, it seems that we are on our way to achieving integration. If so, it does not mean the end of geriatric problems for workers for the blind; it means instead a total rethinking of what we should be doing for elderly blind persons, with a far greater emphasis on what can be done in the way of "geriabilitation" to equip them for living under nonsegregated conditions.

20

The Congenitally Blind

The major distinction to be taken into account in working with blind persons is that between those who *ever* effectively had the use of their sight and those who did not — between the adventitiously and the congenitally blind. The whole sensorium of a once sighted person is organized in terms of sight. How that of a congenitally blind person is organized is still a matter for research and speculation, but we know enough to be sure that it is radically different.

Consequently, while the depth psychology of such a person is the same as that of an adventitiously blind person or anyone else, his "surface psychology" — his mechanism for the reception of ideas — has rather a different pattern. As the philosophical dictum puts it, *Nihil est in intellectu quod non prius fuerit aliquomodo in sensu,* which might be translated as "Nothing is in the psyche which was not first in some way in the sensorium." Since a congenitally blind person has never seen, he cannot visualize, nor does he form visual concepts. A sighted and once sighted person forms his ideas about reality into a mainly visual pattern; a congenitally blind person forms his ideas in some other way.

A congenitally blind person has to use "sighted" language and modes of thought, somehow adapting them to his experience. He has no adequate means, therefore, of giving sighted persons any direct understanding of the sensory terms in which he forms his ideas. For much the same reason, it is hard to see how attempts to estimate how

Chart F

The Deprivations of the Congenitally Blind Compared with the Losses of the Adventitiously Blind[1]

Loss or Deprivation	*Congenitally*	*Adventitiously*
(1) Physical integrity	In his formative years he knows that he is "different" — subject to terrific psychological pressures. More subject to blindisms.	A
(2) Confidence in remaining senses	A Never used sight as a censor. Built up information on remaining senses.	
(3) Reality contact	A Reality contact established in other ways (if he is allowed any freedom of investigation) — except perhaps for tendency to verbalism.	
(4) Visual background	A So far as he may possess far greater appreciation of other sensory backgrounds.	A So far as visualization is concerned.
(5) Light security	A So far as no connection made between lightlessness and lovelessness.	
(6) Mobility	Has always relied on other senses and learned to interpret information they give him.	Potential advantage to person blinded in adult life of retained powers of visualization.

[1] A means a possible advantage to one or other group.

(7) Techniques of daily living	A Has learned them as he grows up.	But visual experience potential advantage in learning new techniques for new situations.
(8) Ease of written communication	A So far as braille is concerned — usually trained in it from childhood as one means of reading and writing. No good means of teaching acceptable handwriting yet devised.	A So far as handwriting is concerned.
(9) Ease of spoken communication		A Because of ability to visualize a social situation; better control of gestures and facial expressions.
(10) Informational progress	A Because of longer experience in interpreting information of other senses.	A Because of broader experience, fund of experiential knowledge, powers of visualization to help assimilate new experiences.
(11) Visual perception of the pleasurable	A From possibility of more adequate substitution.	A From possibility of visualization.
(12) Visual perception of the beautiful	A From possibility of having better trained auditory (and perhaps other) perception of beauty.	A From possibility of visualization.
(13) Recreation	A From greater keenness in use of other senses.	A From once having seen sports played.

Loss or Deprivation	*Congenitally*	*Adventitiously*
(14) Career, etc.	Less possibility of experience usually makes for less opportunity.	A
(15) Financial security	No general statement possible. Blinded person may have savings, but also may have spent them in "sickness expenses" of new blindness.	
(16) Personal independence	A Possibility in reality independence, from long experience in overcoming certain obstacles. But not probably in inner independence, because of almost certain great difficulties in formative years.	A Probably in inner independence.
(17) Social adequacy		A As his broader experience, especially visual experience, is made use of. Less likely to have blindisms.
(18) Obscurity	No general judgment possible as to whether it is easier to be brought up with this problem or to have suddenly to face it.	
(19) Self-esteem	A Insofar as does not suffer from any contrast between present self-estimate and self-image with a previous one.	A Insofar as self-estimate and self-image originally formed under far less serious emotional pressures.
(20) Total personality organization	A Insofar as has not suffered severe blow of sudden multiple deprivation.	A Insofar as emotional problems brought by blindness came to him only after personality formed.

early the effective use of sight begins could ever be successful. Does a person who lost his sight at six months, a year, two years, really remember colors and visual forms, or to what extent does his later imagination, supplied with the words for these sensations, make him think he does?

But whether or not agreement will ever be reached as to whether a child blinded at, say, eighteen months, is to be considered as congenitally or adventitiously blind, there is no doubt that there is a real and qualitative difference between one kind of blindness — its meaning, its effects, and the way in which they should be dealt with — and the other. For, besides this radical difference in "surface psychology," what are "losses" in one case are "deprivations" in the other — and a loss is not the same as a deprivation.

Chart F attempts to evaluate this radical difference, indicating in each case (by the letter A) where the "advantage" would seem to be on one side or the other. The purpose is not to answer the insoluble (though frequently asked) question "Which is better — to be born blind or to become so?" but to bring out the real differences between the problems of the two groups and the different lines along which we should try to help each of them.

One complicating factor that should be taken into account in evaluating any individual situation is the extent to which the congenitally blind person has received a segregated education. On the one hand, certain characteristics may be due to this segregation rather than to congenital blindness in itself. On the other hand, we may be blaming the person's education for consequences which actually result from the fact that he has never seen. And of course, home circumstances, degree of education, opportunities, and the person's individual temperament all have to be taken into account.

But the primary determinant in our work for such a person should be that he is congenitally rather than adventitiously blind. The fact that agencies have not generally recognized this vital distinction in the past is no reason for our not doing so in the future.

21

Special Problems of Those with Additional Physical Deficiencies

1. BLINDNESS AND OTHER MAJOR HANDICAPS

AT THIS point in our study, it may be useful to see how the rehabilitation of blind persons fits into the general picture of rehabilitation work now emerging from the rapid progress of the last decades in various fields. Such a picture will help to clarify our ideas about work with the blind, and it will also guide us in our attempts to aid those who suffer from some other handicap in addition to blindness.

Major handicaps may be classified as (1) *physiatric* (neuromuscular, musculoskeletal, cerebrovascular and cardiovascular, etc. — including, for example, major amputations and all forms of paralysis); (2) *upper sensory* (deafness and "hard-of-hearing," blindness and partial sightedness); (3) *habituative and addictive* (alcoholism and drug addiction); (4) *mental and emotional*; and to make the list complete, we should include (5) *penal* (habitual crime), although this last falls outside the scope of this book.

What we have just seen about blindness is true of the other upper-sensory handicaps: there is a qualitative difference between being congenitally or adventitiously handicapped. And with all handicaps, the impact is quite different on those who have them from birth or childhood, on those struck by them in "the prime of life," and on those struck when they have entered the geriatric period. Since the impact is different, "what to do about it" is different too. Making up for a deprivation is not the same as restoring or substituting for abilities, skills, personality organization that have been lost. We should therefore think of work with handicapped children as "habilitation" rather than rehabilitation if we are clearly to distinguish its special problems from those of work with other groups. Of course, some work with children, and much more with those in the young adolescent group, will be rehabilitation. Nevertheless, much confusion and many mistakes will be avoided if this distinction is kept in mind as basic.

And similarly, those who have entered the geriatric period are not and should not be expected to function with the same efficiency as a young or middle-aged adult. Work with this group in relation to any handicap should therefore be considered as "geriabilitation," to keep its particular problems and goals distinct from those of rehabilitation properly so-called.

Space does not permit us to go into the impact of the first, third and fourth types of handicaps on the younger or the geriatric group, but we should at least see something of the common characteristics of all these types as they affect the middle group, those requiring rehabilitation.

All have two effects in common: a loss of "self" and a loss of relationships with other people. All, that is, strike a cruel blow at self-image and test ego strength to the full (or bring about its collapse). And all put the individual in a new relationship of "difference" to "normal" people (which means, with most of these handicaps, not only that the person seems "different" to himself, but that "normal" people are completely at a loss to understand the meaning and the effect of the handicap).

All four kinds of handicap also involve a "dying"—but of quite a different kind in each type, and different in the subdivisions of each type. For example, the "death" of a newly blinded adult to his sighted life and his sighted self is something quite other than the ego destruction of the addict in whom the wish and the "not-wish" for this destruction coexist. And neither is the same as the "death" to normal active life of the paraplegic.

The recognition of any major handicap as an inevitable fact brings an initial period of shock followed by one of "mourning." Yet here again, the "mourning" is of quite a different kind, for example, with the arm amputee and with the psychotic person on the hazy border line of reality. Effective help through the shock and grief periods will take quite a different form with one or another type. There is serious question, for example, whether persons suffering from a handicap such as quadriplegia should be helped toward (or could in fact sustain) the frank facing of the handicap which is essential in the rehabilitation of blinded persons.

But it is certainly true that the answer to any type of handicap is not to be found in one or another aspect of rehabilitation alone — medical, psychosocial, vocational — but in a total approach which considers the individual as he was, as he is, and as he will be, and works to assist him not only with his own problems but also with those of the environment into which he will move after rehabilitation.

It is also true there is great need for intelligent programs of public education about all major handicaps — not the frightening publicity campaigns which play on terror and pity for fund-raising purposes, but programs designed to form a truly enlightened and civilized mentality which would accept handicaps and handicapped fellow citizens for what they are and be willing to give needed help where and how it really is needed.*

This very general picture will, it is hoped, be of some use when we come to consider the special problems of persons with physical or mental handicaps in addition to blindness — including the question of which is the major handicap in each particular case and consequently how and by whom he can best be helped. It would be useful, if space permitted, to compare blindness with one handicap in each of the other three groups.† But we need at least to compare it rather carefully with the other upper-sensory handicap, deafness, in order to

* A major contribution in this area is the weekly column in the Sunday *New York Times* by Howard A. Rusk, M.D., generally accepted as the greatest expert on rehabilitation in the world today.

† The reader who is interested in some particular handicap and who knows something of its nature might find the twenty losses of blindness useful as a basis for analysis, although some will not apply and some will need to be added in each case.

understand blindness better and also to understand some of the terrible implications of the double handicap of deaf-blindness.

2. DEAFNESS AND BLINDNESS COMPARED

Chart G attempts to make a detailed comparison between deafness and blindness on the basis of the twenty losses already familiar to the reader. In addition, as we have said, generally blindness cuts one off from the world of things and deafness from the world of people (although, as we have seen, because of the loss in spoken communication and its implications of "difference," blindness can very effectively cut one off from the world of normal people). This is a difference which affects the learning processes of children suffering from one handicap or the other.

Deaf children have their greatest difficulties regarding universal ideas. Blind children have their greatest problems with regard to particular ideas. The word, the *verbum,* is readily available to the ear of the blind child, although the recognition of particular things is cut off from him by lack of sight. But the word, the *verbum,* above all other means of communication is the expression of the intellectual concept, the expression (and almost the only possible expression) of the universal idea.

This fact is of great importance. Sight particularizes. We know, of course, the possibility of combining and varying the pictures which sight brings (the purple cow being the favorite example). The sense imagination at best can only put together a number of these particular pictures, thus forming new ones. Hearing, however, is the sense medium for the word. And the word is the expression for the thought — the product not of the imagination but of the intellect.

It is true, of course, that the word, addressed first to the ear, can later become the *written* word, and then come to the mind through the channel of sight. It is also true that words can be translated into word signs, and thus be directly seen rather than heard. Nonetheless,

Chart G

Blindness, Deafness and Deaf-Blindness

Loss	*To the Blind*	*To the Deaf*	*To the Deaf-Blind*
(1) Physical integrity	Much more severe.	"Unhearing ears" not obvious — "deafisms" not like blindisms — inner meaning not so important.	Twofold loss with all the effects of each.
(2) Confidence in the remaining senses	Much more severe.	Greater dependence on other senses but no tendency to distrust them. Loss of confidence in one's own judgment due to loss of confirmation afforded by sound of human voice.	Loss due to blindness becomes much more severe since chief compensating sense also gone.
(3) Reality contact	Due to loss of confidence in remaining senses — comes early in blindness.	Due to loss of human contact — may be very severe with paranoid overtones. Usually comes after a long period of burgeoning suspicions.	Twofold loss sometimes devastating. One great reason for special work with the deaf-blind, lest they be thought psychotic or become so from complete separation from world of things and of people.
(4) Visual or auditory background	Impossible to tell whether loss of visual background more severe than is loss of auditory background to the deaf.	Monotony of soundlessness — loss of unconscious recreation and pleasure *and* of warning of danger — separation from world around needing to be bridged by sight.	Effects of each loss multiplied by effects of other — complete monotony, sense of danger and tension, total loss of subconscious recreation.

		Loss of background of human sounds makes for constant lonesomeness.	
(5) Light (or sound) security	More severe.	Thought of as living in "perpetual silence" (probably as untrue as "perpetual darkness" of blind). But this has nothing like the same connotations and meaning to the person himself or the public.	Notion of living in "silence" adds new horror to public concept — thought of as living in "silent darkness." Even when thought of as "soundless lightlessness," its meaning to the emotions of the person may be very grave.
(6) Mobility	Far more severe.	Some limitation (driving, etc.). Bodily movement not usually hampered. But movement may mean fear, and fear coming from behind.	Here the blind man relies on hearing, the deaf man on sight. With both gone, it means almost complete immobility except for a few.
(7) Techniques of daily living	Far more severe.	No telephone. Difficulties whenever communication with other persons is necessary. But skills and techniques not interfered with.	With compensating sense gone, loss most severe.
(8) Ease of written communication	Far more severe.	Hardly interfered with, except in relation to composition of written material — may lose aural quality of style.	Almost complete — blind man's compensations of radio, Talking Book, etc., all cut off.

Loss	To the Blind	To the Deaf	To the Deaf-Blind
(9) Ease of spoken communication	Less severe.	The most severe loss of all. Difficulty not only of failing to hear, but also of fear of misinterpreting. Own voice may become too low, too loud, too monotonous — may fail to speak, or speak at wrong time. Cut off from life around.	Effect of losses to blind and deaf multiplied — even sign language useless except for signing palm on palm.
(10) Informational progress	Perhaps suffers more from lack of *information*.	Perhaps more from lack of *interpretation*. Easier to keep up with distant events and things that have happened — much harder with things communicated by voice. His easier mobility can bring him to immediate, particularized view of his changing environment — but what it means practically is harder for him to find out.	Here blind and deaf rely on other sense. With both gone loss almost impossible to overcome.[1]
(11) Visual (or auditory) perception of the pleasurable.	Greater for most people. But has advantage that ability to recall visual images and to construct	Less loss since usually less satisfaction taken in auditory than in visual perception.	Both losses greatly magnified.

[1] The word "almost" is important here. Those of us who know a number of deaf-blind persons are aware of the amazing manner is which some can overcome the double handicap. The public generally knows the stories of Helen Keller and Robert Smithdas, both of whom completed college and received graduate degrees although totally deaf and totally blind.

	new ones usually greater than to recall and construct auditory ones.		
(12) Visual (or auditory) perception of the beautiful.	Impossible to say which is the greater loss.		Almost intolerable for those who had these powers.
(13) Recreation	Much more severe.	Music, lectures, radio, conversation, etc., gone — enjoyment of sports may be lessened, in some made more difficult. But activity far less restricted.	Any recreation involving other persons almost an impossibility, plus all the restrictions imposed by each handicap separately.
(14) Career, etc.	More serious.	Professional positions seriously interfered with — sales jobs, etc., difficult to hold; yet white-collar and laboring jobs available. Feelings about employing deaf not so strong; possibility or adaptation of job, etc., seems easier.	Almost impossible to convince an employer that such a person might be useful, or that job might be adapted.
(15) Financial security	More severe.	Greater likelihood of job, usually lesser sickness expenses and lesser expenses incident to the handicap.	Both sickness expenses and expenses incident to the handicap increased. Income usually stopped. For many, anything like financial security gone.

<table>
<tr><th>Loss</th><th>To the Blind</th><th>To the Deaf</th><th>To the Deaf-Blind</th></tr>
<tr><td>(16) Personal independence</td><td colspan="2">Much greater as to reality independence.
Impossible to make any judgment about inner independence.</td><td>Whatever the degree of inner independence, impossible to imagine much greater degree of reality dependence.</td></tr>
<tr><td>(17) Social adequacy</td><td>Rejected and pitied.</td><td>Rejected and ridiculed. Failure to hear taken as failure to understand, sign of low intelligence. Public has impatience rather than awe for the deaf. Builds up feelings in deaf person, setting vicious circle going.</td><td>So great that few can or are in a position to overcome it.</td></tr>
<tr><td>(18) Obscurity</td><td>More generally severe.</td><td>But perhaps much more severe in intimate social situations. Also difficulty in using sign language in public places.</td><td>Again, double handicap multiplies loss.</td></tr>
<tr><td>(19) Self-esteem</td><td colspan="2">Impossible to make any general judgment either about self-estimate or self-image. Blind person more severely handicapped, but effect of each loss on individual is what matters here. Separation from people might affect deaf person's self-esteem and self-image very gravely.</td><td>List of losses indicates number of heavy blows to self-estimate — effect on self-image incalculable.</td></tr>
<tr><td>(20) Total personality organization</td><td colspan="2">Impossible to make any evaluation of which handicap has most serious effects. No statistics available as to relative incidence of mental illness or breakdown in both groups. The blows dealt by the two handicaps are of different character — different effects might be expected. Paranoia said to be more common among deaf, but disputed and no proofs available.</td><td>Multiplicity and intensity of traumatic blows so great that many personality structures unable to withstand them without disorganization.</td></tr>
</table>

the auditory rather than the visual sense is the first channel for the reception of universal ideas, of universal concepts.

This will certainly have different effects on the person who has always been deaf than on the person who lost hearing after the maturing of his intellectual processes, especially when the latter has acquired the ability to read the written word. It needs to be kept in mind, however, in considering the education of the deaf child, and hence in working with the adult who has never had the sense of hearing. This is not to suggest that the latter does not have the power of forming universal concepts, but rather to make us realize something of the difficult process by which he acquired that ability (and the fact that words, the expression of universal thoughts, may at one time have been "strangers" to him). This particular difference between deafness and blindness also points up the need for giving blind children every opportunity for perceiving particular things by the means still available to them, and in the case of blinded adults, for helping them keep in touch with the world of the particular by the various means outlined in the second part of this book.

One more difference might be suggested: deafness deprives a person of the means of perceiving what is going on or coming up behind him, blindness of what is going on or coming at him in front. Thus the loss of hearing leaves a person more susceptible to threats from behind; fear is something overtaking him, something over his shoulder. But the loss of sight means greater susceptibility to threats from in front; fear is what may lie ahead. This difference may be one of the factors contributing to the reported higher incidence of paranoia among the deaf than among the blind.

Chart G is worked out on the basis of how blindness and deafness affect the otherwise healthy normal adult. But the "reality" and the psychological losses of deafness, like those of blindness, affect each individual differently. Groupings must be made among the deaf as among the blind according to age and age of onset according to physical and mental health. Again, the problems raised by the various degrees of hearing loss are equivalent to those raised by the various degrees of loss of sight (although the distinctions between "deaf" and hard of hearing" and the degrees of hearing loss and residual hearing are far more widely recognized and discussed among workers with the deaf than their equivalents, as yet, among workers with the blind — so much so that the deaf and the hard of hearing are in many cases set up as two different groups, with different agencies working for each). The use of hearing aids, equivalent to that of corrective glasses, has long been familiar, but the new electronic aids — which can greatly "magnify" hearing for some persons — bring many new hopes and new complications into work for the deaf. And, as in work with the blind, the factor of prognosis — the opinion of the medical experts and of the individual himself on his prospects of remaining at the present level of loss, of improving or growing worse — is of the greatest importance for his adjustment to the handicap.

As in our own field, work for the deaf may be motivated by a philosophy of segregation or one of integration in connection with adults and with the education of deaf children. The fact that deafness is under many circumstances not so noticeable as blindness has helped to discourage segregation in the adult field, yet many present-day factors have strengthened it.

Closer to our special difficulties with segregation and integration in the emotional tensions aroused is the question of lip reading versus "signing." The lip reading (or, better, "speech reading," since other factors besides the movement of the lips are involved) school of thought holds that the cultivation of this ability (with a corresponding voice production) is absolutely necessary if the deaf person is to live a normal life in a normal society. Moreover, deaf children should not be taught the sign language at all or be exposed to it, not only because this would lead to a neglect of lip reading, but also because the use of signs restricts the child to ideas concerned with particular concrete things and results in the failure to grasp the general concepts and universal ideas expressed by words.

The "signer" school of thought has no objection to children or adults learning to lip-read. But, it is felt, a nonauditory sign language is the natural resource of the deaf; they will use signs anyway and

should be taught to use the recognized sign language
fail to teach the sign language or, worse still, to restric
is the poorest type of preparation for life. There are al
tions in which lip reading is impossible. Moreover, they sa
voice production is restricted to the very few, and even here it is not a perfect means of communication.

To the signers, it appears that their position is that of the "moderates," since very few of them are opposed to teaching lip reading; rather, they believe in the use of both methods. What seems like moderation to some, however, seems like compromise to others, and compromise where there is no room for compromise.

Obviously, only an expert in work for the deaf has any right to decide on the merits of these two schools of thought. But it is important for us to be aware of them because of their effects on deaf persons who later become blind and on the education of the deaf-blind. In both these groups, we find some who are products of one school and some of the other; and we find that deaf persons generally are divided into the group trained in one way and that trained in the other.

All these factors need to be kept in mind in analyzing the situation of any deaf person who has become or is becoming blind or of a blind person becoming deaf whom we need to aid by the proper referrals.

In concluding this comparison of deafness with blindness, it is interesting to note that deaf people usually seem to believe blindness to be the worse handicap of the two, while blind people believe it would be far worse to be deaf. One reason for this is that it has been traditional among agencies in each field to teach the individual to minimize his own handicap. There is also the natural desire we all feel to escape from facing the severity of our own handicaps, from admitting how handicapped we are.

Stronger than either of these two factors, however, is that of the great dependence which each group places on the sense lost by the other. The blind person has cultivated his hearing to make up for the loss of sight, the deaf person his sight. Consequently, the severity of all the losses related to confidence in the other senses is enormously increased for the deaf person who becomes blind or the blind person who becomes deaf.

3. THE DEAF-BLIND

One might think that the number of deaf-blind persons would be decreasing with the advances of science. Unfortunately, this is not true. Because of the increase in life expectancy, more people are living to an age when they may lose both sight and hearing, more blind people to an age when they may become deaf as well, and more deaf people to an age when they may become blind.

Perhaps because of the great fame of Helen Keller, most of us tend to think of the deaf-blind only as those who have been so, and totally so, since early childhood. There are indeed such persons. The deaf and blind child, cut off both from sight knowledge of the particular and hearing knowledge of the universal, has far more than twice the difficulties of the blind or deaf child to overcome; yet the examples of Helen Keller, Richard Kinney and Robert Smithdas show that such persons can accomplish far more than do innumerable normally equipped people.

But by far the greater number of deaf-blind persons, and the group whose numbers are increasing, are those who become so in later life, by any of the possible combinations of loss of sight or hearing separately or of both together at one age or another.

In analyzing each individual's situation and how we can best give him the special help he needs, we need to take into account just when he became deaf and when blind, with the effects of each on his training, education, type of work, status, etc. And we also need to take into account the actual degree of loss of sight and of hearing in each case. For not all the deaf-blind are totally deaf and totally blind. There are any number of possible variations between total loss of both senses and the accepted definition of deaf-blindness: "the state of being deprived of sight within the legal definition of blindness and deprived of hearing to an extent which interferes with normal activity."

In Chart G, we outline the impact of deaf-blindness on a person who in adult life totally loses the use of both senses, in order to bring out the total meaning of this handicap — a meaning which must be modified in accordance with lesser degrees of loss of either sense. No summary or description can exaggerate the magnitude of this twofold handicap. But there is danger that it might seem to exaggerate the possibility of overcoming it. The task of overcoming it is, indeed, a very great one. Yet it has been done; it is possible.

The American Foundation for the Blind maintains a national consultative service on the problems of the deaf-blind and is the most important resource for information in this area. The Industrial Home for the Blind in Brooklyn, New York, is the outstanding direct service agency in the United States. *Rehabilitation of Deaf-Blind Persons* (seven volumes), published by the Industrial Home for the Blind as the result of a joint project with the Office of Vocational Rehabilitation, the United States Department of Health, Education and Welfare, should greatly stimulate the progress of work in this field.* And, as we have seen, such progress is particularly necessary today since the numbers of deaf-blind persons are increasing.

4. SPECIAL PROBLEMS OF BLIND PERSONS WITH A PARTIAL HEARING LOSS

Even a slight hearing loss may be a serious matter to a blind person, since he depends so heavily on this sense. He cannot "speech read" even to the extent that most of us do unconsciously, especially when the speaker's voice is low or hard to understand, and so a hearing loss that he would hardly be aware of if he had his sight may interfere with spoken communication. And a slight loss in one or both ears may even more seriously affect his ability to orient himself

* See also *Report: Committee on Services for the Deaf-Blind to the World Assembly of the World Council for the Welfare of the Blind*, Rome, Italy, 1959.

and his mobility, by interfering with his power to localize sounds. As we saw earlier, the human ear has two different ranges for high-frequency and low-frequency sounds, and it is possible that the blind person with a deficiency in one range can learn to use the other more effectively. Nevertheless, any hearing loss in either range cuts down on the total amount of sound received and on one or another kind of sound, and so limits the occasions on which the power of localization can be used.

Again, reflection detection, type C, which apparently depends on acute hearing in the high frequencies may be interfered with by a hearing loss in that range.

A hearing loss in one ear may be as serious as in both; any inequality in hearing power between the two ears can distort judgment of direction of sound, and so interfere with orientation. This is not a hopeless situation. There is a real possibility of relearning and of retraining so that the person whose hearing differs notably from one ear to the other can localize sound.

In view of all this, a blind person might well be considered "deaf," that is, deprived of hearing to an extent sufficient to interfere with normal activity, when his loss is much less than that of a sighted person. If a 25 decibel loss is disabling to the latter, a 15 decibel loss might well be considered disabling to the former. But even a loss less than disabling can be important.

Since hearing aids are now as socially acceptable as glasses, it might be thought that they would provide the answer to the difficulties of blind persons with slight hearing losses. But this is not necessarily true. The aids so far developed are helpful in one kind of sound perception but are apt to limit or cut out another entirely. Any instrument that must be inserted into the ear, for example, may by this fact tend to cut down on the reception of auditory cues very important to the blind person. Or a monaural hearing aid with a chest microphone may completely distort directional cues, making sounds that are closest to the microphone seem to be closest to the ear. A blinded person with such a monaural aid should certainly be shown the value of revolving the microphone like a direction finder to determine the direction of a sound by the changing strength and weakness of the signal, and also to make what allowance he can for the distortion.

There is also the possibility of a binaural hearing aid with a separate microphone for each receiver, these microphones to be brought as close to each ear as possible. It would be helpful also to have both aids attached to a single power source, so that one would not run down before the other.

But no hearing aid so far developed is the ideal answer to all the problems of blind persons, since none of them reproduces the whole normal range of sound; what is useful for social purposes may be distorting for travel purposes and vice versa.

In view of the special importance of hearing, every blind person should certainly be urged to have regular audiological testing, and at the least sign of any hearing difficulty should be referred to an otologist for evaluation and treatment. When this is done, an attempt should be made to make sure the audiologist and/or otologist has an understanding of the special meaning of any hearing loss to a blind person.

5. PROBLEMS RAISED BY OTHER PHYSICAL DISABILITIES

Diabetes. In a day when an increasing amount of blindness in the young to middle age group is caused by diabetes, it is especially important that the worker for the blind have some notion of the handicap of diabetes itself.

The advance of diabetes often causes sensory loss, including that of finer cutaneous discrimination. It often happens, therefore, that newly blinded diabetics believe that they do not have sufficient tactile acuity to learn braille. Experience shows that this is rarely so: the great block to braille is not lowered acuity but *attitude.*

A device has now been perfected for the self-administration of insulin by the blind, the use of which should certainly be taught to the blind diabetic, as it removes an area of frustrating dependence. No method has yet been developed for the blind diabetic to make his own urine tests, although some attempts are being made to work one out.* Blindness adds to the difficulties of the foot care so necessary for the diabetic, but the average blind diabetic can easily learn the principles of such care and carry them out if they are taught him. This topic, consequently, deserves special attention in the rehabilitation center.

Some workers for the blind have an idea that diabetics develop some sort of special "diabetic personality," making them difficult to work with. Although various somatopsychic findings have been made with regard to diabetes, this notion would rather seem to be the result of the fact that in the last decade diabetic retinopathy has brought many workers for the blind into contact for the first time with a considerable group of newly blinded persons who are in the young active age group and who have a sufficient amount of education, experience and ambition to be dissatisfied with a stereotyped job. In consequence, some of this group show a will of their own, which not every worker is accustomed to.

Loss of use of hand or arm. The idea that a blinded person who has suffered a single arm or hand amputation must immediately be fitted with a prosthesis should give way to second thoughts. An artificial hand or arm cannot feel, and this poses a special problem for the blind person. In some cases, there may be reason for the prosthetic arm; in others, it may be much better for the person to make use of the sensitive stump for the sake of the information it can convey.

Another special difficulty for the blind person with an artificial arm (or an arm which lacks sensation) is the fact that he cannot tell where the end of the arm is. (Anyone who has had the experience of waking up at night with his arm asleep can get some concept of the problem.) Even after one gains complete control of a prosthetic arm, it rarely if ever becomes a part of the body image.

It is important that rehabilitation centers for the blind make

* St. Paul's now has its first prototype of a device for this purpose.

proper use of the field of physical medicine whenever these added handicaps are involved; and also that the personnel of such centers be aware of the existence of such devices as typewriters designed for the person with the use of a left hand only or a right hand only, and of special typing courses so that persons with only one arm may use ordinary typewriters.

One further suggestion might be included here: — the possibility of the Krukenberg operation, whereby in cases of hand amputation the bones of the arm may be surgically separated to form a claw-shaped hand. This ingenious operation may be of untold value in allowing some blinded persons to carry on independently in many areas where they could not otherwise. But if this operation is at all possible, there should be a great deal of psychological study of the patient and of the meaning of such a hand to him before deciding on it. For some it can be most useful; for others it can be too traumatic to be helpful.

A blind person who has lost both hands or both arms is naturally under a tremendous disadvantage. Usually in such cases only one side is fitted with prosthesis, and here (if one or both arms remain) there is often indication for the Krukenberg operation on one side. But in every instance there must be the greatest care for individual prescription. The best source of experienced consultation is the Veterans Administration, Blind Section.

Leg amputation or severe leg injury. The prosthetic leg, or even the weak or shortened leg, can add greatly to the mobility problems of blinded persons. The tendency to turn in a circle may be so great as to be almost impossible to overcome, and of course such a leg or foot does not convey all the information a normal one does. An orthopedic cane, as we saw earlier, is inadequate for the blind person's needs. But the use of the Hoover cane with an artificial foot or leg poses a special problem, and one which calls for wide knowledge and experience on the part of the mobility therapist who is to handle it.

Quadriplegia. Fortunately the combination of quadriplegia and blindness is most rare. When the dependence of either handicap is added to that of the other, the most hopeful rehabilitation personnel will be overwhelmed by the problem. One of the most severe and least recognized losses for the quadriplegic is that of kinesthetic awareness and the self-knowledge of one's own body (while having false pain references within the body). When this and the other losses of the quadriplegic are combined with the losses resulting from blindness, the condition too closely resembles the experimental situation described by the National Institute of Mental Health in March 1956, in which the researcher suspended himself naked in a tank of fluid at body temperature for hours, his head enclosed in a soundproof blackout helmet. The researcher soon found that the isolation led him into a world of vivid hallucination. The only relief from this situation for the blind quadriplegic is through his sense of hearing.

Multiple sclerosis. The combination of multiple sclerosis and blindness is known to most workers for the blind, since sight loss is part of the multiple sclerosis syndrome. The problem in most cases is primarily one of medicine and physical rehabilitation, but the worker in the field of blindness should have some knowledge of the nature of the disease. Unless he knows of its periods of remission and of the high incidence of euphoria, he may be badly misled in his handling of these cases.

Cerebral palsy, etc. Work with the young blind child with cerebral palsy has its very special difficulties. The extreme limitations in function, particularly in the area of co-ordination, make training extremely difficult. The American Foundation for the Blind has attempted to bring together some material on this twofold problem, and some of the centers for physical rehabilitation have had limited experience in attempting to work it out.

In the case of the adult blind person who is the victim of a stroke or cerebral accident, workers for the blind should realize that the centers for physical rehabilitation are doing a great deal for the hemiplegic that at one time was thought impossible. The optimum functioning of the body is so important to the blind person that in the event of a stroke or cerebral accident, every attempt should be made to have the very best consultation in the field of physical medicine.

Some forms of cerebral damage produce the condition called hemianopsia, in which the vision of one side, and the same side, of both eyes is impaired or totally lost. Such a condition may lead elderly persons, in particular, to give up all reading because of the difficulty of finding the beginning of each new line with half the normal field of vision thus a blank. Dr. Richard E. Hoover offers the suggestion that such persons might regain reading by the simple expedient of holding the paper or book vertically or at an oblique angle so that successive lines would be within the remaining field of vision.

Aphasia. Every indication from life expectancy tables and present medical knowledge points to a great increase in the number of blind aphasiacs in the decades ahead. I know of no studies in either the field of work with the blind or in that of speech and hearing to prepare us to meet this problem.

22

Special Problems of Blind Persons Suffering from Mental Illness or Feeble-mindedness

1. THE MENTALLY ILL

AMONG the blind, as among the sighted, there are certainly persons who suffer from the third type of handicap in the classification given in Chapter 21, that of drug addiction or alcoholism. Some alcoholics become blind, and some blind persons become alcoholic. (It is interesting to note that in a few cases, alcoholics who have become blind have stopped drinking, blindness apparently satisfying their masochistic need.) Material published by Alcoholics Anonymous is available in braille and on Talking Books. Beyond this, in view of the study and research now going on in the fields of alcoholism and drug addiction, perhaps all that we can do at present is to see to it that the person gets the best treatment available, and to offer our specialized knowledge of the problems of blindness and our help at least with its reality problems. Or, if the person is already undergoing treatment, we can offer our co-operation and assistance with the problems raised by his blindness.

With regard to those suffering from mental illness in addition to blindness, our task can be somewhat more clearly laid out.

In the general population, mental illness is found in all age groups, but especially in the upper age brackets where processes of senility have begun. This is equally true of the blind, but since more than 50 per cent of the blind persons in this country are over sixty-five years of age, there is, as would be expected, a higher quota of deteriorative illness. In addition, there are those persons who have become severely ill mentally as a result of blindness.

Some of each group now living in the normal community may well remain and be treated in the community; some of each group might benefit greatly in a hospital situation; some will already be under the shelter and support of the hospital environment.

The concern of agencies for the blind with regard to these people should take three forms: interest in their immediate treatment; interest in their environment; and aid toward necessary research.

If their treatment is already in capable hands, our part is to offer our co-operation to the doctor or hospital in charge of it. We will frequently find that experts in the field of mental health will welcome our knowledge of the emotional effects of blindness and/or our direct assistance in solving some of its reality problems while they work on the others.

But we frequently meet blind persons who need such treatment and are not yet receiving it, possibly because either the individual or those around him did not recognize the need. Psychiatrically oriented caseworkers in our agencies can be of great assistance here, being able to recognize the need, to help the individual and his family to recognize it also and to see that he gets it, and to work with the psychiatrist or hospital in the treatment itself.

All of us in larger agencies in the general field need also to be aware of the psychiatric resources available in our community, in addition to retaining our own consultant psychiatric staff. Some large agencies in large cities might well set up resources of their own to which blind persons might bring their mental or emotional problems — in the form, perhaps, of clinics staffed (on at least a part-time basis) with experts who have had special training and, if possible, experience in dealing with the problems of blindness. The fact that blindness is a shared traumatic experience can lead to an ideal situation for the use of group therapy in the treatment of many kinds of mental difficulties.

With psychiatrically oriented caseworkers on our staffs, we can also work with the environment of the person who is not hospitalized, helping with any problems in his family situation or his general living situation which may be aggravating his mental condition or interfering with its cure.

Because of the heavy percentage of blindness and of mental illness in the upper age brackets, a larger percentage of blindness is to be found in mental hospitals and institutions than among the general population. If our interest is in *all* blind persons, it should certainly extend to these people. They need our special assistance just as do the blind among the general population, and they could benefit from many of our services — except that too often we forget that these people also are properly our concern. If we were to organize work for the hospitalized blind, we should find both blind and sighted volunteers to carry it out, with the further possibility of aid from other patients.

One of the greatest tasks of social workers in mental hospitals is that of finding homes in the community for their physically handicapped patients when they are ready for discharge — a task that is far more difficult when the handicap is blindness. Our agencies might well offer their co-operation here to attempt to place discharged blind patients in the most favorable environment possible.

As to research in this field, while the depth psychology of blind persons is in no way different from that of the sighted, blinded persons are so uncommon in the experience of the average psychiatrist (being less than one in five hundred in the general population) that the special problems of adjustment to blindness have in no way been part of his training. There is a great need, consequently, to collect the meager literature now available on these problems and to put it in some form available to psychiatrists and caseworkers and to our agencies.

There is need too of some group study of blind patients in mental hospitals. The study would necessarily have to be on the highest professional level, with a team of researchers working on measurement and on social studies of all factors prior to illness as well as on the actual treatment. Such a study conducted in any state mental health division would benefit the individual patients involved by focusing added attention on their particular problems. It might also prove of inestimable value in the indications it might discover as to methods of prevention and treatment of mental illness for other blind persons. What is more, it might shed much light on the nature of proper adjustment to blindness by its analysis of abnormal adjustments.

And there is need here also for much more study of and work on the special problems of emotionally disturbed blind (and deaf-blind) children.

2. THE FEEBLE-MINDED*

In considering what we can do for those who are feeble-minded as well as blind, we need to remember, first, that the problems of blindness, and still more of deaf-blindness, may make a person *appear* feeble-minded when in fact he is not. It is all too easy for a blind or deaf-blind child to be diagnosed as feeble-minded and even as completely unteachable and untrainable, when in fact his intelligence is quite normal, but he is mentally and emotionally disturbed and/or has not been given means for normal development or proper training. Such a child might be consigned to a purely custodial institution and be sent on to other similar institutions as he grew

* The terms "feeble-minded" and "mentally defective" seem more straightforward and less misleading than the escape words into which experts have been forced today: "mentally retarded," "exceptional," "special." Such persons are those whose intellects function feebly at best; their mental equipment is defective. "Retarded" conveys the idea of a late starter who is likely to catch up in time; using this term for the feeble-minded confuses his condition with that of the child who is truly retarded (now referred to as "apparently retarded"); that is, the child who appears to have an inadequate intelligence quotient but is in fact temporarily blocked by emotional problems. Using "retarded" for "feeble-minded" thus helps to prevent truly retarded children from having their quite different needs analyzed and cared for. Moreover, calling feeble-minded children (or retarded for that matter) "exceptional" or "special," besides being a form of escapism, has the unfortunate effect of giving the public a vague feeling that exceptional brilliance in a child is as unfortunate and peculiar as exceptional dullness — that only the average is normal.

older. But if the mistake were rectified, and he could receive the psychiatric and other help he needs, he might be capable of normal healthy development.

Thus one great need here is to work with specialists in testing and in mental health to ascertain as accurately as possible whether a given individual truly is feeble-minded or not. Secondly, we need to remember that there are many degrees of feeble-mindedness, from those who are totally lacking in the possibility of any mental development to those just below the lower limit of the "normal" IQ range. For those incapable of any mental development, purely custodial care, whether at home or in an institution, is all that can be given. But modern studies seem increasingly to indicate that persons who are capable of any mental development are capable, under the right conditions, of considerably more than was at one time supposed. Modern rehabilitation work, in special schools and in centers offering both classes and consultative and casework service with the families, is enabling an increasing number of such persons to take a place in the regular community.

In a recent study* of mentally defective persons, made by testing them for intellectual performance at the beginning and end of a five-year period under favorable conditions, the IQ mean gain ranged from 9.1 for the younger group (whose mean age was twenty at the first testing) to 4.4 for the oldest group (mean age fifty at first testing). Even in this older group, there were some individuals whose gain was 10.

The problems of blindness enormously increase the difficulties of helping feeble-minded persons of any age to attain whatever degree of development they are capable of. Yet since it has been shown that with the proper care (which includes the "T.L.C." now a recognized element in all the therapeutic arts) and training, such persons are capable of development (and the nearer the normal IQ the greater the potentiality), we should certainly do whatever is possible

* "The Effect of Age on the Intellectual Performance of Mental Defectives" by Anne Dell, M.A., and John P. Zubek, Ph.D. *Journal of Gerontology*, Vol. 15, No. 3, 1960.

to co-operate with the experts in this field and to expand the resources and opportunities available.

At present, purely custodial care is available for the blind child who is completely feeble-minded — capable of no mental development — as for his sighted counterpart. But the number of such children is infinitesimally small.

For the feeble-minded blind child capable of mental development, proper resources at present are available in few places. For sighted children, resources exist both in the community and in special institutional schools. In the community classes, they are educated or trained to live in the community according to their capacity. In the special institutions, they receive custodial care and, according to their capacity, opportunities for recreation, training and education. But for the most part, these resources other than the purely custodial are closed to blind children similarly handicapped, since generally neither community classes nor institutional schools are equipped to give them the special help they need and consequently are unwilling to take them. The schools for the blind are in the same case. The less the degree of feeble-mindedness — the greater the capacity — of such a child, the greater the tragedy for him and for his parents. These children, therefore, form an in-between group, deserving of our special attention and interest.

This is particularly true of those children who were diagnosed at an early age as entirely mentally incapacitated and placed in a custodial, nonremedial institution. Such institutions are often overcrowded and understaffed, with no one having the special knowledge or the time to do anything about the special case of the blind child. We should, therefore, do anything that can be done to urge a rediagnosis wherever there is a possibility that a mistake may have been made.

Parents of a child born blind, who gives signs of being feeble-minded as well, may need to be informed about the special schools where such a child will receive special diagnosis and treatment. One of these is the Royer-Greaves School for the Blind at Paoli, Pennsylvania, where Dr. Jessie Royer Greaves has been doing outstanding work for these doubly handicapped children. The other is the recently established Ransome Green Unit of the Walter E. Fernald School in Waltham, established by the State of Massachusetts especially for feeble-minded blind children. There are also some diagnostic centers such as the Boston Center for Blind Children (formerly known as the Blind Babies' Nursery). Increased interest in the problems of the feeble-minded, especially children and adolescents, is being shown, for example, in the New York area, while the National Association for Retarded Children, Inc., 386 Park Avenue South, New York City, provides a center for information and assistance.

Adults with the same double handicap who are living in the community may have special and severe problems regarding residence, recreation and job placement — and these are the people for whom we may need to operate segregated programs. Depending on the degree of blindness and of feeble-mindedness in each case, they may or may not need the special protection and care of segregation with regard to residence and recreation. They will ordinarily not be able to compete in the sighted employment fields, where the blind person actually needs an "extra something" to get along. Moreover, the difficulties of a high level of adjustment to blindness will be too great for them (although something approaching an adjustment may come more easily to them than to the more intelligent).

These persons certainly need our help, and we should never neglect them for the sake of the success we may have in the rehabilitation of persons of greater capacity. Yet in helping them we need to avoid the error of equating all blind persons with this group, of planning or leveling down all our programs mainly in reference to their needs. And we must use the greatest care not to mistake the emotionally disturbed and maladjusted intelligent blind person for the feeble-minded one, simply because he does not have the present ability to make his true self known.

23

Special Problems of Those with Some Degree of Sight

1. THOSE WITH A MINIMAL DEGREE OF RESIDUAL SIGHT

As WE saw earlier, in connection with the false "darkness" conception of blindness, there are some persons deprived of sight who perceive some light — enough to tell light from dark and, in some cases, to distinguish very vague shapes and colors. When a person has been thus blinded in adult life, his reception of this small amount of light poses a special problem in rehabilitation.

Such a person, having functioned all his life in terms of sight, will still attempt to do so, even though he now has so little sight left that it is of no practical value. He will try so hard to make use of this modicum remaining to him that he will not be able to concentrate on developing the use of his other senses. His almost useless remaining degree of vision thus becomes a barrier to his rehabilitation.

This problem can and should be overcome during rehabilitation training by the use of optical occluders (with the sanction of an ophthalmologist in each case), worn during the greater part of the day, particularly during all skill courses.

In making occluders a requirement for the training of such persons, the rehabilitation personnel should be aware of all the possible psychological implications, particularly to a trainee with poor or doubtful prognosis, and be ready to handle the occasional case of shock induced under the trauma of the occluder. But the benefits of using occluders are so great as to make them an essential tool in the rehabilitation of such blinded persons. During the occluded period, the trainee learns to receive and interpret the information given him by his other senses to the degree he needs for normal living. When he does remove the occluders, he invariably finds that he has come to rely on his other senses and to have confidence in them to a degree previously unknown, and also that his small degree of residual sight now functions more accurately than before because he is not attempting to use it for more than what it can really give him. In one instance at St. Paul's, a trainee who had functioned for some months with a minimal degree of residual sight returned home after training with occluders with so much more efficient a use of this sight that he now refers to the period *before* rehabilitation as "the time when I was blind" — although his degree of vision itself remains the same.

But the problems of the child born with a small degree of residual sight should be handled quite differently. In this case, his central sense begins, from the moment when he is aware of anything outside himself, to organize its workings in terms of this extremely limited vision. He does not have the blinded adult's problem of needing to reorganize a central sense accustomed to work in terms of normal vision. Such a child should, therefore, be taught to use his limited vision to the utmost, restricted only by the possibility of eye damage as indicated by a competent ophthalmologist. A limited use of occluders might be helpful in such a case, but only in special sessions for the direct training of his other senses and never as a part of an ordinary class situation.

2. THE PARTIALLY SIGHTED

If an ordinary member of the public were asked to define blindness, he would almost certainly say, "Why, it means you can't see." And this agrees with the dictionary definition of "blind" as "sightless" or "destitute of the sense of sight."

So far in this book we have been discussing the problems of persons blind in this sense of the word, of persons who "can't see." But according to the legal definition, there are a considerable number of "blind" persons who can read ordinary newsprint, distinguish one person from another by sight and a bill of one denomination from another. Some of them even (though they shouldn't) drive automobiles.

These are frequently the "blind" whose spectacular athletic feats are reported in the press, who appear in "believe it or not" columns for some achievement such as having completed a successful career with the military police after graduation from a school for the blind. These are the "blind" who often make the reports of job placements by agencies for the blind look impressive, although the totally blind remain unemployed. These are the "blind" who make it difficult to find out anything precise about the opening up of new jobs for the truly blind, since the reports only state that the person placed was "blind," without mentioning his degree of sight.*

The fact that persons with so much sight are called blind adds to the public's misunderstanding of blindness and of what blind persons can and cannot do (it certainly contributes to the idea of a magic sixth sense), and it causes confusion in work for the blind.

Yet these people have not labeled themselves as blind; it is agencies for the blind who have done so. And the greatest harm caused by the label is the harm it does to these people themselves. It is very likely that when the term was first applied to any one of them, he resented and rejected it — when, for example, he received a letter from an agency for the blind, not asking his help but offering him help.

When a child at the upper limits of legal blindness is sent to a school for the blind, his whole tendency at first is to point out to everyone that he is not really blind and to reject any unnecessary assistance. Yet there is a limit to the number of times he can go on trying to interpret his degree of sight to his public. After a time (whatever it does to his feelings about himself) he will accept the label of blindness and the assistance, and let the "stupid people" be-

* An exception worth noting is VA Pamphlet 7-10, *Occupations of Totally Blinded Veterans of World War II and Korea.*

lieve, if they insist on it, that he is blind. That so many children go through this process without apparently damaging their general straightforwardness and character is in some ways amazing.

The partially sighted adult encounters the same difficulty. Even his own family cannot understand his "blindness." To those around him, he appears to be able to see more at one time than another, to claim more sight than he has in order to bluff the neighbors or less sight in order to obtain sympathy. His state of health, weather and light conditions all make a difference in what and how much he can see at any given moment. But how can he explain this when he has been labeled "blind" — and nobody seems to realize that he is, indeed, severely handicapped but is not *blind?* Thus he suffers the emotional disturbances of a severe visual handicap which everyone around him knows is labeled "blindness," *plus* those added by the knowledge that he isn't really blind (but fears he may become so, whatever the doctor says) and yet is being treated as if he were (and feels deeply guilty at accepting such treatment).

And finally, these persons are not at home with the sighted, because the sighted public does not understand their "blindness." Nor are they at home with the blind, because blind persons do not believe that these persons really are blind like themselves.

It is true that many partially sighted people generously use their time and abilities to act as guides and friends to truly blind people, and that their own reduction of sight makes them conscious of many of the problems of blindness. (One partially sighted woman gave it as her opinion that persons such as herself were put into the world to act as helpers for the totally blind!) And it is also true that the truly blind often accept the partially sighted as their "natural" guides and aids. (Many totally blind persons will say, "But if you took the partially sighted children out of schools for the blind, who would act as guides for the totally blind ones?" Dr. Richard E. Hoover offers the suggestion that this may be the reason why schools for the blind have never tackled the problem of mobility.)

Yet to the trained psychiatric observer, however much persons of both groups may protest that they feel at home with those of the other, it is obvious that the partially sighted feel guilty with the truly blind because they do not share their handicap, and the truly blind feel resentful about the partially sighted as if these were going under false pretenses. (This is hardly surprising, since it is the partially sighted who make the truly blind feel really frustrated — when, for example, they carry off the prizes in "blind" sports and get the jobs in "blind" employment.)

In work for the blind, we have been taking it for granted that our task includes work for these people as well as for the "really blind." Yet we generally make very little of this aspect of our work in our publicity. We may occasionally mention the fact that some blind people are not totally blind, but in such a vague way as to let the public think that none of our clients can see more than shadows or outlines. What reason can there be for this phenomenon other than the fact that we ourselves are also disturbed by our including people who can see under the term "blind"?

These people *are* handicapped and severely so. They *do* need help and should be given it. But their handicap is not blindness; it is partial sightedness. And it is unfair to them, to those who are blind and to the general public to continue to call them so. Moreover, it does no ultimate good to our work, both because it confuses the progress of work with the truly blind and because many of the public become cynical about our appeals when they see people receiving help as "blind" who obviously are *not* blind.

In view of all this, it seems clear that we should first of all clarify our own ideas about the distinct handicap of partial sightedness. People suffering from this handicap not only see less than normally sighted people (both as regards direct and peripheral vision), but in many cases their sight is distorted, making shapes grotesque, forms misshapen, and colors weakened and blurred.

In its psychological aspects, their handicap is in some ways greater than that of blindness, because of the difficulties involved in accepting it and in interpreting it to others. Chart H gives a more detailed analysis of the losses (or deprivations) of partial sightedness as compared with those of blindness. While the reality losses are inevi-

Chart H

LOSSES AFFECTING THE PARTIALLY SIGHTED

(1) Physical integrity	Nowhere as severe as for the blind except as tied in with the idea that they are "blind."
(2) Confidence in remaining senses	Some difficulties, but much less severe. Many continue to use sight as censor.
(3) Reality contact	Not the same loss of contact with reality, but special difficulty of living in a fog-shrouded, distorted world.
(4) Visual background	Reduction, but no real loss: may be very unpleasant, but not monotonous.
(5) Light security	Not lost at all.
(6) Mobility	Some loss: no driving, some danger in traffic, on stairs, etc. But nothing like the same loss — such people frequently act as guides to the blind.
(7) Techniques of daily living	Relatively much less severe.
(8) Ease of written communication	More or less of the "ease" has gone, but not the possibility of it. Newly developed low vision aids are helping a great deal.
(9) Ease of spoken communication	Not great loss except in large gatherings, or in failure to recognize a friend or an acquaintance.
(10) Informational progress	Diminished but not lost.
(11) Visual perception of the pleasurable	Many can still see with relative clarity many of the objects the sight of which brings pleasure.
(12) Visual perception of the beautiful	Distortion and limitation, but not complete loss.
(13) Recreation	Some loss, but very little in comparison.
(14) Career, etc.	Severe loss. Some job opportunities and possibilities of advancement completely closed. But in

	no way limited as for blind — except as closed off by label of "blindness."
(15) Financial security	Not same expenses, but certainly not financially secure. Should remain eligible when necessary for Aid to Totally and Permanently Disabled.
(16) Personal independence	Reality independence nowhere nearly so greatly affected. If feelings of dependence, due in great part to label of blindness.
(17) Social adequacy	Major loss — due mainly to false label.
(18) Obscurity	Little or no loss. Easy to "pass."
(19) Self-esteem	Loss in self-estimate severe, though much less. Self-image impossible to compare.
(20) Total personality organization	When greatly affected, due mainly to label of "blindness" and difficulty of accepting it.

table, the psychological ones are in great part the effect of being labeled and treated as "blind," and would be greatly mitigated or removed if this label were removed and the handicap of partial sightedness recognized for what it is.

Ideally, it would seem that the education of partially sighted children should be entirely nonsegregated, except for "special aids" and "special aids consultants" available in the schools to these children as a group distinct from the blind.

The rehabilitation of persons overtaken in adult life by this handicap is, in the "reality" order, a question mainly of teaching them to use the sight they have to the best advantage. While no programs have been worked out as yet, it is clear that these must be completely distinct and separate from those for blinded persons.

Vocational rehabilitation for persons becoming partially sighted should be carried out under the auspices of general agencies for rehabilitation rather than those for the blind. And actually, general agencies should be able to do a better job, since their task will not be hampered by the emotional reactions of employers to the word "blind." (And with agencies for the vocational rehabilitation of the blind restricting their work to those who really are blind, the latter also would have a better opportunity to find job openings.)

Casework, recreation aids and the many other services that might be needed in individual cases also could be offered to the partially sighted by a general agency rather than by an agency for the blind. In general, once partial sightedness begins to be thought of and dealt with as a distinct handicap, persons so handicapped should have only the same kind of contact with agencies for the blind as does a sighted person — not as a client, but as a contributor or a volunteer (and they may turn out to be some of our best volunteers).

Any such change-over in our present practice is tied in with the need to work toward the formulation of a new legal definition of blindness. Even though the present one is accepted almost universally in this country, voices have begun to be raised here and there against its misleading and harmful effects; * two committees are now at work studying the present definition.

There must be some exact definition of blindness, and it must include those who receive a little light but still "cannot see." A new definition which would be closer to the general common-sense idea of "blind" and to the realities of the situation would need to be worked out after consultation by leading ophthalmologists, workers for the blind, totally blind and partially sighted persons and experts in the field of sight conservation. In such a new definition, it would seem that loss of lower field vision should be considered as more damaging than that of upper field, and that prognosis also should be taken into account. Above all, the attempt should be made to base the new definition on *efficiency* of vision rather than on acuity.

And it would seem as though, at the same time, some definition of the limits of partial sightedness as a distinct form of disabling handicap should also be worked out, so that, for one thing, qualified

* See "A New Look at the Definition of Blindness" by Richard E. Hoover, M.D., in *Proceedings* AAWB, 1957.

adults needing relief could receive it under the "fourth category" of Federal-state relief, Aid to the Permanently and Totally Disabled," rather than, as at present, through Aid to the Needy Blind.

Such a radical change-over from our present practice would, of course, have to be made gradually, so as not to be upsetting to the individuals involved. For the partially sighted persons now receiving our services, we might well make it optional to continue with us or to transfer to a general agency. But persons coming to us for the first time should, as soon as the change-over is to be realized, be immediately referred to a general agency, so that at no time would the label of blindness be attached to them.

From some of the partially sighted thus released we can expect gratitude, but from many nothing but resentment — since they have finally rationalized their acceptance of the label, it will seem like a personal affront to be told that they really aren't blind after all.

The same reaction can be expected from some agency workers who for years have been convincing themselves and the public of the rightness of the present definition. To accept the idea that it has not been right or in the best interests of those they have been helping will not be easy.

And it is true that many agencies will have to suffer great inconvenience, to put it mildly, in making such a change-over. Our unit costs will rise if an organization using the same number of workers and the same size building then serves only the truly blind. Our public appeals may not at first produce the same results and, in the case of state agencies, allocations will be cut when the numbers of the partially sighted are no longer added to those of the blind in our figures of persons served. If we depend on our partially sighted clients for their assistance as guides to the blind, etc., we may have to make rearrangements or find that our costs are going up.

There is, however, so much and such varied work to be done for the truly blind that in the end, with an intelligent program of public education, we need not necessarily find either our work cut down or our finances seriously affected. But even if this were to happen, most of us will be willing to suffer whatever inconvenience is involved for the sake of the greater service we could then render to blind persons — and to the partially sighted by not treating them as blind — and because our agencies will be the better for it.

24

Special Problems Posed by Prognosis

1. PREPARING FOR BLINDNESS

EVERY experienced worker with the blind has been asked, "What can be done for a person who suddenly learns from the doctor that he has an incurable eye disease and will inevitably become blind? How do you help him prepare for blindness?"

There is certainly no program that can be recommended to everyone threatened with loss of sight — the person's temperament and circumstances, whether the prognosis is for sudden or gradual onset of blindness and how soon, all make a great difference in what would be desirable or practical. The following, therefore, are intended only as very general suggestions.

Many people have an idea that under such circumstances it would be wise to learn braille. But as a matter of fact, it is almost impossible for a still-sighted person to learn braille tactually, as it must be learned. And the slight advantage that might be gained by an acquaintance with braille before blindness would be more than offset by the traumatic emotional effect. Braille is a symbol of blindness; except in very unusual circumstances, it should not be learned until a person actually is blind.

Another common idea is that it would be helpful to get acquainted with blind people. Many persons threatened with loss of sight give themselves, for example, to volunteer work in agencies for the blind (almost as if following the injunction, "Make unto you friends of the mammon of iniquity; that when you shall fail they may receive you . . ."). Aside from questions of their emotional fitness for direct volunteer work, it is very poor policy for such persons to identify in this way with blind persons or with agencies. They only cause themselves added emotional disturbance or make such activity a way of avoiding the development of what would be a normal emotional pattern under the circumstances, thus interfering with, rather than assisting, any preparation for blindness.

Still another idea, that of "seeing all that one can see while there is still time," might be acceptable if it is properly understood. If it means a series of trips filled with morbid emotion, or somehow satiating the sense of sight, or most certainly if it implies the satisfying of some voyeuristic need, it makes no sense and would only make the approach of blindness more disturbing. But if a person has planned all his life to see certain parts of the world or certain works of art, and if he has sufficient emotional balance to go and enjoy these things, with the clear recognition that the onset of blindness is not going to mean the end of all pleasure and delight — then he should be encouraged to do so.

The suggestion is also sometimes made that such a person should read about blind persons, especially stories of persons who have in one way or another succeeded in overcoming their handicap and achieving remarkable things. Here again, the emotional effect would in most cases be additionally disturbing rather than helpful. The reading that would be most generally useful would be material concerned with the human senses, to gain as complete a knowledge as possible of the potential and the limitations of each. In some cases, a person might do well to obtain and read material connected with his particular type of work or a particular interest, material which would be more difficult to assimilate after the onset of blindness.

Again, such a person could very usefully begin to train his other senses, alerting himself to the information they give him and checking on it by the feedback he can still furnish himself with by sight. He might also take or give himself a course in touch typewriting, if he does not already possess this skill. This would have none of the traumatic effects of learning braille, and would enable him to continue written communication after blindness with practically no break. Some individuals might also be advised to develop an interest and acquire proficiency in some type of sport or hobby or other form of recreation that they could continue after blindness.

In many cases, also, it would be desirable before the onset of blindness to make a change-over from a type of work which would be difficult to continue to one that could more easily be maintained after rehabilitation. For example, the stenographer-secretary in a job entailing filing and other tasks in which sight is essential might try to transfer to a job involving only typing and similar nonvisual tasks. The lawyer in a branch demanding considerable use of sight might take the steps needed to transfer to another, or the doctor in general practice or some specialization demanding sight might use the period before blindness to take specialized training in medical administration.

Few people will be able to do more than make moves or plans such as these to improve their financial security before the onset of blindness. But some could change plans involving unnecessary expense, or make plans for the most sensible budgeting possible.

During such a period of "preparation" for blindness, the chief problems will of course be psychological. If these seem to be becoming overwhelming, the intelligent person will call for expert help sooner rather than later — either seeking the aid of a psychiatrist or, if the problems are less severe, of a community family agency to furnish casework service. For some people, the depression and fright in this period are so severe as to cause real suicidal tendencies. Clearly, any indications of this kind call for immediate professional aid.

Certain workers for the blind feel that their experience in the field has prepared them for the eventuality of losing their sight. I certainly cannot say this of myself. I am not sure that there is really any good preparation. And I fear that if anything should ever happen to my own good sight, I would prove a very frightened and quite helpless blind person. I hope, however, that I would be able to accept the psychosocial help I would so badly need.

2. PROGNOSIS AND REHABILITATION

Everyone working in the field of blindness should have a supreme awareness of the distinction between the actual medical (objective) prognosis and the patient's own (subjective) prognosis. Even though the doctor has spelled out his prognosis clearly and the patient appears to accept it, he may hold to a prognosis that is quite different. The doctor may have said not to worry about his sight and the patient may still be convinced that he is on his way to total blindness. The doctor may have told him that he will certainly lose his sight within a stated time, and the patient may feel sure that he will remain at his present level of vision. To a totally blind patient, the doctor may have said that there is good prospect for his regaining his vision, and the patient may not believe it. Or the doctor may state that there is no possible treatment that can restore his sight, and the patient may still cling to false hopes.

In the first two parts of this book, we considered the problems of the blinded person whose medical advisers have told him that there is no hope of his sight being improved or recovered. The task of rehabilitation here is to help him to accept the verdict with all that it implies, to go through the "shock" and mourning periods and to begin to build his new life. When the patient is clinging to false hopes of improvement, part of our task is to help him recognize the fact that they are false.

But the problem is much more difficult when blindness is still coming on but is not yet complete. One trainee at St. Paul's, for example, with a deteriorating eye condition and a prognosis for eventual complete loss of sight, was so preoccupied with the battle between fear and false hope that he had great difficulty with the rehabilitation program. In his own words: "I feel as if it is eleven o'clock and I am to be executed at midnight. But it is always eleven o'clock." *

A prognosis containing any hope, however tenuous, also blocks the rehabilitation process. One man who had lost a great deal of sight through war injuries went through a period of several months during which the doctors kept trying operations on the desperate chance that they could hold what sight he had left and perhaps restore even more. During all this period, he was extremely difficult to work with. But after the last operation, when the doctors had been unable to save any sight and there was no further hope, he began his rehabilitation training and is now a highly successful and well-balanced person.

When the prognosis is good for a return of vision after a time, there is no benefit in attempting any rehabilitation training. Sometimes, for example, a doctor will send a patient to a rehabilitation center during the period when he is waiting for his eye condition to be right for a corneal transplant. Such a trainee, though totally blind during this period, cannot make progress in rehabilitation, since he does not need to accept the *fact* of permanent blindness.

In general, therefore, a person should be admitted to rehabilitation training only after any expected change in his condition has taken place. Exceptions will have to be made in cases where sight goes gradually over a long period of time, or where the possible operation for the recovery of vision is to take place at some indefinite future date. Both socially and economically, persons in such circumstances cannot put off rehabilitation indefinitely. But when they are accepted for training, the staff needs always to be aware of the added difficulty these cases present.

In every instance, rehabilitation needs to take into consideration the trainee's prognosis as well as the doctor's, and to involve psychiatric help where this is needed.

* Stewart R. Smith, M.D., brings out the psychiatric implications as "the impending shadow of death."

PART FOUR

Organized Work for the Blind

25

Institutions and Agencies

1. VIEWPOINT

Basic to any consideration of organized work for the blind is the question of the fundamental viewpoint or "philosophy of blindness" animating and directing both work and workers. If blindness is such an overwhelming handicap that nothing can be done except to ease the lot of blind persons, then segregation for education, for work, for recreation, for housing is the only possible answer. But if blindness, though indeed a major and multiple handicap, is one that can be overcome to a degree that makes normal life and work possible for the majority of blind persons, then our effort should be toward their integration into sighted society.

"Segregation" has certainly become a loaded word. In our day, few Americans outside of historically prejudiced areas want to be put in the position of favoring segregation of any kind. Those of us who oppose segregation for the blind have to admit that the use of the term adds heat rather than light to the discussion. Yet "segregation" and "integration" are the accepted terms, and they seem to be the only terms available to describe the two existing philosophies, attitudes, methods of working with blind persons.

Segregation, as a method of dealing with blind persons, has the weight of history behind it. Time and again in the past, blind persons have been gathered into groups for purposes of training or employment; "asylums," institutions and schools were sources of some of the greatest advances in work for the blind. And the philosophy of segregation is still operative in work for the blind today. There are those even in professional agencies who are recommending the establishment of "training shops," and those who favor many other forms of segregated activities (often disguised under the now popular term "group work").

We shall try, therefore, as objectively as possible, to indicate the arguments still advanced for segregation, and then attempt to show why, however necessary and even beneficial it may have been in the past, it is no longer so today—that progress in work for the blind now lies in the direction of integration.

Segregation, it is said, is the most economical way of dealing with the problems of the blind: economical financially because it is always cheaper and easier to build and maintain institutions and buildings for services than to render community services over a widespread area. And economical also from the viewpoint of services. Less of our specialists' valuable time is wasted in travel if we gather all our clients at one central point. What is more, segregation makes it easier to build up our services; with many blind persons gathered at one place, we have a better opportunity to convince potential volunteers—as well as potential benefactors—of the value of the services which we are rendering.

Again, it is said, tension and frustration must always exist among blind persons who are competing in a sighted society, where the odds are heavily stacked against them. Furthermore, it is said, blindness shared with other blind persons gives one an opportunity to find strength in a group situation, and thus its impact is greatly lessened.

Or, again, we often hear that only the blind can truly understand the blind. "Sighted people can never give them true understanding. Let them be together, as they really want to be. Some few sighted persons can understand the handicap, and these should be the workers at the segregated centers for the blind. Then, from their fellow blind and from these few understanding workers, the blind will find something of happiness, and also gain some training."

Blind persons are not really wanted in sighted groups anyhow, it is argued: "They realize they are not wanted and thus will be always unhappy in any situation among sighted people." Or again, it is said that placing blind persons in sighted situations leads only to their being babied, as, for example, placing a blind child in a sighted school. "The blind person will be far better off among people who will not be impressed by his handicap and will not spoil him." Moreover, it is argued, in a segregated situation, where many blind persons of his own group are gathered together, the blind person will not only learn from observing what others do, he will also be actually inspired to greater effort to overcome his handicap and to become a normal person.

This is not to suggest that the only force promoting segregation comes from without, from sighted agency workers or from the sighted public. Actually, as we saw earlier, segregation of the blind, like any type of segregation, has an impetus from within as well as from without. There are indeed blind persons who feel at home only with other blind persons. There are blind persons who feel that they can compete for employment only with other blind persons. There are those who seek not only employment, but also their housing and their recreation among the blind. (This is particularly true, and for good reason, of persons who are graduates of residential schools for the blind, in which their companionships and their friendships were formed among the blind, and no real opportunity was offered for making friends among the sighted.) But this does not mean that we should accept, let alone enforce, this situation.

Admittedly, history shows that segregation has in the past given certain benefits to certain groups. Perhaps, even, segregation was a necessary stage in the progress of work with the blind. But the fact that segregation was the only practicable method of dealing with the blind in certain bygone situations in no way proves or even suggests that we must restrict ourselves to this method today.

Segregation, in terms of workers and cost, is undoubtedly the most economical method of dealing with the blind. But whether it is truly economical has to be considered in terms of results. And many of us believe that the results of an integrated program so far outweigh those of a segregated one as to make the segregation program in most cases distinctly *un*economical. Whereas it may be true that a gathering of blind persons in one place can strongly influence a sighted group, there is a very real danger that this influence will work against our ultimate objectives. It may impress and loosen purse strings, but it is not calculated to show the public about the "normalcy" of blind persons, no matter what type of publicity is used.

As to the argument that blind persons themselves seek segregation, the reasons have been discussed earlier. The solution is not to yield to, and thus increase, this desire for segregation, but to help these blind persons in every way so that they will not feel a need to escape from society as they have known it.

It is also true that there is strength to be derived from a group situation — when the group situation is controlled and is envisaged as temporary. The danger is that this strength will deteriorate into a "misery loves company" situation, draining the strength of the individual and replacing it by a dependence on the group. Moreover, segregation has the terribly unfortunate result of building up minority feelings. It increases group hostilities rather than releasing them (as a group therapy situation might do), and, in extreme instances, actually leads almost to a group paranoia.

As for the tensions and frustrations of competition with the sighted, we must realize that while there is truth here, it is not *all* the truth. We must also consider the fact that even greater tension and often true personality damage may result from running away from competition.

No matter how complete the contentment of blind persons in a segregated situation may appear to be, they have, and cannot help having, an underlying resentment at this situation which has cut them off from the breadth of choice of friends and companions which a sighted society could give them. Segregation deprives blinded persons of all manner of normal interpersonal relationships and rewarding experiences; of its very nature it is bound to lead to decreased gratification in every area.

If blind persons are not truly welcomed in sighted circles, the solution is to do something about those blind persons and about those sighted circles. Particularly with regard to the latter, segregation is bad. How can we ever hope to educate the public about blindness and blind people if we keep the latter as a group apart? With regard to public relations and public education, this method of handling the problem of blindness gets us nowhere, since it is calculated to foster the notion, already far too prevalent, that the blind are somehow vaguely and unalterably "different."

Certainly it is true that only the blind have an experiential knowledge of blindness and therefore a true *realization* of its meaning. This does not, however, preclude the possibility that sighted people can be educated so as to gain a true intellectual understanding of blindness and that some can be trained so as to achieve also that empathy which is of such great importance. Actually, in some situations the blind person may benefit from the objectivity and detachment of the capable sighted worker, and in other situations from the blind worker's emotional recognition of the total impact of blindness.

Certainly we have all seen cases in which sighted groups, overwhelmed by their own emotional feelings about blindness, were spoiling blind persons (children and adults). But here again, the solution is not to place blind persons where the public can't spoil them, but to enlighten the public so thoroughly that it will not do the spoiling.

Finally, with regard to the group learning situation, the danger always exists that it will be learning for a blind rather than for a sighted world, learning for an escape rather than for a reality situation. The very results of the learning may, then, be harmful rather than helpful to the individual. And similarly concerning the inspiration to be derived from others within the group: while there is truth in this, ways other than segregation can often be found to accomplish the same thing—whether by using various media of communication to educate the blind individual about the successes and attitudes of other blind persons, or by bringing him into contact with other blind individuals who can give him something of what the group might give along these lines without all the hazards of segregated group situations.

Segregation, therefore, does not seem to be the adequate or the necessary solution to the problems of most blind persons. It may, it is true, be the only solution available, in our time at least, for some of those who have other handicaps in addition to blindness. Those who are handicapped by extremely low intelligence, for example, may not be able to make their way in a sighted society, to work in sighted industry, to be trained in sighted surroundings. Or again, those with severe additional physical handicaps, particularly deafness added to blindness, may under present circumstances need the protection of segregation. Eventually, though, sufficient progress may have been made toward integration so that many of this group also will be freed from this necessity.

When an elderly person feels that nothing can be done to face the double burden of old age and blindness, and we are unable to overcome this attitude, it may be that segregated conditions supplying extra services may be necessary. But even now, a better answer is often found in a home for the aged than in a segregated home for the aged blind.

Those who are handicapped by severe emotional difficulties—who have strong neurotic feelings about society and the dangers facing them in a sighted world—may or may not be aided by *temporary* segregation while they are being helped to overcome these difficulties.

And finally, for the newly blinded, temporary segregation in a training situation may be of assistance, *if* so handled that its temporary nature is always uppermost in mind. But it is of the utmost importance that group recreation in the center be discouraged, that a time limit be established so that the segregation will be known to be temporary, and that it be clearly recognized that the whole purpose of the segregation is to achieve integration when that time limit has been reached. (Certainly, this reasoning against segregation does not apply in any way to the formation of blind persons' organizations, the sole purpose of which is periodical meetings to achieve greater progress in the field of work with the blind, or to protect their rights under prevailing or proposed legislation.)

Segregation, then, while it cannot be wholly eliminated, *must be limited* and increasingly so. Whether the impetus toward it comes from the blind or from sighted workers and agencies for the blind, segregation is surrender and escape. It is a surrender to the difficulties of blindness rather than a conquering of them. It is an escape from sighted society, and — on the part of the sighted as well as the blind — it is an escape from facing the realities of the world in which we live; it is escape from living with, and recognizing our own feelings about, blindness.

When the impetus toward segregation comes from agencies for the blind, it manifests a lack of confidence in their ability to integrate the blind person and a lack of confidence in the innate power of the blind person to be integrated. Most often the agencies are not acting so much out of their own inner feelings — since they have not yet examined their own feelings — as acting on historical precedent. But the precedent itself was born of the feeling that it is hopeless to try to integrate blind persons (just as now we say that in some circumstances it is hopeless to try to integrate certain groups of the doubly handicapped).

In any case, whereas in the past segregation of the blind for many purposes may have seemed like the best or the only way of coping with a practically hopeless situation, it has now become, because of progress* made in knowledge in the last decades, a defeatist way of coping with a potentially hopeful situation. We have come to a stage of development in work for the blind in which our only real progress must come from the integration of blind persons in a sighted community. The twofold aim of agencies for the blind henceforth must,

* Unlike other forms of social progress, which often occur first in large population centers, the opportunity for this progress is greater in rural and suburban areas or small cities. Unfortunately, the more populous centers are under pressure to maintain or establish segregated programs.

therefore, be to restore blinded persons to their rightful place in sighted society, and to educate that society so that it can accept the adjusted blind person without being overwhelmed by its own fears and feelings.

2. SPECIAL WORKSHOPS FOR THE BLIND

Among institutions for the blind, the public is perhaps most generally aware of the special schools which have contributed so much to advances in work for the blind. We have already discussed these schools in speaking of the educational needs of blind children. The other most generally known institution for the blind is the special workshop, although the public is usually quite vague as to the different kinds of shops, their nature and purposes.

Historically, organized work for the blind has made great use of such special shops, usually listed under the general name "sheltered shops," since the intention of most of them was, in fact, to shelter blind persons from the direct person-to-person competition involved in regular employment in the everyday world. But many of them were established with the quite different intention of serving as a transition to other employment. This type of shop was intended to be a training shop in which blind persons were taken in as learners until they had been prepared for jobs in regular industry.

In the days when such *training shops* were first established, they constituted a step forward — one which was of great importance and full of promise. For they gave recognition to the fact that blind persons need special training and that if properly trained they would be employed in regular jobs. Moreover, the training was given under at least simulated employment circumstances. Given the attitude of those times toward blindness and blind persons, the establishment of these shops was a new and hopeful departure. (In fact, in the so-called "newer countries" as of today, they might have a similar value.)

But for the most part these shops made no attempt to distinguish between the congenitally and the adventitiously blind. Since employment possibilities were so limited in the public climate of their time, they could give little consideration to the previous education, training or work experience of their clients. But the greatest difficulty in most cases was that they became in fact not only the training centers they were designed to be, but also regular centers of continued employment. Rather than discharge the clients whom they could not place, they kept them as permanent employees.

Two courses can be taken in such a situation. One is that of keeping on, for the sake of the shop, not only those who cannot be employed but also the most capable who might find other employment. The other is to continue to place the most capable in regular jobs. But then the shop soon has a permanent core of less capable workers. New clients, capable or not, are trained in an atmosphere necessarily permeated by the nonemployability of this permanent core group. Soon the shop becomes so oriented that it cannot train for regular industry or other outside employment; it trains for a sheltered atmosphere only.

There is, certainly, some need for sheltered shops that are not designed to be anything else. But even if a training shop could keep to its original purpose, which is practically impossible, it can serve no useful purpose today. Persons blinded in adult life — the great majority of whom have had work experience — need primarily training for *blindness*. The rehabilitation center is, therefore, today's successor to the training shop as originally conceived. And when such a person needs specialized training for a new type of work, industrial or otherwise, as we have already seen, he can receive it more effectively in a regular school or course for that type of work.

The congenitally blind and others who never had work experience before blindness were the group which made greatest use of the training shops of the past. Some people still seem to feel that there is need for special training shops for graduates of schools for the blind. But, as we saw earlier, this is an insult to the residential schools. What is needed is not further segregated training, but special counseling to aid such young people in making the double adjustment to adult life and to life in sighted society. If special professional or industrial or some other type of training is needed, this should be obtained at the appropriate sighted educational institution.

But the problem here actually seems to center on those graduates of schools for the blind who are in one way or another below average, and so are possible candidates for the permanent sheltered shop.

The *sheltered shop* strictly so-called is a center for the permanent employment of blind persons not capable of competition with the sighted. The workers are actually not employees but clients of the agency operating the shop, which is necessarily subsidized by the agency, and sometimes heavily so. The purpose of such a shop is to keep its clients occupied and to provide them with some sort of income along with the occupation.

As we have seen, there is a place for such sheltered shops to take care of persons of low intelligence. They also may be needed for the group of those who would be among the "fringe employees" in the regular labor force if they had their sight, and also for some who would be just above the fringe level. For one thing, fringe jobs are almost completely closed to the blind, and for another, blindness requires that a person have "something extra" to compete. The very word "handicap" suggests this. But there are a number of blind persons, just as there are a number of sighted persons, who do not have this extra and thus often must be numbered among the incapable so far as employment in a sighted situation is concerned. For these types of person, the sheltered shop may still fill a real need.

Another group who might be considered are those blinded persons to whom some added handicap gives low work tolerance; they might be capable of part-time work in industry, but cannot be placed. But if there is a choice, even these persons should be not in a sheltered shop for the blind, but in one designed for that other handicap which is the cause of their low work tolerance.

Thus the sheltered shop, if it is to be maintained at all, should be honestly recognized and publicized for what it is: not a "blind workshop," but a special solution for that group of marginal workers whose inability to find work in the sighted labor market is simply due to the fact that they are "marginal." At present, unfortunately, many of these shops, as well as those that combine both sheltered and "production" shop characteristics, house many highly capable workers who, in the ideal situation, would never be allowed in them.

The third type, the *production shop*, is one which has eliminated much of the "shelter" to be found in the sheltered shop strictly so-called. It is a shop for the segregated employment of blind persons who would actually be capable of holding positions in outside industry. It cannot afford to take the *less* capable blind worker, since it is working in competition with sighted industry; its workers are not clients but employees who earn their pay. Such a shop is not subsidized, but either operates at a profit or at least breaks even.

But the sheltered production shop seldom exists in this pure state. In many communities one finds shops which attempt to be training shops, sheltered shops in the strict sense, and production shops all at once. Or one might come across a shop which has some of the characteristics of the production shop but is financially subsidized, to some extent directly and to some extent indirectly by sheltering laws and exemptions.

Some of these shops were established by groups of public-spirited citizens who did not fully understand the true needs of blind persons in their own community and so thought of the shop as providing an ideal solution. Often, though, the founders did realize that the segregated shop (production or otherwise) was not the ideal but believed it to be the best solution to be hoped for in their own day. They thought (and some people still think) of the shops as a momentary necessity when, at a given time in history, sighted employers are unwilling to employ capable blind persons at tasks which they can accomplish. To these people, the shop seems a necessary evil, at a bad employment period or in a bad employment area, and the only possible way of giving capable blind persons some occupation, some earnings, and the preservation of some respectability.

We must admit that such times and places have existed and may exist in the historical development of the employment of blind persons. But we must also keep in mind the fact that the production shop ceases to fulfill its purpose when it becomes confused with a training shop or with the sheltered shop in the strict sense. This fact is important for many reasons, one of them being that the production shop, to fulfill its real purpose, must be run with efficiency in mind, for production on a scale which can compete (and compete fairly) with sighted competition. As soon as it ceases to be so conducted, paternalism creeps in. After paternalism comes the destruction of morale; and then one of the prime purposes of the shop is no longer achieved.

Production shops for the blind are sometimes criticized for employing sighted people for certain jobs. The criticism is possibly justified in certain cases, but generally speaking, the use of sight where sight will speed up efficiency is wise and is in the best interests of the blind workers. The task of the production shop is to employ blind persons in such a way that those blind persons will receive an adequate return for their labor; and the very best way of doing this may be to combine the sighted and the sightless jobs, giving each to the one who can perform it most efficiently.

But even if the production shop succeeds in keeping to its original nature and purpose, it necessarily has the danger, not only of segregation in a work situation, but of the further advancement of segregation outside the work situation — into recreation, even housing, and finally even into ways of thinking. Even if the shop sponsors resist segregation, the workers come to it naturally from being placed together at work. Soon they are meeting together in the evening, having their recreation together, living in the same neighborhood — and all too soon, the will to live in a sighted world is destroyed, and all the frustrations which segregation entails soon follow. (The reader might well consider for how few of the losses optimum rehabilitation can take place in a sheltered shop situation, even of the production variety, and how many of them are actually magnified.)

Moreover, the capable blind persons now in such shops might well find themselves in much better jobs if the money used to subsidize these shops were used instead for placement work to find jobs for these and other such persons in regular industry.

Under any circumstances, the special industrial shop for blind persons has the very serious disadvantage of reinforcing a stereotype that *all* blind persons should be in industrial jobs. Even without shops, too many workers for the blind (including placement personnel) fall prey to the temptation to train for industrial employment or to place in industry blind persons who under no circumstances should be in an industrial setting. There is nothing wrong with jobs in industry, but most sighted people are not industrial workers, and there is no reason why most blind persons should be.

At best, then, the production shop must be considered as a temporary expedient, formerly forced on agencies for the blind and on the blind employees by the unwillingness of the general public to recognize the potentialities of blind persons.

But, obviously, sheltered shops of the production variety, and the other types of sheltered shops, cannot suddenly be done away with. Agencies for the blind have erected them and given to blind persons an implicit contract of continued employment. If we have erected a world of the blind, and have led or driven people into it, the solution of the problem it poses is not to destroy that world. It is rather to make sure that we lead or drive no others into it, and at the same time that we take steps to enable as many individuals as possible to leave it.

The latter course is difficult, but it should be taken insofar as it lies within our power. We have an obligation to these people to employ them as long as we have led them to believe we would employ them, or until they have worked through their individual problems so successfully that they are ready to leave the sheltering care of the shop.

There is considerable discussion today as to whether shops which employ only handicapped persons should be unionized. So long as production shops exist, there seems every reason why they should be organized, in recognition of the employees' dignity as laboring men (and not by some paternalistic company union). The question of the unionization of training shops and sheltered shops strictly so-called is somewhat more complicated, since the workers are either students or clients. In such shops it seems indicated at least that representatives of organized labor should sit on their boards, not only from the standpoint of community co-operation, but to protect the rights of labor in the community from unfair competition and to guard the rights of the blind workers who are the students or clients in these shops.

To summarize: we should be working away from the training shop entirely, and from the production shop as anything but a temporary necessity, in which case it should be *only and entirely* a production shop; we should plan finally to retain only the sheltered shop strictly so-called, and this only to the extent that is absolutely necessary under the circumstances.

3. THE WORK OF AGENCIES, NOW AND IN THE FUTURE

Organized work for the blind, as this book may have indicated, is very much in a state of transition today. The public has the general impression that everything possible is being done for the blind: people make contributions, they buy brooms and belts to "help the blind," they know of schools, they see blind persons with dog guides and canes, they have a vague feeling that "a lot is being done for people like that nowadays." But the newcomer to the field is often appalled that the work is so little advanced — after so many years.

People have been blind since the dawn of history. In one or another culture they have been deified as possessing special powers, neglected, or cared for as helpless. But until the last century, with the invention of braille, so far as we know, nothing widespread was done to help blind people overcome the handicap of blindness in a positive way. In our times have come the guide dog, the Talking Book and many devices and inventions. But considering the progress in social, scientific and technological fields, it is amazing how little is yet being done to attack the problems of blindness — except in a few scattered instances.

Modern work for the adult blind grew out of the schools for the blind founded in the last century. Something had to be done to help the graduates of these schools, and so volunteers were found to read to them, to guide them about, to run recreational programs for them, and so on. Perhaps some sociologist of the future will be able to give the causes of the extraordinary fact that after all these years of special schools and special programs, the idea of some magic "compensation," some "sixth sense," has so generally blocked any constructive work to help the blind person use his own senses. A newly blinded person might ask for a few hints about recognizing sounds from someone blind for a long time, but until the Army's program for the blinded servicemen of World War II, nothing had been worked out in the way of systematic help for blinded persons in this — as it would seem — most obviously necessary area. And even now, work along these lines is practically limited to the total rehabilitation centers.

In the same way with mobility — one blind man might hand on to another a few tips about using the orthopedic cane, but otherwise blind and blinded persons have been left to their own devices to find out how to walk or grope or fumble along — or be guided. The guide dog was a great step toward rehabilitation and independence here — and at last mobility therapy and the professional training of mobility therapists are under way. But here again, many institutions and agencies still do not recognize the vital importance of mobility training, nor the necessity for training the blind person's senses on the one hand and training the therapist on the other.

Again, it seems extraordinary that as yet there is so little recognition of the need for distinguishing the different problems of the congenitally blind from those of the adventitiously blind, or for distinguishing the truly blind from the partially sighted.

The sociologist of the future will also, perhaps, be able to account for the strange fact that in these days of social studies and integration consciousness, the segregation of the blind is still hotly defended and continually promoted, and discover why there is as yet so little recognition of the fact that this is a minority group problem, needing the same sort of study and public education as the problem of minority racial and religious groups. And why also, when so many workers for the blind defend the thesis that the blind are "just like everyone else," so many agencies and those who staff them continue to put on publicity campaigns which reinforce in many different ways the idea that blind persons are different, strange, pitiable, peculiar.

It is true that much has been done in many single areas of restoration. But here again, it is extraordinary how not only the public, but agencies and workers fasten on the idea of one or another restoration as all-sufficient. Financial security, job restoration (any job), mobility, Talking Books or braille, and, lately, "adjustment" — each in turn is too often seized upon as the total answer to *all* the problems of blindness.

Yet, very slowly, the realization is beginning to grow that on the one hand, blindness is a multiple handicap, requiring many-phased restoration, and that on the other hand, each blind person is an individual with his own particular needs who must be helped as an individual.

These realizations open out almost unlimited possibilities, some of which have been indicated in this book. So many exist already and so many new ones are opening out every day that there is certainly no need for any overlapping of services in a given area, nor any excuse for the waste of time, effort and money that can come from agency rivalry. Ideally, we should be working toward a setup in which, in every geographical area, every blind person could have reasonably available the specialized help he needs. This would include aid in the process of *his* rehabilitation and the provision of continuing services such as volunteer readers, information as to legislation and new devices. It would also include, on a nationwide

basis, research* to open out, gather together, and utili[illegible]
possibilities of restoration.

Occasionally a worker for the blind seems to believe th[illegible]
efforts to integrate blind persons into the community m[illegible]
greater and greater success, we are approaching the day when there will be no longer any need for specialized agencies dealing specifically with the problems of blindness. But the progress of modern work with the blind seems to indicate the exact opposite.

Tackling the problems of blindness holds so many unknowns for the average "nonblind" agency that the blind person directed to such an agency for advice and assistance regarding his handicap usually gets lost in the shuffle. General agencies are needed to cope with all the other difficulties a blinded person may have, but they cannot be expected to have the special knowledge and skills needed to work with his blindness problems. Moreover, the more possibilities of restoration are developed, the more need there will be for staffs of well-trained experts in the various fields to actualize these possibilities for more and more blind persons: for the young and for the old, for the otherwise fully equipped and for those with all the various additional handicaps. There is also great need for separate work to be done in the rehabilitation of the partially sighted. And there will long be need for intelligent and well-directed volunteers to act as "eyes for the blind" in situations where eyes are indispensable.

In this many-sided work, there is room for both state and private agencies — state agencies, as has already happened in various areas, taking over certain work that has been pioneered by private agencies, leaving them, with their more flexible setup, free to develop further possibilities. For example, formerly private agencies

* Two recent actions of the United States Office of Vocational Rehabilitation are important here. One concerns a grant to the Shilling Laboratory at Groton, Connecticut, for its auditory research. The other involves a major contract with the Massachusetts Institute of Technology for broad areas of sensory research. Through this office in recent years, the Federal Government has stimulated basic and applied research in all areas of rehabilitation.

had to supply most of the emergency financial aid for blind persons, and this forced them to concentrate mainly on the attempt to restore financial security. In recent years, Federal-state Aid to the Needy Blind has taken over a good deal of this work, leaving these agencies free to work at other types of restoration. The most effective fundamental division of labor among agencies in any given area would be by services — so that any blind person could find the various kinds of help he needed provided by one or another.

But as work with the blind continues to develop, we need to keep one thing very much in mind. The task of agencies for the blind is to deal with the *various problems of blindness* affecting their clients and the public, *not* to deal with *all the problems of blind persons*. The more we specialize in our particular work, referring the blind person to other agencies for those of his problems that are not blindness problems, the more effectively all his needs will be served. This policy will aid in integrating the blind person himself into the sighted community, and aid in integrating our own work and our own agency into the general picture. If we try to deal with all the problems of our clients because they are blind, we cut them and ourselves off from the benefits of others' work and other points of view. Our clients are, once again, being unnecessarily segregated, and we are also segregating ourselves.

In a developing field such as this, it is, moreover, of the utmost importance that we constantly evaluate and re-evaluate our own work and what services we are emphasizing; what may be important work for us to carry out at one period may not be the most important contribution we could be making even a brief time later. Thus prudent flexibility and the ability to learn are of the essence in work for the blind today.

It is extremely necessary that we come to evaluate our work in the light of its contribution to the total goal set up by our philosophy of work for the blind. The number of services rendered and the number of people served by our agencies are valuable statistics to have on hand. But the best yardstick of our progress toward the restoration of blind persons on the one hand and of society on the other is, in the final analysis, not so much the number of people served as the number who have been served so well that they no longer need the services of our agency. Our final purpose is to help as many blind persons as possible to achieve such an adjustment to their blindness that they are free from dependence on us and from abnormal dependence on anyone.

26

Those Who Work for the Blind

1. THE WORKER — BLIND OR SIGHTED

"IF AGENCIES for the blind will not themselves employ blind persons as members of their staffs, how can they expect others to employ them, and what does it suggest with regard to their own confidence in the blind?" This line of argument is one which many organizations would have difficulty in contending with. Yet it is sometimes used to oversimplify what is often a complex question: who is to be preferred as a worker in staffing agencies for the blind — a sighted person or a blind person?

The individual blind worker is the first and most immediately involved. Possibly the best possible job or professional appointment for him may be one with an organization for the blind. But it is equally possible that his best opportunity may be with some other organization. The very fact of finding a position outside of work for the blind might be of extreme importance from the viewpoint of his self-confidence.

The individual blind worker must also be considered from the standpoint of his own growth in skills. The professional worker particularly may be far better off if he finds employment outside of work for the blind, for the sake of his own development and growth in skills. Because of his own experience as a blind person, he may be altogether too close to work for the blind to make it possible for him to obtain his complete professional growth within the field, unless at some time in his career he broadens himself by proper, supervised experience outside it.

The client also needs to be considered. It may be that the relationship between blind worker and blind client will be of the best, but the mere fact of blindness is not enough to guarantee this. Sometimes, the fact of common blindness may interfere with proper relations. The blind worker may be so satisfied with his own success at overcoming his handicap that he cannot properly sympathize with the client's failure to do so. Or again, his success may be a barrier from the client's viewpoint. Or he may be so closely identified with the blind client as to have a common feeling without being able to assist in working out the client's basic difficulties. But it is also possible that his example may be so fine and his understanding so complete that perhaps he, and he alone, could aid the blind person.

The problem of public education also enters into the picture. Agencies for the blind must certainly give example to other agencies by employing blind workers. But there is also the argument that the employment of the blind by agencies for the blind is not conducive to good education of the public, who might come to feel that blind workers are mainly for agencies for the blind, rather than learning thereby the general value of blind workers.

The question of employing blind workers (which often comes down to giving *priority* to blind workers, something rather akin to veterans' preference) has to be considered also in its effect on intra-agency relations — the relationships between various workers, blind and sighted, on the agency staff. On the one hand, the complete refusal to hire new blind workers or to advance blind workers already employed leads to natural feelings of resentment on the part of blind staff members. The resentment is turned toward the sighted workers who are "taking their jobs away." On the other hand, if the policy of the agency gives special privileges to blind workers, advancing them ahead of sighted workers who are doing superior work, the reverse happens: the sighted now turn the resentment onto the blind.

Either way, we destroy the morale of our staff workers and lessen our ability to work for the good of the blind. The effects of such decreased morale on agency growth are easy to see. Soon we are unable to attract good new workers, either blind or sighted, because of the friction within the agency. Either blind or sighted workers (depending on our policy) know that they have no chance for advancement with our agency, and therefore come to us for a brief time only or not at all. Finally, too consistent an adherence to the policy of hiring all blind workers, or at least of giving them a heavy preference, can mean an "inbreeding" in the work: our former clients become our workers, who in turn deal with new clients or set a policy for dealing with new clients. Little in the way of new blood comes into the agency, little in the way of new ideas; and there is less and less likelihood of the objective evaluation and re-evaluation of the agency in the light of progress in the field. Our new workers are not getting the breadth of experience and supervision which makes for the growth of individual skills, and the agency is failing to get the benefit of workers with such breadth.

Thus the question is extremely involved, and it is further complicated by the fact that it deals with more than one type of employee, with more than one job or professional opportunity—in agencies for the adult blind, the employment of, among others, administrators, supervisors, caseworkers, relief workers, home teachers, legislative analysts, orienters, business managers, public relations representatives, researchers, receptionists, shop foremen, shop salesmen, stenographers, job counselors, and placement agents.

Since practically every one of these jobs is offered also by agencies other than those for the blind, our first and greatest task here is to persuade these other agencies to open up opportunities to blind persons. More than any other group, social agencies would seem to have this obligation. And, by virtue of their training, the personnel of these agencies should not be subject to the emotional blocks against blind workers which we find among the public at large. General social agencies certainly have little excuse for building up feelings which keep them from hiring capable blind persons (capable blind caseworkers, for example). Yet, strangely enough, it is some of the supposedly enlightened social agencies which suggest to blind workers that they should find their employment exclusively in the field of work with the blind.

To many readers this will appear to be just so much "good theory," because they are up against the present fact of discrimination against blind workers. (While this situation cannot be handled by any state or government fair employment practices policy, compulsory or otherwise, in many instances agencies for the blind might form an area "antidiscrimination committee" which would hear complaints regarding discrimination because of blindness and make proper representations to those responsible in cases where unfair practices have been established.) To many workers, this discrimination provides the primary motivation for seeking a position with an agency for the blind. And obviously, it is an unanswerable motivation unless we can open up enough opportunities elsewhere so that blind persons will have a choice.

To some other blind workers, a strong motivation is the supposed security of the job with the agency for the blind. In their minds, an agency for the blind is less likely to dismiss them than other agencies might be. There can be little quarrel with the idea of seeking job security, although it should never become a prime motivation in choosing between jobs. But the implication that an agency for the blind might lower its standards rather than release a worker (simply because the worker is blind) is something that calls for some self-examination on the part of the agency. This does not mean that we should be ruthless, but that our employment policy should be the same with regard to blind and sighted alike, recognizing the equal dignity and responsibilities of both.

Still other blind workers are motivated to seek positions in agencies for the blind because they feel that only here will they truly be "accepted." Here we are coming very close to the surrender involved in segregation. The difficulties which promote this surrender should not be minimized—difficulties for which the attitude of sighted persons is largely responsible. Yet the answer is not to be found in surrender, but in work with the environment causing the difficulty and in work with the individual who may himself be in part responsible.

Sometimes, too, workers have deep unconscious motivations for seeking to work in agencies dealing with clients who have the same handicap. And at times, these deeper reasons can seriously interfere with the possibility of their doing capable work for the agency and its blind clients.

Perhaps the most common motive, or at least the most common argument advanced, for the employment of blind workers by agencies for the blind is that the experience of being blind makes a person capable of understanding the problems of other blind people, or, as it is more often stated, blindness. This belief contains a basic fallacy. No amount of experience in undergoing disaster will, of itself, help us to understand other people; we are certainly in a far better position than we would be otherwise to realize the horror visited on others who undergo these catastrophes, but this does not in itself guarantee that we will understand the *people* who suffer from it.

"Only the blind can understand the blind" is another statement which we hear many times in this same connection. Beside it should always be placed the other statement: "Not all the blind can understand the blind." It is true that no sighted person can have a full *realization* of what blindness is. For a brief time we can get something of the feeling of it, but it is not entire, and necessarily we soon escape from it back into our sighted lives. Sighted persons who forget this fact and act as if they had a full realization of what it is to be blind are a real menace and should not be allowed in work for the blind. But what *is* important in understanding blind persons is to understand *persons*—and neither blindness nor sight guarantees this ability (or is a hindrance to possessing it).

If experience in being blind is not a guarantee that anyone will know blind people, neither is it an adequate substitute for good training. The fact that a man is blind no more qualifies him to be a trained caseworker (without training), or a trained counselor (without training), or a trained administrator (without training) than it qualifies him to be an ophthalmologist.

But it is also true that many blind persons with good training seek opportunities in work for the blind because they have a special interest in this field. They may give a great deal more of themselves to their work than would the person to whom it is just another job. The disaster worker who has undergone disaster is less likely to be a time-server. It is quite possible, therefore, that the motivations of the blind applicant may be of the highest (both on the surface and underneath); his ability may be of the greatest; and his training and experience may be of the best.

Still, with some of our agencies he would have difficulty in finding employment. And the fact that this is so brings us to another phase of this complex question: the reasons why some of us who head agencies for the blind block on the subject of appointing blind workers to our staffs.

Some sighted persons who administer agencies for the blind undoubtedly do not really believe all they teach about the competency or the "normalcy" of blind persons. No matter how they have rationalized their position to themselves, they talk about one blind person who was a failure, proceed to exaggerate his failure and then to generalize from it about all blind workers. Or they generalize in the same way from the personality difficulties of one individual who was difficult to work with in an agency.

Underneath, probably many of the agency heads who resist the idea of employing blind workers do so because blind workers may be a threat to their own jobs. Or, more likely, they are a threat to their own feelings of security—by somehow suggesting to them their own incompetence. This may seem farfetched, but it is a human reaction. It can be felt by the sighted golfer who watches the good blind golfer; by the tennis player of normal physique faced by the good one-armed tennis player. The fact that others can succeed with a handicap is too much for some insecure people without handicaps to take.

Sometimes, again, this feeling against blind workers grows out of an inner guilt. Strangely enough, it is possible for us to feel guilty for not having experienced the handicap that another has. We may know our unworthiness before God, and wonder that He has allowed others to suffer and us to go free. Or — and quite different — we may have *feelings* of unworthiness for which we *feel* that we should be punished — and such feelings may well interfere with our hiring of blind workers.

Furthermore, some of us who are agency heads may be unwilling to accept any inconvenience which may be involved in employing blind workers; we may not be flexible enough to make any rearrangements of our system which might be involved.

Blind administrators of agencies for the blind also can have feelings which cause them to resist the employment of blind persons on their staffs. Other blind persons may seem a threat to them and their security. And if they are not adjusted to their blindness, they may have strong feelings of rejection toward others who are blind, feelings which express their own resentment toward their handicap and themselves.

It is clear, then, that there is no ready and universal answer to the question of using blind or sighted persons in staffing an agency for the blind. The answer must depend not only on the persons involved, but also on the degree of progress made in integrating persons who are blind into the general community. When no jobs are open for competent blind persons elsewhere, we must be especially alert to opportunities for them with our agencies — *if* they are capable of filling those positions as well as another person. But we must always insist that excellency, not blindness, is *the* qualification. The good of the great number of our blind clients cannot be sacrificed for the immediate satisfaction of the one blind person looking for a job.

At the same time, we must keep in mind the goal of placing blind workers in general agencies (and general business and industry) rather than in specialized agencies for the blind. We must see to it that individual professional workers, blind and sighted, are encouraged to get as broad and as good a training and experience as possible in these general agencies before we take them on our staffs (for both their good and the good of the agency). And, always, we must remember that (except for the few jobs where, other things being equal, blindness is a positive asset) blindness must not be a consideration, either positive or negative, in our engaging staff.

2. THE VOLUNTEER

To the agency in a position to make use of their services, volunteers can be of the greatest assistance. Their value can be twofold: to supply services to the agency and to supply services to the blind individual.

The volunteers who give their services to the *agency* are sometimes more difficult to obtain — volunteers who will raise funds, stuff envelopes, deliver bundles, sweep the office, etc. The fact that the work is not directly with the client makes it less attractive. Yet such work makes possible the existence of many agencies, and therefore makes possible whatever work they accomplish for their blind clients.

The volunteers who work directly with the blind have one function which should be written in large letters in a prominent place in every agency: *The Function of the Volunteer is to Supply Eyes.*

For centuries, volunteers have been doing just this for individual blind persons, whether working under agencies for the blind or on their own initiative. But such volunteers, as well as agency executives and individual blind persons, know that volunteers also exist who work their way into various organizations and confuse the purpose of the volunteer by taking on other responsibilities, forgetting that the sole function of the volunteer is to *supply eyes.*

The function of the volunteer as the agent of an organization for the blind is *not* to supply funds to the individual (although he may very well be called upon to report to the agency about the individual's apparent need of funds). It is *not* to lavish gifts upon the blind person. It is *not* to supply intelligence to him or to make decisions for him. It is *not* to educate him and it is *not* to convert him.* It is *not* to make him dependent and it is *not* to possess him. *Nor is it* to use the blind person as a means for solving one's own problems.

Some of these purposes are good in themselves. Others may be good for the person who does them. Still others are bad for the volunteer and bad for the client. But *none* of them is the function of the volunteer as a volunteer for an agency for the blind — except in the specific instance when the volunteer is directed to undertake any one of them in cases of unusual need.

The function of the volunteer working with the combination of old age and blindness may be different; the function of the volunteer working with both incurable dependence and blindness may also be different. There may be other extraordinary exceptions (and there are, of course, the "regular" exceptions: those who volunteer their professional skill — the ophthalmologist, for example, or psychiatrist. But the function of the volunteer working with blindness should be well circumscribed in his mind and in the mind of the agency which uses him.

The activities of volunteers are best used in making up for three losses (mainly, for only two). These are the *loss of written communication* and the *loss of mobility* (and, to some extent, the loss of the techniques of daily living).

In making up for the loss of the ease of written communication, the work of the volunteer may be directly with the blind person, by reading to him. Or it may consist in transcribing braille material for him, or reading onto Talking Books for his later use. In the latter two instances, the volunteer does not come directly into contact with the blind person, working instead through an agency for the blind which has as its purpose the transcription of such material.

* Some readers may find difficulty with this statement about education and conversion. It is said with a complete recognition of the fact that man is made to strive for truth and Truth, and the need of mankind and individual men to achieve truth and Truth, and also of the obligation of each of us as individuals to help other individuals, and mankind generally, to seek and find both. But here we are speaking of the function of the volunteer worker for the blind *qua tale*, a function which we firmly believe is only to *supply eyes*.

Probably the greatest need in the field of volunteer activity for the blind is for some agency to experiment with a large corps of screened, trained volunteers who would go to the homes of a large number of blind persons for a set and limited period each week to read to the blind — not anything of any special importance, but whatever recreational or other reading each individual wanted. These "substitute eyes" would probably be shaken up regularly, moved on to new blind persons. Their job would be different from that of most volunteers; it would almost be a mechanical function.

To restore lost mobility calls for the service of guides and drivers; but while trying to supply such volunteers in sufficient quantity to meet real needs, agencies must be careful not to supply them to such an extent that they increase an attitude of dependence and thus harm the blind person more than they help him.

Sometimes, too, but only occasionally, we run across certain conditions where the volunteers are called on to help in the restoration of the techniques of daily living.

Over and above the service of "supplying eyes," some agencies for the blind supply volunteers for various services which have little if any connection with their clients' blindness — as, for example, the supplying of baby sitters. While recognizing that emergency situations can change the nature of things, I believe that such services could be better supplied by general volunteer agencies, leaving to agencies for the blind the special work of restoration and substitution which is theirs.

Most of us fail by not supplying enough volunteers. But there is also the danger of supplying too many volunteers, or at least of supplying too much volunteer service in a particular case. Finding the happy medium is not easy, and even for the agency with the best ordered volunteer program, great balance is required in the person administering the program in order to supply the service without making the clients more dependent than each is or would want to become.

Most important of all in a good volunteer service is the *quality* of the volunteers — not alone that they be good people, but that they be good for the job. Most agencies have a screening and training process for volunteers who are going to work directly with persons who are blind. Some, however, fail in this — one of the best-known examples of this failure being the case of the agency executive who was discussing a volunteer who had been recommended to open incoming mail in a fund drive. After due consideration, his answer was that the agency did not know enough about her to put her in a position where she would handle money; perhaps she should be used instead as a reader for the blind.

Screening of volunteers who are going to work directly with the blind is an essential part of a volunteer program. It means (in addition to screening out any morally undesirable persons who might by chance volunteer) screening out all those who by nature would seek to dominate the blind, those who would "identify" with the blind, and many fine people whose emotional make-up is such that they could not work in a direct volunteer position without becoming somehow involved in the inner problems of the person who is blind. It does not mean refusing these people, but turning their efforts into other channels where they can perform volunteer service for the agency and, indirectly, for the blind.

It should be recognized, here as elsewhere, that people turn to "good works" of one sort or another from a vast range and variety of motives, some of which may be quite unconscious. For the sake of our clients, we must try to prevent any damage that might be done by the working out of these unconscious motivations, just as we must not prevent any good will from having its due scope.

To carry out such a screening job requires an extraordinary person — one with insight, training, tact, and strength of purpose. In order to include the balanced, the well-motivated, and those emotionally fitted for the purpose, we may have to screen out some of our best friends, and, for that matter, some of the best friends of our agency. Difficult or not, such screening is worthwhile nonetheless, in what it will mean for the increased independence of the blind clients of the agency.

In addition to screening, *training of volunteers* is of paramount importance. Usually the training consists in a general backgrour course on the purpose of work with the blind, the philosophy which is to activate the work of the volunteer, and something about the agency itself. During the whole period in which the volunteer works for the agency, refresher courses are given and the volunteer is kept abreast of progress or change in the field of work with the blind.

In some cases, it may be extremely helpful if agencies can work out for their volunteers a sort of "pledge of restricted activity," or at least a "credo" for volunteers, in order to make sure from the beginning that the worker really understands and intends not to overstep the limits of the work set out for him — limits of time as well as of type of work. Many a blind person has experienceed the volunteer who begins by giving far more time than is required, only to taper off gradually or suddenly, until he is seen no more.

A volunteer program also calls for *good supervision.* The workers must be taught to report to the agency. No matter how unnecessary this may seem to them, or how much like more "red tape," it is of great importance that the agency not only be performing its function through its volunteers but also that it know that it is performing it. In addition to the report of their own activities, the volunteers should be asked to report on any unusual situation affecting the blind persons they are working with, so that the agency may judge when additional services may be required.

Supervising volunteers also implies withdrawing them from a particular case or from volunteer work generally if, for one reason or another, it seems advisable — if, for example, they break appointments without reason, prove themselves incompetent, or show an overzealousness which is not for the good of the blind person to whom they are assigned.

The Pledge of the Volunteer

I pledge myself to be the eyes of the blind.

I will try with all that lies within me to be free of false feelings about blindness — feelings that blind persons are strange or different — feelings that they have a sixth sense or a miraculous compensation — feelings that they are geniuses or that, on the other hand, they have warped or twisted personalities.

I will attempt to realize completely what I am now beginning to recognize, that there is no common personality pattern among blind persons. And I will try always to see each individual blind person with whom I come in contact as an individual human person with an individual human personality.

I promise in speaking of my work never to attempt to raise a false pity for the blind, but only to teach people the truth about blindness, that it is a most severe handicap to which human beings react in their own individual ways.

And my actual relationship to the person to whom I am assigned will be the relationship which is assigned to me. I accept these volunteer opportunities in order that I may assist persons who are blind. Generally speaking, the very best assistance is that in which I am only "substitute eyes." This will mean that I will refrain from any attempt to influence the life or actions of the person who is blind — leaving this to others whose responsibility it may be. I will not try to be mother or father or sister or brother to the person who is blind. I will not allow myself to be financial benefactor to him. Nor will I own or possess him. I will not make him dependent on me — nor myself dependent on him. I pledge myself to be the eyes of the blind — and not to attempt to be something more. If this I do and this I do for God — then my time is indeed well spent — no matter what other problems there may be that I myself would wish to solve.

3. THE BLINDFOLD AS A TRAINING TOOL

As the reader has certainly noted already, there are many controversial aspects in the field of work with the blind — not the least of which is the use of the blindfold. To some people, it is a simple tool which can help teach sighted people about blindness; to others, using a blindfold for this purpose is a kind of play-acting rightly scorned by serious professionals.

Experience shows that the blindfold can be a very valuable adjunct in any training program for the four purposes to be described. But one of the most serious mistakes often made is to use it without the proper safeguards.

We shall mention the special safeguards needed with each use, but the safeguard always necessary is that it should never be used with the idea that it will teach anyone "what it is like to be blind." *No use of the blindfold for any length of time can teach the sighted person what blindness is.* Its value lies simply in its capacity to bring home very quickly to the sighted *some of the reality problems* of blindness. The blindfolded person can learn, as he could in no other way, some of the difficulties involved in such losses as those of mobility, ease of spoken communication, and the techniques of daily living. But he can never grasp from blindfolded experience the experience of blindness; in this sense it *is* play-acting.

(1) *Using the blindfold for new workers.* It is presumed that the new worker for the blind, whether professional or volunteer, will be given a training period of indoctrination into the special problems of blindness and the special techniques required in the field. Such a course can be greatly shortened and its impact strengthened if these workers use the blindfold during the major part of the course.*

No special safeguard is needed here other than insistence on the fact that the use of the blindfold will not teach what it is to be blind, although it would seem that workers sufficiently qualified to be working in the field should not need too much emphasis on this point. In fact, the worker who, after the course, speaks of it as having given him the experience of blindness thereby gives proof that he does not belong in the field.

(2) *Using the blindfold in indoctrinating public groups.* The use of the blindfold on any sizable audience as an aid in teaching them some of the facts about blindness can be very helpful. But it

* All members of the teaching staff at St. Paul's Rehabilitation Center wear the blindfold at least one day a month, as a repeated reminder to them of problems which they might otherwise overlook.

should be remembered that the speaker who, under these circumstances, truly interprets some of the deep and frightening meanings of blindness is treading dangerous ground; it is possible for panic to rise and spread in a blindfolded audience. Yet, unless the speaker gives the deeper interpretation, he may well send away many unthinking people with the impression that now they "know what it is like to be blind." The blindfold may well be used with groups of the public who must be taught much about blindness in a short time, but its use should be only for brief periods, and emotional tension must not be allowed to rise too high.

(3) *Using the blindfold to assist the families of newly blinded persons.* The use of the blindfold by the members of the family of a blind person, while it may be very helpful in showing them some of the "reality" problems of blindness, must be even more thoroughly safeguarded. Above all, it must be remembered that the blindfold experience may be too traumatic for some persons very close to the newly blinded person to undergo. With the family of a blind person, it is more than ever vitally important that they fully apprehend the fact that having worn a blindfold for a brief period does not teach them what blindness is. And it must be made very clear to the blind person himself that the members of his family are not suffering from any such delusion. Few things can be more upsetting to family relations than for a sighted member to appear to believe, or actually to believe, that he fully realizes the meaning of the handicap of the blind person.

(4) *Using the blindfold to control the impact of sighted visitors on a program for blind persons.* Because of the emotional reaction of such a large proportion of the public to blindness and because of the fact that few of them have regular contact with persons who are blind, the problem of visitors to an agency or institution working with blind persons presents a major problem.

On the one hand, the agency desires to have its particular work known, and also to educate the public in the general problems of blindness and in some of the available methods of overcoming these problems. On the other hand, anything that approaches an "open house" in a place where blind persons are living or working invites an attitude of putting the blind persons on display, as in a museum or a zoo, doing a grave disservice to the blind persons who are under observation and offering very little in the way of valuable public education.

Generally speaking, then, any sort of observation tour for non-professional groups is entirely to be ruled out. But if there are occasions when certain groups from the general public must be brought through an establishment where blind persons are active, much of the trauma of the situation can be taken from the blind persons and a more effective tour conducted if the blindfold is used with these visitors.

St. Paul's restricts its visitors to those who have a professional interest in the program, to such an extent that none but professional visitors are allowed to enter classrooms while classes are in session. And even though these visitors are professionals, they must wear blindfolds.

The reasons for this policy are: the blindfolded professional visitor has a greater opportunity to recognize what is actually being given by way of instruction to the person who is blind; he has brought home to him rather forcefully some of the external problems connected with blindness, such as mobility problems, communication problems, and technique problems; he is less distracted by such relatively minor matters as the appearance of the trainee in a classroom situation (particularly important for the professional unaccustomed to working with blind people, who might devote all his attention to watching to see "what blind people do"); he is able to view the classrooms and appurtenances of the center from the viewpoint of the trainee; he hears trainees acting with far greater freedom than they would if they did not know that he was blindfolded (and therefore observes the training center under less artificial circumstances).

This policy also means that trainees are not embarrassed or distracted in their work by the presence of visitors watching their reactions — a point especially important to a completely free classroom atmosphere. The trainee knows that he is not being pitied by sighted persons entering the classroom to observe. He realizes that, in the particular situation, although the blindfolded visitor is not blind, the trainee has the advantage in that he is not disturbed, whereas the blindfolded visitor is probably under some discomfort, or at least is too busy considering the novelty of the situation to regard the blind trainee from a superior position.

If this appears to be a form of overprotection of blind people who are to return to a sighted world, it should be noted that the trainees are given full training in operating securely in the presence of sighted people when they move about the center or the grounds between classes, when they take their mobility instruction in the general community, and when they take their recreation among sighted people in regular sighted circumstances. Yet in the intimacy of a small class situation, they should not be expected to operate as in a goldfish bowl, or to be observed through a one-way glass.

The use of the blindfold as a training tool will perhaps encounter resistance from older workers in the field for many years to come. But it will encounter special resistance from those who find its use too traumatic for them to accept, and yet are unwilling to face their own fears.

Appendix

The Religious Care of the Blind

WE ARE considering the religious care of the blind at the end of this volume because only when we have considered blindness and its meaning are we in a position to view this subject in its full context.

Some people feel that the only thing to be done for the blind from the viewpoint of religion is to sanctify them, to make them holy. This is true if it is taken to mean that the only thing which religion must do for any person, and therefore for the blind person, is to sanctify him. But it is untrue if it is taken to mean that somehow the blind person has a special call to holiness which the rest of mankind does not.

This latter point of view is not religion, but superstition. It is not formal and thought-out superstitition. But it is superstition nevertheless, and not too far removed from that of the primitive tribes who almost deify blind persons, feeling that they are in some way special representatives of God. As with superstitions generally, this grows out of vague fears and hidden emotions. The blind person seems to have special contemplative powers which the rest of us do not possess. This superstition is probably not too far removed in origin from ignorant feelings about the "evil eye."

With this notion goes a feeling of shock when blind persons are guilty of sin — far greater than if they themselves or other sighted persons commit sin. Shock at sin is not a bad thing, certainly, if it is shock at *all* sin and not just at some types of sin, and if it is shock at sins committed by all kinds of people and not just at those committed by some groups. (Difficulties of definition arise here; some kinds of "shock" at sin are not so much the result of a balanced attitude which hates any offense to God as the result of a neurotic unbalance and a disturbed spirituality.) But to be shocked by the sins of blind persons and to take the sins of other human beings for granted is to be superstitious.

Sometimes those who expect blind persons to be more holy than the rest of the human race explain how they feel when a blind person is guilty of violating the law of God: "There they are deprived of a sense that God gave to the rest of us. Wouldn't you think that they would be so near to God that they would be ashamed of this?" No particular logic explains what they are trying to say. It would seem more logical that if there were any difference between the two groups, the burden would be on us who see, on us to whom God has given more in the way of senses. It would seem that if there were to be more shock at the sins of one group than the other, it should be directed at us to whom God has given so much. But there is no particular logic to superstition.

What can be said, if we believe that growth in sanctity is measured by the degree to which we are able to conform our wills to the will of God, is that perhaps blind persons as a group have a greater *opportunity* for a higher degree of sanctity. We can say this (keeping in mind many other factors) on the basis that the will of God has demanded more of them — for them, complete submission to the will of God includes submission to His permissive will with regard to a terrible and multiple handicap from which the rest of us are free.

This brings us immediately into another question: What attitude toward such a handicap does God ask for on the part of the person who bears it? Too many people seem to believe that they must minimize their handicap; otherwise they would not be showing that submission which God demands. Too many seem to be teaching this same notion to the blind: "Treat it as if it were not so bad as it is. Call it a minor burden. Don't think of it as severe, or it will show that you are resentful of God's will."

This strange belief, that the God of Truth would ask us to deny the truth, is hard to understand. When we break an arm, submission to the will of God does not demand that we should call it or think of it as just a "severe strain — kind of pulled the muscles, I guess." When we suffer pain, God does not expect that conformity to His will should make us say or think that it really isn't pain — "kind of itchy, a sort of discomfort."

And when a person is handicapped by blindness, he is not expected to minimize it (any more than he is to exaggerate it). Rather, he is to see it as it is, in its full meaning. Only then can he give meaning to his "Father, not my will, but Thine be done."

Christ in His Passion made no attempt to minimize His terrible suffering. He prayed to be freed from it: "My Father, if it be possible, let this chalice pass from me." This is a prayer that the blind man has every right and every reason to say as he tries to free himself from the handicap of blindness — by restoration of sight and by every other means available — and as he tries to make up in every possible way for the losses of blindness so as to make it less of a handicap than it might be. *Then* Christ prayed, as the handicapped person must also try to do: "But yet not my will but Thine be done."

Love of truth demands that the blind person view his handicap as objectively as possible — admitting to himself its whole burden — seeing for himself how his whole human nature rebels at one aspect of it after another, how his nature resents, rejects, hates his blindness.

If he hides the truth from himself, he may very well discover that the resentment, the rejection, the hatred is being misplaced. It may be turned toward other people; it may be turned toward himself; it may even be turned toward God.

If, in fact, he does grow in sanctity, if his blindness (his acceptance of it) is an instrument of that growth — then, in his progress toward God, he may come to be grateful for that instrument as the "sweet yoke, the light burden" of Christ. It is distinctly possible to hate the *handicap* of blindness while loving the *cross* of blindness.

The whole problem of the existence of evil, both moral and physical, faces us in work with the blind as it does in all contacts with persons undergoing suffering or deprivation. One suggestion, however, is that we might forego the use of the word "affliction," since its connotations are all in the field of punishment, and since it implies more than the *permissive* will of God, and thus too often leads to false conclusions.

There are many other notions that we need to clarify for ourselves and for others. Distinctions between true sanctity and various kinds of false sanctity will have to be made. That "false martyrdom" familiar to every confessor and spiritual director is to be found among the blind as elsewhere. A blind person, like a sighted person, may put on a front such as to make people think he is a martyr, completely submissive to the various blows life is dealing him, while at the same time working himself into a position where, in his suffering, he is dominating all those around him, causing his whole household to revolve around his own will. The false martyr manages to arouse terrible feelings of guilt in those about him for the occasions when they have allowed their doubts of his sincerity to come close to the surface. And with each new upsurge of guilt, the "martyr" is more and more in control. The terrible thing (truly terrible and terrifying) about this sort of thing is that it is not generally consciously done. It all goes on sufficiently beneath the surface so that the "martyr" himself is convinced (or almost convinced) of his selflessness. Submission here, or the appearance of submission, is not born of love; it is instead a cloak for a terrible hostility; it feeds on hate and it nurtures hate.

Then we come across social aberrations, rebellions of one sort or another. We need to learn when these are simply a displacement of resentment and rebellion against the handicap itself. Sinful actions, against the Church, against society, against the marriage laws of God — often among the roots from which these spring will be discovered this same inner rebellion (perhaps unrecognized by the person himself, who may think it is only a part of some "enlightenment" or other), a rebellion against a blindness never accepted because never fully met.

On the moral side (the question of obedience or disobedience to the laws of God) we know to start with, of course, that the laws of God are binding on blind and sighted alike. At the same time, among the circumstances which alter the nature of sin (increasing or decreasing the culpability) are many factors connected with blindness and the experiences diminished by blindness. We shall realize all these things more thoroughly as we know blindness itself more thoroughly.

With regard to the Sunday obligation of public worship, no general statement can be made. Some blind persons are normally excused because they are sick and bedridden. Others are excused because they have severe neurotic problems which make it impossible for them to go among crowds. Others are excused because they are so afraid of travel that they never go anywhere. But there are many blind persons who take part in regular community activities during the week; they get to work and they get to places of recreation. It is a serious error to hold these people generally excused from the obligation simply and solely because of their blindness.

We need to see, too, how *sensibly* different is any form of public worship to the blind person than to the sighted. The whole sacramental system is one in which the material thing is a sign of the spiritual. What appears to the senses signifies what appears to the soul. Unless we stop to consider it, we are apt to overlook the frequency with which the sense appealed to is sight,* where it is the literally "visible" things which lead to the invisible. The recognition of this difficulty is of the greatest importance in assisting with the religious education of children; we must take care to make every-

* This is particularly true if, as in the Roman rite of the Roman Catholic Church at the present time, the liturgical language is one not understood by the people. It is extremely difficult for the average Catholic blind person to keep his mind focused on the altar at Mass. Nor does he have the assistance of a braille missal, since the transcription of the missal into braille would take volumes and prove impractical. For this reason, a group of Catholic priests assigned to work with blind persons unanimously passed a resolution requesting the bishop to petition the Holy See for a further use of the vernacular in the liturgy.

thing tangible in the process of education so that they can know with the greatest clarity what is taking place. It is also of importance in our dealing with and understanding the problems of adult blind persons with regard to religious services.

With regard to religious literature (besides what was said about reading material generally in Chapter 13, Restoration #8), we should be on our guard against multiplying agencies for transcription. Our task it to increase the circulation, not to multiply and duplicate copies of a single book.

In the same connection, it is interesting how large a percentage of the literature in braille is of the "inspirational" variety. Might some of this, at least, be an outgrowth of the superstition mentioned above? Sometimes it appears as if some people had looked at the blind and said, "Here is a group we can force to be holy." In our desire to bring people to God, the temptation always exists to attempt to force holiness on them. But such an effort can never be fruitful. We may force an appearance of holiness, but the holiness can come only from within.

Our task is to allow people to grow up (as indeed God wishes them to grow up), to give to them opportunities for learning about God — at each stage of their growth presenting them with the knowledge of God suited to that stage. We aid them and we assist them in such a way that they will be independent of us. We protect them from the inroads of evil, not in a hothouse but in the world. We shield them from moral harm, not by keeping them from growing, but rather by teaching them to grow so they themselves will choose good and avoid evil.

It is the same with religious literature for the blind. We should attempt in every way to make available to them that religious literature which will assist them to know, love and serve God. But we should attempt no more (and no less) to make their literary fare exclusively religious than we should for a sighted group.

Blindness is a multiple handicap, and the person who is interested in the spiritual welfare of a person who is blind will recognize that fact and come to know as much as possible about blindness in order to assist him. At times, he will turn for special advice to those whose office it is to know more about the special problems of the blind. There is nothing in the nature of blindness, however, which should take the ordinary spiritual care of blind persons out of the regular parish. The special religious organizations for the blind exist so that they can make the blind individual a better member of his parish. The true measure of their success (and the only real justification for their existence) is the extent to which they do this.

Index

Index